OUR VILLAGE

MARY RUSSELL MITFORD

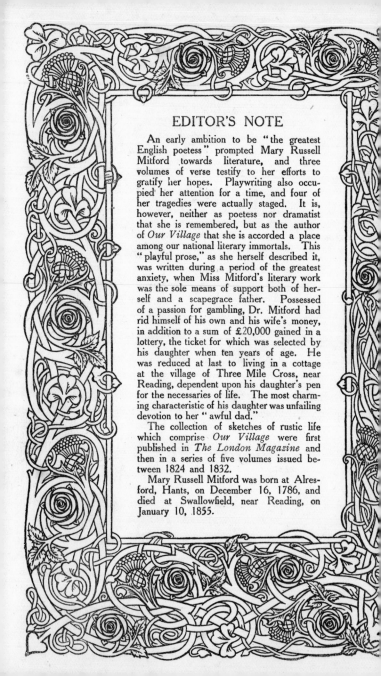

EDITOR'S NOTE

An early ambition to be "the greatest English poetess" prompted Mary Russell Mitford towards literature, and three volumes of verse testify to her efforts to gratify her hopes. Playwriting also occupied her attention for a time, and four of her tragedies were actually staged. It is, however, neither as poetess nor dramatist that she is remembered, but as the author of *Our Village* that she is accorded a place among our national literary immortals. This "playful prose," as she herself described it, was written during a period of the greatest anxiety, when Miss Mitford's literary work was the sole means of support both of herself and a scapegrace father. Possessed of a passion for gambling, Dr. Mitford had rid himself of his own and his wife's money, in addition to a sum of £20,000 gained in a lottery, the ticket for which was selected by his daughter when ten years of age. He was reduced at last to living in a cottage at the village of Three Mile Cross, near Reading, dependent upon his daughter's pen for the necessaries of life. The most charming characteristic of his daughter was unfailing devotion to her "awful dad."

The collection of sketches of rustic life which comprise *Our Village* were first published in *The London Magazine* and then in a series of five volumes issued between 1824 and 1832.

Mary Russell Mitford was born at Alresford, Hants, on December 16, 1786, and died at Swallowfield, near Reading, on January 10, 1855.

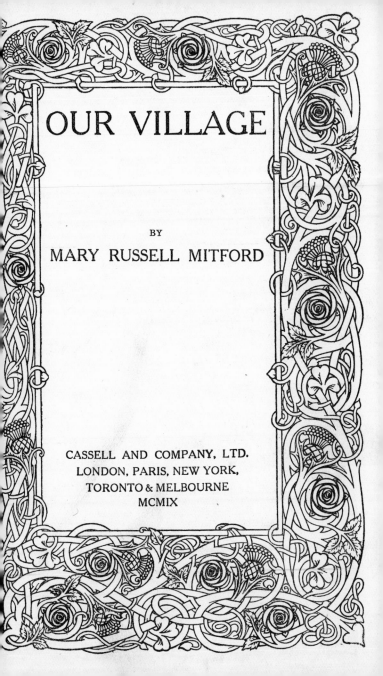

OUR VILLAGE

BY

MARY RUSSELL MITFORD

CASSELL AND COMPANY, LTD.
LONDON, PARIS, NEW YORK,
TORONTO & MELBOURNE
MCMIX

CONTENTS

OUR VILLAGE

OUR VILLAGE

OF all situations for a constant residence, that which appears to me most delightful is a little village far in the country ; a small neighbourhood, not of fine mansions finely peopled, but of cottages and cottage-like houses, "messuages or tenements," as a friend of mine calls such ignoble and nondescript dwellings, with inhabitants whose faces are as familiar to us as the flowers in our garden ; a little world of our own, close-packed and insulated like ants in an ant-hill, or bees in a hive, or sheep in a fold, or nuns in a convent, or sailors in a ship ; where we know every one, are known to every one, interested in every one, and authorised to hope that every one feels an interest in us. How pleasant it is to slide into these true-hearted feelings from the kindly and unconscious influence of habit, and to learn to know and to love the people about us, with all their peculiarities, just as we learn to know and to love the nooks and turns of the shady lanes and sunny commons that we pass every day. Even in books I like a confined locality, and so do the critics when they talk of the unities. Nothing is so tiresome as to be whirled half over Europe at the chariot-wheels of a hero, to go to sleep at Vienna, and awaken at Madrid ; it produces a real fatigue, a weariness of spirit. On the other hand, nothing is so delightful as to sit down in a country village in one of Miss Austen's delicious novels, quite sure before we leave it to become intimate with every spot and every person it contains ;

or to ramble with Mr. White * over his own parish of Selborne, and form a friendship with the fields and coppices, as well as with the birds, mice, and squirrels, who inhabit them ; or to sail with Robinson Crusoe to his island, and live there with him and his goats and his man Friday—how much we dread any new comers, any fresh importation of savage or sailor ! we never sympathise for a moment in our hero's want of company, and are quite grieved when he gets away ; or to be shipwrecked with Ferdinand on that other lovelier island— the island of Prospero, and Miranda, and Caliban, and Ariel, and nobody else, none of Dryden's exotic inventions —that is best of all. And a small neighbourhood is as good in sober waking reality as in poetry or prose ; a village neighbourhood, such as this Berkshire hamlet in which I write, a long, straggling, winding street at the bottom of a fine eminence, with a road through it, always abounding in carts, horsemen, and carriages, and lately enlivened by a stage-coach from B—— to S——, which passed through about ten days ago, and will, I suppose, return some time or other. There are coaches of all varieties now-a-days ; perhaps this may be intended for a monthly diligence, or a fortnight fly. Will you walk with me through our village, courteous reader ? The journey is not long. We will begin at the lower end, and proceed up the hill.

The tidy, square, red cottage on the right hand, with the long well-stocked garden by the side of the road, belongs to a retired publican from a neighbouring town ; a substantial person with a comely wife ; one who piques himself on independence and idleness, talks politics, reads newspapers, hates the minister, and cries out for reform. He introduced into our peaceful vicinage the rebellious

* White's *Natural History and Antiquities of Selborne ;* one of the most fascinating books ever written. I wonder that no naturalist has adopted the same plan.

innovation of an illumination on the Queen's acquittal. Remonstrance and persuasion were in vain ; he talked of liberty and broken windows—so we all lighted up. Oh ! how he shone that night with candles, and laurel, and white bows, and gold paper, and a transparency (originally designed for a pocket handkerchief) with a flaming portrait of her Majesty, hatted and feathered, in red ochre. He had no rival in the village, that we all acknowledged ; the very bonfire was less splendid ; the little boys reserved their best crackers to be expended in his honour, and he gave them full sixpence more than any one else. He would like an illumination once a month ; for it must not be concealed that, in spite of gardening, of newspaper reading, of jaunting about in his little cart, and frequenting both church and meeting, our worthy neighbour begins to feel the weariness of idleness. He hangs over his gate, and tries to entice passengers to stop and chat ; he volunteers little jobs all round, smokes cherry trees to cure the blight, and traces and blows up all the wasps' nests in the parish. I have seen a great many wasps in our garden to-day, and shall enchant him with the intelligence. He even assists his wife in her sweepings and dustings. Poor man ! he is a very respectable person, and would be a very happy one if he would add a little employment to his dignity. It would be the salt of life to him.

Next to his house, though parted from it by another long garden with a yew arbour at the end, is the pretty dwelling of the shoemaker, a pale, sickly-looking, black-haired man, the very model of sober industry. There he sits in his little shop from early morning till late at night. An earthquake would hardly stir him ; the illumination did not. He stuck immovably to his last, from the first lighting up, through the long blaze and the slow decay, till his large, solitary candle was the only light in the place. One cannot conceive anything more perfect than the contempt which the man of transparencies and the man of shoes must have felt for each other on that evening. There was at least as much vanity in the sturdy industry as in the strenuous idleness, for our shoemaker is a man of substance—he employs three journeymen, two lame, and one a dwarf, so that his shop looks like a hospital; he has purchased the lease of his commodious dwelling, some even say he has bought it out and out; and he has only one pretty daughter, a light, delicate, fair-haired girl of fourteen, the champion, protectress, and playfellow of every brat under three years old, whom she jumps, dances, dandles, and feeds all day long. A very attractive person is that child-loving girl. I have never seen any one in her station who possessed so thoroughly that undefinable charm, the lady-look. See her on a Sunday in her simplicity and her white frock, and she might pass for an earl's daughter. She likes flowers, too, and has a profusion of white stocks under her window, as pure and delicate as herself.

The first house on the opposite side of the way is the blacksmith's; a gloomy dwelling, where the sun never seems to shine; dark and smoky within and without, like a forge. The blacksmith is a high officer in our little state, nothing less than a constable; but, alas! alas! when tumults arise, and the constable is called for, he will commonly be found in the thickest of the fray. Lucky would it be for his wife and her eight children if there were no public-house in the land; an inveterate inclination to enter those betwitching doors is Mr. Constable's only fault.

Next to this official dwelling is a spruce brick tenement, red, high, and narrow, boasting, one above another, three sash-windows, the only sash-windows in the village, with a clematis on one side and a rose on the other, tall and narrow like itself. That slender mansion has a fine, genteel look. The little parlour seems made for Hogarth's

old maid and her stunted footboy; for tea and card parties
it would just hold one table; for the rustle of faded silks,
and the splendour of old china; for the delight of four by
honours, and a little snug, quiet scandal between the
deals; for affected gentility and real starvation. This
should have been its destiny; but fate has been unpro-
pitious: it belongs to a plump, merry, bustling dame,
with four fat, rosy, noisy children, the very essence of
vulgarity and plenty.

Then comes the village shop, like other village shops,
multifarious as a bazaar; a repository for bread, shoes,
tea, cheese, tape, ribands, and bacon; for everything, in
short, except the one particular thing which you happen
to want at the moment, and will be sure not to find. The
people are civil and thriving, and frugal withal; they have
let the upper part of their house to two young women (one
of them is a pretty, blue-eyed girl) who teach little children
their A B C, and make caps and gowns for their mammas—
parcel school-mistress, parcel mantua-maker. I believe
they find adorning the body a more profitable vocation
than adorning the mind.

Divided from the shop by a narrow yard, and opposite
the shoemaker's, is a habitation of whose inmates I shall
say nothing. A cottage—no—a miniature house, with
many additions, little odds and ends of places, pantries,
and what not; all angles, and of a charming in-and-out-
ness; a little bricked court before one half, and a little
flower-yard before the other; the walls, old and weather-
stained, covered with hollyhocks, roses, honeysuckles,
and a great apricot-tree; the casement full of geraniums;
(ah, there is our superb white cat peeping out from among
them); the closets (our landlord has the assurance to call
them rooms) full of contrivances and corner-cupboards;
and the little garden behind full of common flowers, tulips,
pinks, larkspurs, peonies, stocks, and carnations, with an
arbour of privet, not unlike a sentry-box, where one

lives in a delicious green light, and looks out on the gayest
of all gay flower-beds. That house was built on purpose
to show in what an exceeding small compass comfort
may be packed. Well, I will loiter there no longer.

The next tenement is a place of importance, the Rose
inn; a whitewashed building, retired from the road
behind its fine swinging sign, with a little bow-window
room coming out on one side, and forming, with our stable
on the other, a sort of open square, which is the constant
resort of carts, waggons, and return chaises. There are
two carts there now, and mine host is serving them with
beer in his eternal red waistcoat. He is a thriving man
and a portly, as his waistcoat attests, which has been twice
let out within this twelvemonth. Our landlord has a
stirring wife, a hopeful son, and a daughter, the belle of
the village; not so pretty as the fair nymph of the shoe-
shop, and far less elegant, but ten times as fine; all curl-
papers in the morning, like a porcupine, all curls in the
afternoon, like a poodle, with more flounces than curl-
papers, and more lovers than curls. Miss Phœbe is fitter
for town than country; and to do her justice, she has a
consciousness of that fitness, and turns her steps town-
wards as often as she can. She is gone to B—— to-day
with her last and principal lover, a recruiting sergeant—
a man as tall as Sergeant Kite, and as impudent. Some
day or other he will carry off Miss Phœbe.

In a line with the bow-window room is a low garden-wall,
belonging to a house under repair—the white house opposite the collar-maker's shop, with four lime-trees before
it, and a waggon-load of bricks at the door. That house
is the plaything of a wealthy, well-meaning, whimsical
person who lives about a mile off. He has a passion for
brick and mortar; and, being too wise to meddle with
his own residence, diverts himself with altering and re-
altering, improving and re-improving, doing and undoing
here. It is a perfect Penelope's web. Carpenters and

brick-layers have been at work for these eighteen months, and yet I sometimes stand and wonder whether anything has really been done. One exploit in last June was, however, by no means equivocal. Our good neighbour fancied that the limes shaded the rooms, and made them dark (there was not a creature in the house but the work- men), so he had all the leaves stripped from every tree. There they stood, poor miserable skeletons, as bare as Christmas under the glowing midsummer sun. Nature revenged herself in her own sweet and gracious manner ; fresh leaves sprang out, and at nearly Christmas the foliage was as brilliant as when the outrage was committed.

Next door lives a carpenter, " famed ten miles round, and worthy all his fame "—few cabinet-makers surpass him, with his excellent wife, and their little daughter Lizzy, the plaything and queen of the village, a child three years old according to the register, but six in size and strength and intellect, in power and in self-will. She manages everybody in the place, her schoolmistress included ; turns the wheeler's children out of their own little cart, and makes them draw her ; seduces cakes and lollypops from the very shop window ; makes the lazy carry her, the silent talk to her, the grave romp with her ; does anything she pleases ; is absolutely irresistible. Her chief attraction lies in her exceeding power of loving, and her firm reliance on the love and indulgence of others. How impossible it would be to disappoint the dear little girl when she runs to meet you, slides her pretty hand into yours, looks up gladly in your face, and says, " Come ! " You must go ; you cannot help it. Another part of her charm is her singular beauty. Together with a good deal of the character of Napoleon, she has something of his square, sturdy, upright form, with the finest limbs in the world, a complexion purely English, a round, laughing face, sunburnt and rosy, large, merry, blue eyes, curling brown hair, and a wonderful play of countenance. She

has the imperial attitudes, too, and loves to stand with
her hands behind her, or folded over her bosom ; and
sometimes, when she has a little touch of shyness, she clasps
them together on the top of her head, pressing down her
shining curls, and looking so exquisitely pretty ! Yes,
Lizzy is queen of the village ! She has but one rival in
her dominions, a certain white greyhound called Mayflower, much her friend, who resembles her in beauty and
strength, in playfulness, and almost in sagacity, and reigns
over the animal world as she over the human. They are
both coming with me, Lizzy and Lizzy's " pretty May."
We are now at the end of the street ; a cross lane, a rope-
walk shaded with limes and oaks, and a cool, clear pond
overhung with elms, lead us to the bottom of the hill.
There is still one house round the corner, ending in a
picturesque wheeler's shop. The dwelling-house is more
ambitious. Look at the fine flowered window-blinds, the
green door with the brass knocker, and the somewhat prim
but very civil person, who is sending off a labouring man
with sirs and curtsies enough for a prince of the blood.
Those are the curate's lodgings—apartments his landlady
would call them : he lives with his own family four miles
off, but once or twice a-week he comes to his neat little
parlour to write sermons, to marry, or to bury, as the case
may require. Never were better or kinder people than
his host and hostess : and there is a reflection of clerical
importance about them since their connection with the
Church which is quite edifying—a decorum, a gravity, a
solemn politeness. Oh, to see the worthy wheeler carry
the gown after his lodger on a Sunday, nicely pinned up
in his wife's best handkerchief !—or to hear him rebuke
a squalling child or a squabbling woman ! The curate is
nothing to him. He is fit to be perpetual churchwarden.

We must now cross the lane into the shady rope-walk.
That pretty white cottage opposite, which stands straggling
at the end of the village in a garden full of flowers, belongs

to our mason, the shortest of men, and his handsome, tall
wife : he, a dwarf, with the voice of a giant ; one starts
when he begins to talk, as if he were shouting through a
speaking-trumpet ; she, the sister, daughter, and grand-
daughter of a long line of gardeners, and no contemptible
one herself. It is very magnanimous in me not to hate
her ; for she beats me in my own way, in chrysanthemums,
and dahlias, and the like gauds. Her plants are sure to
live ; mine have a sad trick of dying, perhaps because
I love them " not wisely, but too well," and kill them with
over-kindness. Half-way up the hill is another detached
cottage, the residence of an officer and his beautiful family.
That eldest boy, who is hanging over the gate, and looking
with such intense childish admiration at my Lizzy, might
be a model for a Cupid.

How pleasantly the road winds up the hill, with its
broad, green borders and hedge-rows so thickly timbered !
How finely the evening sun falls on that sandy excavated
bank, and touches the farm-house on the top of the
eminence ! and how clearly defined and relieved is the
figure of the man who is just coming down ! It is poor
John Evans, the gardener—an excellent gardener till about
ten years ago, when he lost his wife, and became insane.
He was sent to St. Luke's, and dismissed as cured ; but
his power was gone and his strength ; he could no longer
manage a garden, nor submit to the restraint, nor encounter
the fatigue of regular employment : so he retreated to the
workhouse, the pensioner and factotum of the village,
amongst whom he divided his services. His mind often
wanders, intent on some fantastic and impracticable plan,
and lost to present objects ; but he is perfectly harmless,
and full of a child-like simplicity, a smiling contentedness,
a most touching gratitude. Every one is kind to John
Evans, for there is that about him which must be loved ;
and his unprotectedness, his utter defencelessness, have an
irresistible claim on every better feeling. I know nobody

who inspires so deep and tender a pity; he improves all
around him. He is useful, too, to the extent of his little
power; will do anything, but loves gardening best, and
still piques himself on his old arts of pruning fruit-trees
and raising cucumbers. He is the happiest of men just
now, for he has the management of a melon bed—a melon
bed!—fie! What a grand, pompous name was that for
three melon plants under a hand-light! John Evans is
sure that they will succeed. We shall see; as the
chancellor said, "I doubt."

We are now on the very brow of the eminence, close
to the Hill-house and its beautiful garden. On the outer
edge of the paling, hanging over the bank that skirts the
road, is an old thorn—such a thorn! The long sprays
covered with snowy blossoms, so graceful, so elegant, so
lightsome, and yet so rich! There only wants a pool under
the thorn to give a still lovelier reflection, quivering and
trembling, like a tuft of feathers, whiter and greener
than the life, and more prettily mixed with the bright blue
sky. There should, indeed, be a pool; but on the dark
grass-plot, under the high bank, which is crowned by that
magnificent plume, there is something that does almost as
well—Lizzy and Mayflower in the midst of a game of romps,
"making a sunshine in the shady place;" Lizzy rolling,
laughing, clapping her hands, and glowing like a rose;
Mayflower playing about her like summer lightning,
dazzling the eyes with her sudden turns, her leaps, her
bounds, her attacks, and her escapes. She darts round
the lovely little girl, with the same momentary touch that
the swallow skims over the water, and has exactly the
same power of flight, the same matchless ease, and strength,
and grace. What a pretty picture they would make; what
a pretty foreground they do make to the real landscape!
The road winding down the hill with a slight bend, like
that in the High Street at Oxford; a waggon slowly
ascending, and a horseman passing it at a full trot—(ah!

Lizzy, Mayflower will certainly desert you to have a
gambol with that blood-horse!) half way down, just
at the turn, the red cottage of the lieutenant, covered
with vines, the very image of comfort and content;
farther down, on the opposite side, the small, white
dwelling of the little mason: then the limes and the
rope-walk; then the village street, peeping through the
trees, whose clustering tops hide all but the chimneys,
and various roofs of the houses, and here and there some
angle of a wall: farther on, the elegant town of B——,
with its fine old church-towers and spires; the whole
view shut in by a range of chalky hills; and over every
part of the picture, trees so profusely scattered, that it
appears like a woodland scene, with glades and villages
intermixed. The trees are of all kinds and all hues, chiefly
the finely-shaped elm, of so bright and deep a green,
the tips of whose high outer branches drop down with such
a crisp and garland-like richness, and the oak, whose
stately form is just now so splendidly adorned by the
sunny colouring of the young leaves. Turning again
up the hill, we find ourselves on that peculiar charm
of English scenery, a green common divided by the
road; the right side fringed by hedge-rows and trees, with
cottages and farm-houses irregularly placed, and terminated by a double avenue of noble oaks; the left, prettier
still, dappled by bright pools of water, and islands of
cottages and cottage-gardens, and sinking gradually
down to corn-fields and meadows, and an old farm-house,
with pointed roofs and clustered chimneys, looking out
from its blooming orchard, and backed by woody hills.
The common is itself the prettiest spot of the prospect:
half covered with low furze, whose golden blossoms reflect
so intensely the last beams of the setting sun, and alive
with cows and sheep, and two sets of cricketers; one
of young men, surrounded by spectators, some standing,
some sitting, some stretched on the grass, all taking

a delighted interest in the game; the other, a merry group of little boys, at a humble distance, for whom even cricket is scarcely lively enough, shouting, leaping, and enjoying themselves to their hearts' content. But cricketers and country boys are too important persons in our village to be talked of merely as figures in the landscape. They deserve an individual introduction—an essay to themselves—and they shall have it. No fear of forgetting the good-humoured faces that meet us in our walks every day.

WALKS IN THE COUNTRY

FROST AND THAW

JANUARY 23rd.—At noon to-day I and my white grey-hound, Mayflower, set out for a walk into a very beautiful world—a sort of silent fairy-land—a creation of that matchless magician, the hoar-frost. There had been just snow enough to cover the earth and all its covers with one sheet of pure and uniform white, and just time enough since the snow had fallen to allow the hedges to be freed of their fleecy load, and clothed with a delicate coating of rime. The atmosphere was deliciously calm ; soft, even mild, in spite of the thermometer ; no perceptible air, but a stillness that might almost be felt, the sky, rather grey than blue, throwing out in bold relief the snow-covered roofs of our village, and the rimy trees that rise above them, and the sun shining dimly as through a veil, giving a pale, fair light, like the moon, only brighter. There was a silence, too, that might become the moon, as we stood at our little gate looking up the quiet street ; a Sabbath-like pause of work and play, rare on a work-day ; nothing was audible but the pleasant hum of frost, that low, monotonous sound, which is perhaps the nearest approach that life and nature can make to absolute silence. The very waggons as they come down the hill along the beaten track of crisp, yellowish frost-dust, glide along like shadows ; even May's bounding footsteps, at her height of glee and of speed, fall like snow upon snow.

But we shall have noise enough presently : May has

stopped at Lizzy's door; and Lizzy, as she sat on the window-sill with her bright, rosy face laughing through the casement, has seen her and disappeared. She is coming. No! The key is turning in the door, and sounds of evil omen issue through the key-hole—sturdy " Let me outs," and " I will goes," mixed with shrill cries on May and on me from Lizzy, piercing through a low continuous harangue, of which the prominent parts are apologies, chilblains, sliding, broken bones, lollypops, rods, and ginger-bread, from Lizzy's careful mother. " Don't scratch the door, May! Don't roar so, my Lizzy! We'll call for you as we come back."—" I'll go now! Let me out! I will go!" are the last words of Miss Lizzy. Mem. —Not to spoil that child—if I can help it. But I do think her mother might have let the poor little soul walk with us to-day. Nothing worse for children than coddling. Nothing better for children than exercise. Besides, I don't believe she has any—and as to breaking her bones in sliding, I don't suppose there's a slide on the common. These murmuring cogitations have brought us up the hill, and half-way across the light and airy common, with its bright expanse of snow and its clusters of cottages, whose turf fires send such wreathes of smoke sailing up the air, and diffuse such aromatic fragrance around. And now comes the delightful sound of childish voices, ringing with glee and merriment almost from beneath our feet. Ah, Lizzy, your mother was right! They are shouting from that deep, irregular pool, all glass now, where, on two long, smooth, liny slides, half-a-dozen ragged urchins are slipping along in tottering triumph. Half-a-dozen steps bring us to the bank right above them. May can hardly resist the temptation of joining her friends, for most of the varlets are of her acquaintance, especially the rogue who leads the slide—he with the brimless hat, whose bronzed complexion and white flaxen hair, reversing the usual lights and shadows of the human countenance, give so strange and foreign a look to his flat and comic features. This hobgoblin, Jack Rapley by name, is May's great crony; and she stands on the brink of the steep, irregular descent, her black eyes fixed full upon him, as if she intended him the favour of jumping on his head. She does: she is down, and upon him: but Jack Rapley is not easily to be knocked off his feet. He saw her coming, and in the moment of her leap sprung dexterously off the slide on the rough ice, steadying himself by the shoulder of the next in file, which unlucky follower, thus unexpectedly checked in his career, fell plump backwards, knocking down the rest of the line like a nest of cardhouses. There is no harm done; but there they lie, roaring, kicking, sprawling, in every attitude of comic distress, whilst Jack Rapley and Mayflower, sole authors of this calamity, stand apart from the throng, fondling, and coquetting, and complimenting each other, and very visibly laughing, May in her black eyes, Jack in his wide, close-shut mouth, and his whole monkey-face, at their comrades' mischances. I think, Miss May, you may as well come up again, and leave Master Rapley to fight your battles. He'll get out of the scrape. He is a rustic wit—a sort of Robin Goodfellow—the sauciest, idlest, cleverest, best-natured boy in the parish; always foremost in mischief, and always ready to do a good turn. The sages of our village predict sad things of Jack Rapley, so that I am sometimes a little ashamed to confess, before wise people, that I have a lurking predilection for him (in common with other naughty ones), and that I like to hear him talk to May almost as well as she does. " Come, May ! " and up she springs, as light as a bird. The road is gay now; carts and post-chaises, and girls in red cloaks, and, afar off, looking almost like a toy, the coach. It meets us fast and soon. How much happier the walkers look than the riders—especially the frost-bitten gentleman, and the shivering lady with the invisible face, sole passengers of that commodious machine! Hooded, veiled, and bonneted, as she is, one sees from her attitude how miserable she would look uncovered.

Another pond, and another noise of children. More sliding? Oh, no! This is a sort of higher pretension. Our good neighbour, the lieutenant, skating, and his own pretty little boys, and two or three other four-year-old elves, standing on the brink in an ecstasy of joy and wonder! O what happy spectators! And what a happy performer! They admiring, he admired, with an ardour and sincerity never excited by all the quadrilles and the spread-eagles of the Seine and the Serpentine. He really skates well, though, and I am glad I came this way; for, with all the father's feelings sitting gaily at his heart, it must still gratify the pride of skill to have one spectator at that solitary pond who has seen skating before.

Now we have reached the trees—the beautiful trees! never so beautiful as to-day. Imagine the effect of a straight and regular double avenue of oaks, nearly a mile long, arching over-head, and closing into perspective like the roof and columns of a cathedral, every tree and branch incrusted with the bright and delicate congelation of hoar-frost, white and pure as snow, delicate and defined as carved ivory. How beautiful it is, how uniform, how various, how filling, how satiating to the eye and to the mind—above all, how melancholy! There is a thrilling awfulness, an intense feeling of simple power in that naked and colourless beauty which falls, on the earth, like the thoughts of death—death pure, and glorious, and smiling —but still death. Sculpture has always the same effect on my imagination, and painting never. Colour is life.— We are now at the end of this magnificent avenue, and at the top of a steep eminence commanding a wide view over four counties—a landscape of snow. A deep lane leads abruptly down the hill; a mere narrow cart-track, sinking between high banks clothed with fern and furze and low broom, crowned with luxuriant hedge-rows, and famous for their summer smell of thyme.   How lovely these banks are now—the tall weeds and the gorse fixed and stiffened in the hoar-frost, which fringes round the bright, prickly holly, the pendent foliage of the bramble, and the deep orange leaves of the pollard oaks !   Oh, this is rime in its loveliest form !   And there is still a berry here and there on the holly, " blushing in its natural coral," through the delicate tracery, still a stray hip or haw for the birds, who abound here always.   The poor birds, how tame they are, how sadly tame !   There is the beautiful and rare crested wren, " that shadow of a bird," as White, of Selborne, calls it, perched in the middle of the hedge, nestling, as it were, amongst the cold, bare boughs, seeking, poor, pretty thing, for the warmth it will not find.   And there, farther on, just under the bank, by the slender runlet, which still trickles between its transparent fantastic margin of thin ice, as if it were a thing of life—there, with a swift, scudding motion, flits, in short, low flights, the gorgeous kingfisher, its magnificent plumage of scarlet and blue flashing in the sun, like the glories of some tropical bird.   He is come for water to this little spring by the hill-side—water which even his long bill and slender head can hardly reach, so nearly do the fantastic forms of those garland-like icy margins meet over the tiny stream beneath.   It is rarely that one sees the shy beauty so close or so long ; and it is pleasant to see him in the grace and beauty of his natural liberty, the only way to look at a bird.   We used, before we lived in a street, to fix a little board outside the parlour window, and cover it with bread crumbs in the hard weather.   It was quite delightful to see the pretty things come and feed, to conquer their shyness, and do away with their mistrust.   First came the more social tribes, " the robin red-breast and the wren," cautiously, suspiciously, picking up a crumb on the

wing, with the little, keen, bright eye fixed on the window ;
then they would stop for two pecks ; then stay till they
were satisfied. The shyer birds, tamed by their example,
came next ; and at last, one saucy fellow of a blackbird—
a sad glutton, he would clear the board in two minutes—
used to tap his yellow bill against the window for more.
How we loved the fearless confidence of that fine, frank-
hearted creature ! And surely he loved us. I wonder
the practice is not more general. "May! May! naughty
May ! " She has frightened away the kingfisher ; and now
in her coaxing penitence she is covering me with snow.
" Come, pretty May ! it is time to go home."

THAW

January 28th.—We have had rain, and snow, and
frost, and rain again ; four days of absolute confinement.
Now it is a thaw and a flood ; but our light, gravelly
soil, and country boots, and country hardihood, will
carry us through. What a dripping, comfortless day it
is ! just like the last days of November : no sun, no sky,
grey or blue ; one low, overhanging, dark, dismal cloud,
like London smoke : Mayflower is out coursing too,
and Lizzy is gone to school. Never mind. Up the hill
again ! Walk we must. Oh, what a watery world to
look back upon ! Thames, Kennet, London—all over-
flowed ; our famous town, inland once, turned into a
sort of Venice ; C. park converted into an island ; and
the long range of meadows from B. to W. one huge,
unnatural lake, with trees growing out of it. Oh, what
a watery world !—I will look at it no longer. I will walk
on. The road is alive again. Noise is re-born. Waggons
creak, horses splash, carts rattle, and pattens paddle
through the dirt with more than their usual clink. The
common has its old, fine tints of green and brown, and
its old variety of inhabitants, horses, cows, sheep, pigs,

and donkeys. The ponds are unfrozen, and cackling geese and gabbling ducks have replaced the lieutenant and Jack Rapley. The avenue is chill and dark, the hedges are dripping, the lanes knee-deep, and all nature is in a state of " dissolution and thaw."

THE FIRST PRIMROSE

MARCH 6th.—Fine March weather : boisterous, blustering, much wind and squalls of rain ; and yet the sky, where the clouds are swept away, deliciously blue, with snatches of sunshine, bright, and clear, and healthful, and the roads, in spite of the slight, glittering showers, crisply dry. Altogether, the day is tempting, very tempting. It will not do for the dear common, that wind-mill of a walk ; but the close, sheltered lanes at the bottom of the hill, which keep out just enough of the stormy air, and let in all the sun, will be delightful. Past our old house, and round by the winding lanes, and the workhouse, and across the lea, and so into the turnpike road again—that is our route for to-day. Forth we set, Mayflower and I, rejoicing in the sunshine, and still more in the wind, which gives such an intense feeling of existence, and, co-operating with brisk motion, sets our blood and our spirits in a glow. For mere physical pleasure there is nothing, perhaps, equal to the enjoyment of being drawn in a light carriage against such a wind as this, by a blood-horse at his height of speed. Walking comes next to it ; but walking is not quite so luxurious or so spiritual ; not quite so much what one fancies of flying, or being carried above the clouds in a balloon.

Nevertheless, a walk is a good thing ; especially under this southern hedge-row, where nature is just beginning to live again ; the periwinkles, with their starry blue flowers, and their shining, myrtle-like leaves, garlanding the bushes ; woodbines and eldertrees pushing out their small, swelling buds ; and grasses and mosses springing forth in every variety of brown and green. Here we are at the corner where four lanes meet, or rather where a passable road of stones and gravel crosses an impassable one of beautiful but treacherous turf, and where the small, white farm-house, scarcely larger than a cottage, and the well-stocked rick-yard behind, tell of comfort and order, but leave all unguessed the great riches of the master. How he became so rich is almost a puzzle; for, though the farm be his own, it is not large; and though prudent and frugal on ordinary occasions, Farmer Barnard is no miser. His horses, dogs, and pigs are the best kept in the parish—May herself, although her beauty be injured by her fatness, half envies the plight of his bitch Fly; his wife's gowns and shawls cost as much again as any shawls or gowns in the village; his dinner parties (to be sure they are not frequent) display twice the ordinary quantity of good things—two couples of ducks, two dishes of green peas, two turkey poults, two gammons of bacon, two plum-puddings; moreover, he keeps a single-horse chaise, and has built and endowed a Methodist chapel. Yet is he the richest man in these parts. Everything prospers with him. Money drifts about him like snow. He looks like a rich man. There is a sturdy squareness of face and figure; a good-humoured obstinacy; a civil importance. He never boasts of his wealth, or gives himself undue airs; but nobody can meet him at market or vestry without finding out immediately that he is the richest man there. They have no child to all this money; but there is an adopted nephew, a fine, spirited lad, who may, perhaps, some day or other, play the part of a fountain to the reservoir.

Now turn up the wide road till we come to the open common, with its park-like trees, its beautiful stream, wandering and twisting along, and its rural bridge. Here we turn again, past that other white farm-house, half hidden by the magnificent elms which stand before it.

Ah! riches dwell not there, but there is found the next best thing—an industrious and light-hearted poverty. Twenty years ago Rachel Hilton was the prettiest and merriest lass in the country. Her father, an old game-keeper, had retired to a village ale-house, where his good beer, his social humour, and his black-eyed daughter, brought much custom. She had lovers by the score; but Joseph White, the dashing and lively son of an opulent farmer, carried off the fair Rachel. They married and settled here, and here they live still, as merrily as ever, with fourteen children of all ages and sizes, from nineteen years to nineteen months, working harder than any people in the parish, and enjoying themselves more. I would match them for labour and laughter against any family in England. She is a blithe, jolly dame, whose beauty has amplified into comeliness; he is tall, and thin, and bony, with sinews like whipcord, a strong, lively voice, a sharp, weather-beaten face, and eyes and lips that smile and brighten when he speaks into a most contagious hilarity. They are very poor, and I often wish them richer; but I don't know—perhaps it might put them out.

Quite close to farmer White's is a little ruinous cottage, whitewashed once, and now in a sad state of betweenity, where dangling stockings and shirts, swelled by the wind, drying in a neglected garden, give signal of a washer-woman. There dwells at present in single blessedness, Betty Adams, the wife of our sometimes gardener. I never saw any one who so much reminded me in person of that lady whom everybody knows, Mistress Meg Merrilees —as tall, as grizzled, as stately, as dark, as gipsy-looking, bonneted and gowned like her prototype, and almost as oracular. Here the resemblance ceases. Mrs. Adams is a perfectly honest, industrious, painstaking person, who earns a good deal of money by washing and charing, and spends it in other luxuries than tidiness—in green tea, and gin, and snuff. Her husband lives in a great family,

ten miles off. He is a capital gardener—or rather he
would be so, if he were not too ambitious. He undertakes
all things, and finishes none. But a smooth tongue, a
knowing look, and a great capacity of labour, carry him
through. Let him but like his ale and his master, and he
will do work enough for four. Give him his own way,
and his full quantum, and nothing comes amiss to him.

Ah, May is bounding forward! Her silly heart leaps
at the sight of the old place—and so in good truth does
mine. What a pretty place it was—or rather, how pretty
I thought it! I suppose I should have thought any place
so where I had spent eighteen happy years. But it was
really pretty. A large, heavy, white house, in the simplest
style, surrounded by fine oaks and elms, and tall, massy
plantations shaded down into a beautiful lawn by wild
overgrown shrubs, bowery acacias, ragged sweet-briers,
promontories of dog-wood, and Portugal laurel, and bays
overhung by laburnum and bird-cherry; a long piece of
water letting light into the picture, and looking just like a
natural stream, the banks as rude and wild as the shrubbery, interspersed with broom, and furze, and bramble,
and pollard oaks covered with ivy and honeysuckle; the
whole enclosed by an old mossy park paling, and terminating in a series of rich meadows, richly planted.
This is an exact description of the home which, three
years ago, it nearly broke my heart to leave. What a
tearing up by the root it was; I have pitied cabbage-
plants and celery, and all transplantable things, ever
since; though, in common with them, and with other
vegetables, the first agony of the transportation being
over, I have taken such firm and tenacious hold of my new
soil, that I would not for the world be pulled up again,
even to be restored to the old beloved ground—not even
if its beauty were undiminished, which is by no means the
case; for in those three years it has thrice changed
masters, and every successive possessor has brought

the curse of improvement upon the place ; so that between
filling up the water to cure dampness, cutting down trees
to let in prospects, planting to keep them out, shutting up
windows to darken the inside of the house (by which
means one end looks precisely as an eight of spades would
do that should have the misfortune to lose one of his
corner pips), and building colonnades to lighten the out,
added to a general clearance of pollards, and brambles,
and ivy, and honeysuckles, and park palings, and irregular
shrubs, the poor place is so transmogrified, that if it had
its old looking-glass, the water, back again, it would not
know its own face.   And yet I love to haunt round about
it : so does May.   Her particular attraction is a certain
broken bank full of rabbit burrows, into which she
insinuates her long, pliant head and neck, and tears her
pretty feet by vain scratchings ; mine is a warm, sunny
hedge-row, in the same remote field, famous for early
flowers.   Never was a spot more variously flowery :
primroses yellow, lilac white, violets of either hue, cowslips,
oxslips, arums, orchises, wild hyacinths, ground ivy,
pansies, strawberries, heart's-ease, formed a small part
of the Flora of that wild hedge-row.   How profusely they
covered the sunny open slope under the weeping birch,
" the lady of the woods "—and how often have I started
to see the early innocent brown snake, who loved the
spot as well as I did, winding along the young blossoms,
or rustling among the fallen leaves !   There are primrose
leaves already, and short, green buds, but no flowers ;
not even in that furze cradle so full of roots, where they
used to blow as in a basket.   No, my May, no rabbits !
no primroses !   We may as well get over the gate into
the woody winding lane, which will bring us home again.

Here we are making the best of our way between the
old elms that arch so solemnly overhead, dark and
sheltered even now.   They say that a spirit haunts this
deep pool—a white lady without a head.   I cannot say

that I have seen her, often as I have paced this lane at deep midnight, to hear the nightingales, and look at the glowworms—but there, better and rarer than a thousand ghosts, dearer even than nightingales or glowworms, there is a primrose, the first of the year ; a tuft of primroses, springing in yonder sheltered nook, from the mossy roots of an old willow, and living again in the clear, bright pool. Oh, how beautiful they are—three fully blown, and two bursting buds ! How glad I am I came this way ! They are not to be reached. Even Jack Rapley's love of the difficult and unattainable would fail him here : May herself could not stand on that steep bank. So much the better. Who could wish to disturb them ? There they live in their innocent and fragrant beauty, sheltered from the storms, and rejoicing in the sunshine, and looking as if they could feel their happiness. Who would disturb them ? Oh, how glad I am I came this way home !

VIOLETING

MARCH 27th.—It is a dull, grey morning, with a dewy feeling in the air; fresh, but not windy; cool, but not cold; the very day for a person newly arrived from the heat, the glare, the noise, and the fever of London, to plunge into the remotest labyrinths of the country, and regain the repose of mind, the calmness of heart, which has been lost in that great Babel. I must go violeting— it is a necessity—and I must go alone; the sound of a voice, even my Lizzy's, the touch of Mayflower's head, even the bounding of her elastic foot, would disturb the serenity of feeling which I am trying to recover. I shall go quite alone, with my little basket, twisted like a bee-hive, which I love so well, because *she* gave it to me, and kept sacred to violets and to those whom I love; and I shall get out of the highroad the moment I can. I would not meet any one just now, even of those whom I best like to meet.

Ha!—Is not that group—a gentleman on a blood-horse, a lady keeping pace with him so gracefully and easily—see how prettily her veil waves in the wind created by her own rapid motion!—and that gay, gallant boy, on the gallant white Arabian, curveting at their side, but ready to spring before them every instant—is not that chivalrous-looking party Mr. and Mrs. M., and dear B.? No! the servant is in a different livery. It is some of the ducal family, and one of their young Etonians. I may go on. I shall meet no one now; for I have fairly left the road, and am crossing the lea by one of those wandering paths, amidst the gorse, and the heath,

34

and the low broom, which the sheep and lambs have made—a path turfy, elastic, thymy and sweet, even at this season.

We have the good fortune to live in an unenclosed parish, and may thank the wise obstinacy of two or three sturdy farmers, and the lucky unpopularity of a ranting madcap lord of the manor, for preserving the delicious green patches, the islets of wilderness amidst cultivation, which form, perhaps, the peculiar beauty of English scenery. The common that I am passing now—the lea, as it is called—is one of the loveliest of these favoured spots. It is a little sheltered scene, retiring, as it were, from the village; sunk amidst higher lands—hills would be almost too grand a word: edged on one side by one gay highroad, and intersected by another; and surrounded by a most picturesque confusion of meadows, cottages, farms, and orchards; with a great pond in one corner, unusually bright and clear, giving a delightful cheerfulness and daylight to the picture. The swallows haunt that pond; so do the children. There is a merry group round it now; I have seldom seen it without one. Children love water, clear, bright, sparkling water; it excites and feeds their curiosity; it is motion and life.

The path that I am treading leads to a less lively spot, to that large, heavy building on one side of the common, whose solid wings, jutting out far beyond the main body, occupy three sides of a square, and give a cold, shadowy look to the court. On one side is a gloomy garden, with an old man digging in it, laid out in straight dark beds of vegetables, potatoes, cabbages, onions, beans; all earthly and mouldy as a newly-dug grave. Not a flower or flowering shrub! Not a rose-tree or currant-bush! Nothing but for sober, melancholy use. Oh, different from the long irregular slips of the cottage-gardens, with their gay bunches of polyanthuses and crocuses, their wallflowers sending sweet odours through the narrow casement, and their gooseberry trees bursting into a brilliancy of leaf, whose vivid greenness has the effect of a blossom on the eye! Oh, how different! On the other side of this gloomy abode is a meadow of that deep, intense emerald hue, which denotes the presence of stagnant water, surrounded by willows at regular distances, and like the garden, separated from the common by a wide, moat-like ditch. That is the parish workhouse. All about it is solid, substantial, useful; but so dreary! so cold! so dark! There are children in the court, and yet all is silent. I always hurry past the place as if it were a prison. Restraint, sickness, age, extreme poverty, misery, which I have no power to remove or alleviate—these are the ideas, the feelings, which the sight of those walls excites; yet, perhaps, if not certainly, they contain less of that extreme desolation than the morbid fancy is apt to paint. There will be found order, cleanliness, food, clothing, warmth, refuge for the homeless, medicine and attendance for the sick, rest and sufficiency for old age, and sympathy—the true and active sympathy which the poor show to the poor—for the unhappy. There may be worse places than a parish workhouse—and yet I hurry past it. The feeling, the prejudice, will not be controlled.

The end of the dreary garden edges off into a close-sheltered lane, wandering and winding, like a rivulet, in gentle " sinuosities " (to use a word once applied by Mr. Wilberforce to the Thames at Henley), amidst green meadows, all alive with cattle, sheep, and beautiful lambs, in the very spring and pride of their tottering prettiness; or fields of arable land, more lively still with troops of stooping bean-setters, women and children, in all varieties of costume and colour; and ploughs and harrows, with their whistling boys and steady carters, going through, with a slow and plodding industry, the main business of this busy season. What work bean-setting is! What a reverse of the position assigned to man to distinguish him

from the beasts of the field! Only think of stooping
for six, eight, ten hours a-day, drilling holes in the earth
with a little stick, and then dropping in the beans one by
one. They are paid according to the quantity they plant :
and some of the poor women used to be accused of clumping
them—that is to say, of dropping more than one bean
into a hole. It seems to me, considering the temptation,
that not to clump is to be at the very pinnacle of human
virtue.

Another turn in the lane, and we come to the old house
standing amongst the high elms—the old farm-house,
which always, I don't know why, carries back my imagination to Shakespeare's days. It is a long, low, irregular
building, with one room, at an angle from the house,
covered with ivy, fine white-veined ivy ; the first floor of
the main building projecting and supported by oaken
beams, and one of the windows below, with its old casement
and long narrow panes, forming the half of a shallow
hexagon. A porch, with seats in it, surmounted by a
pinnacle, pointed roofs, and clustered chimneys, complete
the picture ! Alas ! it is little else but a picture ! The
very walls are crumbling to decay under a careless landlord
and ruined tenant.

Now a few yards farther, and I reach the bank. Ah !
I smell them already—their exquisite perfume steams
and lingers in this moist, heavy air. Through this little
gate, and along the green south bank of this green wheat-
field, and they burst upon me, the lovely violets, in tenfold
loveliness. The ground is covered with them, white
and purple, enamelling the short, dewy grass, looking but
the more vividly coloured under the dull, leaden sky.
There they lie by hundreds, by thousands. In former
years I have been used to watch them from the tiny green
bud, till one or two stole into bloom. They never came
on me before in such a sudden and luxuriant glory of simple
beauty—and I do really owe one pure and genuine pleasure

to feverish London! How beautifully they are placed, too, on this sloping bank, with the palm branches waving over them, full of early bees, and mixing their honeyed scent with the more delicate violet odour! How transparent and smooth and lusty are the branches, full of sap and life! And there, just by the old mossy root, is a superb tuft of primroses, with a yellow butterfly hovering over them, like a flower floating on the air. What happiness to sit on this tufty knoll, and fill my basket with the blossoms! What a renewal of heart and mind! To inhabit such a scene of peace and sweetness is again to be fearless, gay, and gentle as a child. Then it is that thought becomes poetry, and feeling religion. Then it is that we are happy and good. Oh, that my whole life could pass so, floating on blissful and innocent sensation, enjoying in peace and gratitude the common blessings of Nature, thankful above all for the simple habits, the healthful temperament, which render them so dear! Alas! who may dare expect a life of such happiness? But I can at least snatch and prolong the fleeting pleasure, can fill my basket with pure flowers, and my heart with pure thoughts; can gladden my little home with their sweetness; can divide my treasures with one, a dear one, who cannot seek them; can see them when I shut my eyes; and dream of them when I fall asleep.

THE COWSLIP-BALL

MAY 16th.—There are moments in life when, without any visible or immediate cause, the spirits sink and fail, as it were, under the mere pressure of existence ; moments of unaccountable depression, when one is weary of one's very thoughts, haunted by images that will not depart—images many and various, but all painful ; friends lost, or changed, or dead ; hopes disappointed even in their accomplishment ; fruitless regrets, powerless wishes, doubt and fear, and self-distrust and self-disapprobation. They who have known these feelings (and who is there so happy as not to have known some of them ?) will understand why Alfieri became powerless and Froissart dull ; and why even needlework, the most effectual sedative, that grand soother and composer of woman's distress, fails to comfort me to-day. I will go out into the air this cool pleasant afternoon, and try what that will do. I fancy that exercise, or exertion of any kind, is the true specific for nervousness. "Fling but a stone, the giant dies." I will go to the meadows, the beautiful meadows ! and I will have my materials of happiness, Lizzy and May, and a basket for flowers, and we will make a cowslip-ball. "Did you ever see a cowslip-ball, my Lizzy ?" "No." "Come away, then ; make haste ! run Lizzy ! "

And on we go, fast, fast ! down the road, across the lea, past the workhouse, along by the great pond, till we slide into the deep, narrow lane, whose hedges seem to meet over the water, and win our way to the little farm-house at the end. "Through the farm-yard, Lizzy ; over the gate ; never mind the cows ; they are quiet enough."—

" I don't mind 'em," said Miss Lizzy, boldly and truly, and with a proud, affronted air, displeased at being thought to mind anything, and showing by her attitude and manner some design of proving her courage by an attack on the largest of the herd, in the shape of a pull by the tail. " I don't mind 'em."—" I know you don't, Lizzy ; but let them alone, and don't chase the turkey-cock. Come to me, my dear ! " and, for a wonder, Lizzy came.

In the meantime, my other pet, Mayflower, had also gotten into a scrape. She had driven about a huge, unwieldly sow, till the animal's grunting had disturbed the repose of a still more enormous Newfoundland dog, the guardian of the yard. Out he sallied, growling, from the depth of his kennel, erecting his tail, and shaking his long chain. May's attention was instantly diverted from the sow to this new playmate, friend or foe, she cared not which ; and he of the kennel, seeing his charge unhurt, and out of danger, was at leisure to observe the charms of his fair enemy, as she frolicked around him, always beyond the reach of his chain, yet always, with the natural instinctive coquetry of her sex, alluring him to the pursuit which she know to be vain. I never saw a prettier flirtation. At last the noble animal, wearied out, retired to the inmost recesses of his habitation, and would not even approach her when she stood right before the entrance. " You are properly served, May. Come along, Lizzy. Across this wheat-field, and now over the gate. Stop ! let me lift you down. No jumping, no breaking of necks, Lizzy ! " And here we are in the meadows, and out of the world. Robinson Crusoe in his lonely island had scarcely a more complete or a more beautiful solitude.

These meadows consist of a double row of small enclosures of rich grass-land, a mile or two in length, sloping down from high arable grounds on either side, to a little nameless brook that winds between them with a course which, in its infinite variety, clearness, and rapidity, seems to emulate the bold rivers of the north, of whom, far more than of our lazy southern streams, our rivulet presents a miniature likeness. Never was water more exquisitely tricksy—now darting over the bright pebbles, sparkling and flashing in the light with a bubbling music, as sweet and wild as the song of the woodlark; now stretching quietly along, giving back the rich tufts of the golden marsh-marigolds which grow on its margin; now sweeping round a fine reach of green grass, rising steeply into a high mount, a mimic promontory, whilst the other side sinks softly away, like some tiny bay, and the water flows between, so clear, so wide, so shallow, that Lizzy, longing for adventure, is sure she could cross unwetted; now dashing through two sand-banks, a torrent deep and narrow, which May clears at a bound; now sleeping, half hidden, beneath the alders, hawthorns, and wild roses, with which the banks are so profusely and variously fringed, whilst flags,* lilies, and other aquatic plants, almost cover the surface of the stream. In good truth, it is a beautiful brook, and one that Walton himself might have sitten by and loved, for trout are there; we see them as they dart up the stream, and hear and start at the sudden plunge when they spring to the surface for the summer flies. Izaak Walton would have loved our brook and our quiet meadows; they breathe the very spirit of his own peaceful-

---

* Walking along these meadows one bright sunny afternoon, a year or two back, and rather later in the season, I had an opportunity of noticing a curious circumstance in natural history. Standing close to the edge of the stream, I remarked a singular appearance on a large tuft of flags. It looked like bunches of flowers, the leaves of which seemed dark, yet transparent, intermingled with brilliant tubes of bright blue or shining green. On examining this phenomenon more closely, it turned out to be several clusters of dragon-flies, just emerged from their deformed chrysalis state, and still torpid and motionless from the wetness of their filmy wings. Half-an-hour later we returned to the spot and they were gone. We had seen them at the very moment when beauty was complete and animation dormant. I have since found nearly a similar account of this curious process in Mr. Bingley's entertaining work, called *Animal Biography.*

ness, a soothing quietude that sinks into the soul. There is no path through them, not one; we might wander a whole spring day and not see a trace of human habitation. They belong to a number of small proprietors, who allow each other access through their respective grounds from pure kindness and neighbourly feeling; a privilege never abused; and the fields on the other side of the water are reached by a rough plank, or a tree thrown across, or some such homely bridge. We ourselves possess one of the most beautiful; so that the strange pleasure of property, that instinct which makes Lizzy delight in her broken doll, and May in the bare bone which she has pilfered from the kennel of her recreant admirer of Newfoundland, is added to the other charms of this enchanting scenery; a strange pleasure it is when one so poor as I can feel it! Perhaps it is felt most by the poor, with the rich it may be less intense—too much diffused and spread out, becoming thin by expansion, like leaf-gold; the little of the poor may be not only more precious, but more pleasant to them; certain that bit of grassy and blossomy earth, with its green knolls and tufted bushes, its old pollards wreathed with ivy, and its bright and babbling waters, is very dear to me. But I must always have loved these meadows, so fresh, and cool, and delicious to the eye and to the tread, full of cowslips, and of all vernal flowers: Shakespeare's song of spring bursts irrepressibly from our lips as we step on them—

> " When daisies pied, and violets blue,
>   And lady-smocks all silver white,
>   And cuckoo-buds of yellow hue,
>   Do paint the meadows with delight,
>   The cuckoo then on every tree——"

" Cuckoo! cuckoo!" cried Lizzy, breaking in with her clear, childish voice; and immediately, as if at her call, the real bird, from a neighbouring tree (for these meadows are dotted with timber like a park), began to echo my

lovely little girl, "Cuckoo! cuckoo!" I have a prejudice
very unpastoral and unpoetical (but I cannot help it, I
have many such) against this "harbinger of spring."
His note is so monotonous, so melancholy; and then the
boys mimic him; one hears "Cuckoo! cuckoo!" in
dirty streets, amongst smoky houses, and the bird is hated
for faults not his own. But prejudices of taste, likings, and
dislikings, are not always vanquishable by reason; so,
to escape the serenade from the tree, which promised to
to be of considerable duration (when once that eternal
song begins, on it goes ticking like a clock)—to escape that
noise, I determined to excite another, and challenged
Lizzy to a cowslip-gathering; a trial of skill and speed,
to see which would soonest fill her basket. My stratagem
succeeded completely. What scrambling, what shouting,
what glee from Lizzy! twenty cuckoos might have sung
unheard whilst she was pulling her own flowers, and
stealing mine, and laughing, screaming, and talking
through all.

At last the baskets were filled, and Lizzy declared victor;
and down we sat, on the brink of the stream, under a
spreading hawthorn, just disclosing its own pearly buds,
and surrounded with the rich and enamelled flowers of
the wild hyacinth, blue and white, to make our cowslip-
ball. Every one knows the process: to nip off the tuft
of flowerets just below the top of the stalk, and hang each
cluster nicely balanced across a riband, till you have a
long string like a garland; then to press them closely
together, and tie them tightly up. We went on very
prosperously, *considering*—as people say of a young lady's
drawing, or a Frenchman's English, or a woman's tragedy,
or of the poor little dwarf who works without fingers, or
the ingenious sailor who writes with his toes, or generally
of any performance which is accomplished by means
seemingly inadequate to its production. To be sure we
met with a few accidents. First, Lizzy spoiled nearly

all her cowslips by snapping them off too short ; so there
was a fresh gathering ; in the next place, May overset
my full basket, and sent the blossoms floating, like so
many fairy favours, down the brook ; then, when we were
going on pretty steadily, just as we had made a superb
wreath, and were thinking of tying it together, Lizzy,
who held the riband, caught a glimpse of a gorgeous butterfly, all brown and red and purple, and skipping off to pursue
the new object, let go her hold ; so all our treasures were
abroad again. At last, however, by dint of taking a
branch of alder as a substitute for Lizzy, and hanging the
basket in a pollard-ash, out of sight of May, the cowslip-
ball was finished. What a concentration of fragrance
and beauty it was ! golden and sweet to satiety ! rich
to sight, and touch, and smell ! Lizzy was enchanted,
and ran off with her prize, hiding amongst the trees in the
very coyness of ecstasy, as if any human eye, even mine,
would be a restraint on her innocent raptures.

In the meanwhile I sat listening, not to my enemy
the cuckoo, but to a whole concert of nightingales, scarcely
interrupted by any meaner bird, answering and vying with
each other in those short, delicious strains which are to the
ear as roses to the eye ; those snatches of lovely sound
which come across us as airs from heaven. Pleasant
thoughts, delightful associations, awoke as I listened ; and
almost unconsciously I repeated to myself the beautiful
story of the Lutist and the Nightingale, from Ford's
Lover's Melancholy. Here it is. Is there in English
poetry anything finer ?

> " Passing from Italy to Greece, the tales
>   Which poets of an elder time have feign'd
>   To glorify their Tempe, bred in me
>   Desire of visiting Paradise.
>   To Thessaly I came, and living private,
>   Without acquaintance of more sweet companions
>   Than the old inmates to my love, my thoughts,
>   I day by day frequented silent groves

And solitary walks.   One morning early
This accident encounter'd me : I heard
The sweetest and most ravishing contention
That art and nature ever were at strife in.
A sound of music touch'd mine ears, or rather,
Indeed, entranced my soul ; as I stole nearer,
Invited by the melody, I saw
This youth, this fair-faced youth, upon his lute
With strains of strange variety and harmony
Proclaiming, as it seem'd, so bold a challenge
To the clear choristers of the woods, the birds,
That as they flock'd about him, all stood silent,
Wondering at what they heard.   I wonder'd too.
A nightingale,
Nature's best skill'd musician, undertakes
The challenge ; and for every several strain
The well-shaped youth could touch, she sang him down.
He could not run divisions with more art
Upon his quaking instrument than she,
The Nightingale, did with her various notes
Reply to.
Some time thus spent, the young man grew at last
Into a pretty anger, that a bird,
Whom art had never taught clefs, moods, or notes,
Should vie with him for mastery, whose study
Had busied many hours to perfect practice.
To end the controversy, in a rapture
Upon his instrument he plays so swiftly,
So many voluntaries, and so quick,
That there was curiosity and cunning,
Concord in discord, lines of different method
Meeting in one full centre of delight.
The bird (ordain'd to be
Music's first martyr) strove to imitate
These several sounds ; which, when her warbling throat
Fail'd in, for grief down dropt she on his lute,
And brake her heart.   It was the quaintest sadness
To see the conqueror upon her hearse
To weep a funeral elegy of tears.
He looked upon the trophies of his art,
Then sigh'd, then wiped his eyes ; then sigh'd and cry'd,
' Alas ! poor creature, I will soon revenge
This cruelty upon the author of it.
Henceforth this lute, guilty of innocent blood,
Shall never more betray a harmless peace

To an untimely end ; ' and in that sorrow,
As he was pashing it against a tree,
I suddenly stept in."

When I had finished the recitation of this exquisite
passage, the sky, which had been all the afternoon dull
and heavy, began to look more and more threatening ;
darker clouds, like wreaths of black smoke, flew across
the dead leaden tint ; a cooler, damper air blew over the
meadows, and a few large, heavy drops splashed in the
water. " We shall have a storm. Lizzy ! May ! where
are ye ? Quick, quick, my Lizzy ! run, run ! faster,
faster ! "

And off we ran ; Lizzy not at all displeased at the
thoughts of a wetting, to which, indeed, she is almost
as familiar as a duck ; May, on the other hand, peering
up at the weather, and shaking her pretty ears with mani-
fest dismay. Of all animals, next to a cat, a greyhound
dreads rain. She might have escaped it ; her light feet
would have borne her home long before the shower ; but
May is too faithful for that, too true a comrade, under-
stands too well the laws of good-fellowship ; so she waited
for us. She did, to be sure, gallop on before, and then stop
and look back, and beckon, as it were, with some scorn in
her black eyes at the slowness of our progress. We in the
meanwhile got on as fast as we could, encouraging and
reproaching each other. " Faster, my Lizzy ! Oh, what
a bad runner ! "—" Faster, faster ! Oh, what a bad
runner ! " echoed my sauce-box. " You are so fat,
Lizzy, you make no way ! "—" Ah ! who else is fat ? "
retorted the darling. Certainly her mother is right ;
I do spoil that child.

By this time we were thoroughly soaked, all three.
It was a pelting shower, that drove through our thin
summer clothing, and poor May's short glossy coat, in
a moment. And then, when we were wet to the skin,
the sun came out, actually the sun, as if to laugh at our

plight; and then, more provoking still, when the sun was shining, and the shower over, came a maid and a boy to look after us, loaded with cloaks and umbrellas enough to fence us against a whole day's rain. Never mind! on we go, faster and faster; Lizzy obliged to be most ignobly carried, having had the misfortune to lose a shoe in the mud, which we left the boy to look after.

Here we are at home—dripping; but glowing and laughing, and bearing our calamity most manfully. May, a dog of excellent sense, went instantly to bed in the stable, and is at this moment over head and ears in straw; Lizzy is gone to bed too, coaxed into that wise measure by a promise of tea and toast, and of not going home till to-morrow, and the story of Little Red Riding Hood; and I am enjoying the luxury of dry clothing by a good fire. Really, getting wet through now and then is no bad thing, finery apart; for one should not like spoiling a new pelisse, or a handsome plume; but when there is nothing in question but a white gown and a straw bonnet, as was the case to-day, it is rather pleasant than not. The little chill refreshes, and our enjoyment of the subsequent warmth and dryness is positive and absolute. Besides, the stimulus and exertion do good to the mind as well as body. How melancholy I was all the morning! how cheerful I am now! Nothing like a shower-bath— a real shower-bath, such as Lizzy and May and I have undergone, to cure low spirits. Try it, my dear readers, if ever ye be nervous—I will answer for its success.

THE HARD SUMMER

AUGUST 15th.—Cold, cloudy, windy, wet. Here we are, in the midst of the dog-days, clustering merrily round the warm hearth like so many crickets, instead of chirruping in the green fields like that other merry insect, the grasshopper; shivering under the influence of the *Jupiter Pluvius* of England, the watery St. Swithin; peering at that scarce personage, the sun, when he happens to make his appearance, as intently as astronomers look after a comet, or the common people stare at a balloon; exclaiming against the cold weather, just as we used to exclaim against the warm. "What a change from last year!" is the first sentence you hear, go where you may. Everybody remarks it, and everybody complains of it; and yet in my mind it has its advantages, or at least its compensations, as everything in nature has, if we would only take the trouble to seek for them.

Last year in spite of the love which we are now pleased to profess towards that ardent luminary, not one of the sun's numerous admirer's had courage to look him in the face: there was no bearing the world till he had said "good-night" to it. Then we might stir: then we began to wake and to live. All day long we languished under his influence in a strange dreaminess, too hot to work, too hot to read, too hot to write, too hot even to talk; sitting hour after hour in a green arbour, embowered in leafiness, letting thought and fancy float as they would. Those day-dreams were pretty things in their way; there is no denying that. But then, if one half of the world were to dream through a whole summer, like the sleeping

48

Beauty in the Wood, what would become of the other ?

The only office requiring the slightest exertion which I performed in that warm weather was watering my flowers. Common sympathy called for that labour. The poor things withered, and faded, and pined away ; they almost, so to say, panted for draught. Moreover, if I had not watered them myself, I suspect that no one else would ; for water last year was nearly as precious hereabout as wine. Our land-springs were dried up ; our wells were exhausted ; our deep ponds were dwindling into mud ; and geese, and ducks, and pigs, and laundresses, used to look with a jealous and suspicious eye on the few and scanty half-buckets of that impure element, which my trusty lackey was fain to filch for my poor geraniums and campanulas and tuberoses. We were forced to smuggle them in through my faithful adherent's territories, the stable, to avoid lectures within doors ; and at last even that resource failed ; my garden, my blooming garden, the joy of my eyes, was forced to go waterless like its neighbours, and became shrivelled, scorched, and sunburnt, like them. It really went to my heart to look at it.

On the other side of the house matters were still worse. What a dusty world it was, when about sunset we became cool enough to creep into it ! Flowers in the court looking fit for a *hortus siccus* ; mummies of plants, dried as in an oven ; hollyhocks, once pink, turned into Quakers ; cloves smelling of dust. Oh, dusty world ! May herself looked of that complexion ; so did Lizzy ; so did all the houses, windows, chickens, children, trees, and pigs in the village ; so above all did the shoes. No foot could make three plunges into that abyss of pulverised gravel, which had the impudence to call itself a hard road, without being clothed with a coat a quarter of an inch thick. Woe to white gowns ! woe to black ! Drab was your only wear.

Then, when we were out of the street, what a toil it was to mount the hill, climbing with weary steps and slow upon the brown turf by the way-side, slippery, hot, and hard as a rock ! And then if we happened to meet a carriage coming along the middle of the road—the bottomless middle—what a sandy whirlwind it was ! What choking ! what suffocation ! No state could be more pitiable, except, indeed, that of the travellers who carry this misery about with them. I shall never forget the plight in which we met the coach one evening in last August, full an hour after its time, steeds and driver, carriage and passengers, all in dust. The outsiders, and the horses, and the coachman, seemed reduced to a torpid quietness, the resignation of despair. They had left off trying to better their condition, and taken refuge in a wise and patient hopelessness, bent to endure in silence the extremity of ill. The six insides, on the contrary, were still fighting against their fate, vainly struggling to ameliorate their hapless destiny. They were visibly grumbling at the weather, scolding at the dust, and heating themselves like a furnace, by striving against the heat. How well I remember the fat gentleman without his coat, who was wiping his forehead, heaving up his wig, and certainly uttering that English ejaculation, which, to our national reproach, is the phrase of our language best known on the continent. And that poor boy, red-hot, all in a flame, whose mamma, having divested her own person of all superfluous apparel, was trying to relieve his sufferings by the removal of his neckerchief—an operation which he resisted with all his might. How perfectly I remember him, as well as the pale girl who sat opposite, fanning herself with her bonnet into an absolute fever ! They vanished after a while into their own dust ; but I have them all before my eyes at this moment, a companion picture to Hogarth's Afternoon, a standing lesson to the grumblers at cold summers.

For my part, I really like this wet season. It keeps

us within, to be sure, rather more than is quite agreeable ; but then we are at least awake and alive there, and the world out of doors is so much the pleasanter when we can get abroad. Everything does well, except those fastidious bipeds, men and women ; corn ripens, grass grows, fruit is plentiful ; there is no lack of birds to eat it, and there has not been such a wasp-season these dozen years. My garden wants no watering, and is more beautiful than ever, beating my old rival in that primitive art, the pretty wife of the little mason, out and out. Measured with mine, her flowers are naught. Look at those hollyhocks, like pyramids of roses ; those garlands of the convolvulus major of all colours, hanging around that tall pole, like the wreathy hop-bine ; those magnificent dusky cloves, breathing of the Spice Islands ; those flaunting double dahlias ; those splendid scarlet geraniums, and those fierce and warlike flowers, the tiger-lilies. Oh, how beautiful they are ! Besides, the weather clears sometimes—it has cleared this evening ; and here are we, after a merry walk up the hill, almost as quick as in the winter, bounding lightly along the bright green turf of the pleasant common, enticed by the gay shouts of a dozen clear, young voices, to linger awhile, and see the boys play at cricket.

I plead guilty to a strong partiality towards that unpopular class of beings, country boys ; I have a large acquaintance amongst them, and I can almost say, that I know good of many and harm of none. In general, they are an open, spirited, good-humoured race, with a proneness to embrace the pleasures and eschew the evils of their condition, a capacity for happiness, quite unmatched in man, or woman, or a girl. They are patient, too, and bear their fate as scape-goats (for all sins whatsoever are laid, as matters of course, to their door), whether at home or abroad, with amazing resignation ; and, considering the many lies of which they are the objects, they tell

wonderfully few in return. The worst that can be said of
them is, that they seldom, when grown to man's estate,
keep the promise of their boyhood ; but that is a fault to
come—a fault that may not come, and ought not to be
anticipated. It is astonishing how sensible they are to
notice from their betters, or those whom they think such.
I do not speak of money, or gifts, or praise, or the more
coarse and common briberies—they are more delicate
courtiers ; a word, a nod, a smile, or the mere calling of
them by their names, is enough to insure their hearts
and their services. Half-a-dozen of them, poor urchins,
have run away now to bring us chairs from their several
homes. "Thank you, Joe Kirby! you are always first—
yes, that is just the place—I shall see everything there.
Have you been in yet, Joe ? "—" No, ma'am ! I go in
next."—" Ah, I am glad of that—and now's the time.
Really, that was a pretty ball of Jem Eusden's !—I was
sure it would go to the wicket. Run, Joe ! They are waiting for you." There was small need to bid Joe Kirby
make haste ; I think he is, next to a race-horse, or a greyhound, or a deer, the fastest creature that runs—the most
completely alert and active. Joe is mine especial friend,
and leader of the "tender juveniles," as Joel Brent is of the
adults. In both instances this post of honour was gained
by merit, even more remarkably so in Joe's case than in
Joel's ; for Joe is a less boy than many of his companions
(some of whom are fifteeners and sixteeners, quite as tall
and nearly as old as Tom Coper), and a poorer than all,
as may be conjectured from the lamentable state of that
patched, round frock, and the ragged condition of those
unpatched shoes, which would encumber, if anything
could, the light feet that wear them. But why should
I lament the poverty that never troubles him ? Joe is
the merriest and happiest creature that ever lived twelve
years in this wicked world. Care cannot come near him.
He hath a perpetual smile on his round, ruddy face, and

a laugh in his hazel eye that drives the witch away. He works at yonder farm on the top of the hill, where he is in such repute for intelligence and good-humour, that he has the honour of performing all the errands of the house, of helping the maid, the mistress, and the master, in addition to his own stated office of carter's boy. There he works hard from five till seven, and then he comes here to work still harder, under the name of play—batting, bowling, and fielding, as if for life, filling the place of four boys; being, at a pinch, a whole eleven. The late Mr. Knyvett, the king's organist, who used in his own person to sing twenty parts at once of the hallelujah chorus, so that you would have thought he had a nest of nightingales in his throat, was but a type of Joe Kirby. There is a sort of ubiquity about him; he thinks nothing of being in two places at once, and for pitching a ball, William Grey himself is nothing to him. It goes straight to the mark like a bullet. He is king of the cricketers from eight to sixteen, both inclusive, and an excellent ruler he makes. Nevertheless, in the best-ordered states there will be grumblers, and we have an opposition here in the shape of Jem Eusden.

Jem Eusden is a stunted lad of thirteen, or thereabout, lean, small, and short, yet strong and active. His face is of an extraordinary ugliness, colourless, withered, haggard, with a look of extreme age, much increased by hair so light that it might rather pass for white than flaxen. He is constantly arrayed in the blue cap and old-fashioned coat, the costume of an endowed school to which he belongs; where he sits still all day, and rushes into the field at night, fresh, untired, and ripe for action, to scold, and brawl, and storm, and bluster. He hates Joe Kirby, whose immovable good-humour, broad smiles, and knowing nods, must certainly be very provoking to so fierce and turbulent a spirit; and he has himself (being, except by rare accident, no great player)

the preposterous ambition of wishing to be manager of
the sports. In short, he is a demagogue in embryo, with
every quality necessary to a splendid success in that
vocation—a strong voice, a fluent utterance, an incessant iteration, and a frontless impudence. He is a great
" scholar " too, to use the country phrase ; his " piece,"
as our village schoolmaster terms a fine sheet of flourishing
writing, something, between a valentine and a sampler,
enclosed within a border of little coloured prints—his last,
I remember, was encircled by an engraved history of Moses,
beginning at the finding in the bulrushes, with Pharaoh's
daughter dressed in a rose-coloured gown and blue feathers
—his piece is not only the admiration of the school, but of
the parish, and is sent triumphantly round from house to
house at Christmas, to extort halfpence and sixpences
from all encouragers of learning—*Montem* in miniature.
The Mosaic history was so successful, that the produce
enabled Jem to purchase a bat and ball, which, besides adding to his natural arrogance (for the little pedant actually
began to mutter against being eclipsed by a dunce, and
went so far as to challenge Joe Kirby to a trial in Practice,
or the Rule of Three), gave him, when compared with the
general poverty, a most unnatural preponderance in the
cricket state. He had the ways and means in his hands—
(for, alas ! the hard winter had made sad havoc among
the bats, and the best ball was a bad one)—he had the
ways and means, could withhold the supplies, and his
party was beginning to wax strong, when Joe received a
present of two bats and a ball for the youngsters in
general and himself in particular—and Jem's adherents
left him on the spot—they ratted, to a man, that very
evening. Notwithstanding this desertion, their forsaken
leader has in nothing relaxed from his pretensions or his
ill-humour. He still quarrels and brawls as if he had a
faction to back him, and thinks nothing of contending with
both sides, the ins and the outs, secure of out-talking the

whole field. He has been squabbling these ten minutes, and is just marching off now with his own bat (he has never deigned to use one of Joe's) in his hand. What an ill-conditioned hobgoblin it is ! And yet there is something bold and sturdy about him, too. I should miss Jem Eusden.

Ah, there is another deserter from the party ! my friend the little hussar—I do not know his name, and call him after his cap and jacket. He is a very remarkable person, about the age of eight years, the youngest piece of gravity and dignity I ever encountered ; short, and square, and upright, and slow, with a fine, bronzed, flat visage, resembling those convertible signs, the Broad-Face and the Saracen's-Head (which, happening to be next-door neighbours in the town of B., I never knew apart), resembling, indeed, any face that is open-eyed and immovable, the very sign of a boy ! he stalks about with his hands in his breeches pocket, like a piece of machinery ; sits leisurely down when he ought to field, and never gets farther in batting than to stop the ball. His is the only voice never heard in the *mêlée* ; I doubt, indeed, if he have one, which may be partly the reason of a circumstance that I record to his honour, his fidelity to Jem Eusden, to whom he has adhered through every change of fortune, with a tenacity proceeding, perhaps, from an instinctive consciousness that the loquacious leader talks enough for two. He is the only thing resembling a follower that our demagogue possesses, and is cherished by him accordingly. Jem quarrels for him, scolds for him, pushes for him ; and but for Joe Kirby's invincible good-humour, and a just discrimination of the innocent from the guilty, the activity of Jem's friendship would get the poor hussar ten drubbings a-day.

But it is growing late. The sun has set a long time. Only see what a gorgeous colouring has spread itself over those parting masses of clouds in the west—what

a train of rosy light ! We shall have a fine sunshiny day
to-morrow—a blessing not to be under-valued, in spite
of my vituperation of heat. Shall we go home now ?
And shall we take the longest but prettiest road, that by
the green lanes ? This way, to the left, round the corner
of the common, past Mr. Welles's cottage, and our path
lies straight before us. How snug and comfortable that
cottage looks ! Its little yard all alive with the cow
and the mare, and the colt almost as large as the mare,
and the young foal, and the great yard-dog, all so fat !
Fenced in with hay-rick, and wheat-rick, and bean-stack,
and backed by the long garden, the spacious drying-
ground, the fine orchard, and that large field quartered
into four different crops. How comfortable this cottage
looks, and how well the owners earn their comforts !
They are the most prosperous pair in the parish—she a
laundress, with twenty times more work than she can do,
unrivalled in flounces and shirt-frills, and such delicacies
of the craft ; he, partly a farmer, partly a farmer's man,
tilling his own ground, and then tilling other people's—
affording a proof, even in this declining age, when the circumstances of so many worthy members of the community
seem to have " an alacrity in sinking," that it is possible
to amend them by sheer industry. He, who was born in
the workhouse, and bred up as a parish boy, has now,
by mere manual labour, risen to the rank of a land-owner,
pays rates and taxes, grumbles at the times, and is called
Master Welles—the title next to Mister—that by which
Shakespeare was called—what would man have more ?
His wife, besides being the best laundress in the county,
is a comely woman still. There she stands at the spring,
dipping up water for to-morrow—the clear, deep, silent
spring, which sleeps so peacefully under its high, flowery
bank, red with the tall spiral stalks of the foxglove and
their rich, pendant bells, blue with the beautiful forget-
me-not, that gem-like blossom, which looks like a living

jewel of turquoise and topaz. It is almost too late to see its beauty ; and here is the pleasant shady lane, where the high elms will shut out the little twilight that remains. Ah, but we shall have the fairies' lamps to guide us, the stars of the earth, the glowworms ! Here they are, three almost together. Do you not see them ? One seems tremulous, vibrating, as if on the extremity of a leaf of grass ; the others are deeper in the hedge, in some green cell, on which their light falls with an emerald lustre. I hope my friends the cricketers will not come this way home. I would not have the pretty creatures removed for more than I care to say, and in this matter I would hardly trust Joe Kirby—boys so love to stick them in their hats. But this lane is quite deserted. It is only a road from field to field. No one comes here at this hour. They are quite safe ; and I shall walk here to-morrow and visit them again. And now, good night ! beautiful insects, lamp of the fairies, good night !

NUTTING

SEPTEMBER 26th.—One of those delicious autumnal days, when the air, the sky, and the earth seemed lulled into a universal calm, softer and milder even than May. We sallied forth for a walk, in a mood congenial to the weather and the season, avoiding, by mutual consent, the bright and sunny common, and the gay highroad, and stealing through shady, unfrequented lanes, where we were not likely to meet any one—not even the pretty family procession which in other years we used to contemplate with so much interest—the father, mother, and children, returning from the wheat-field, the little ones laden with bristling close-tied bunches of wheat-ears, their own gleanings, or a bottle and a basket which had contained their frugal dinner, whilst the mother would carry her babe, hushing and lulling it, and the father and an elder child trudged after with the cradle, all seeming weary and all happy. We shall not see such a procession as this to-day ; for the harvest is nearly over, the fields are deserted, the silence may almost be felt. Except the wintry notes of the redbreast, nature herself is mute. But how beautiful, how gentle, how harmonious, how rich ! the rain has preserved to the herbage all the freshness and verdure of spring, and the world of leaves has lost nothing of its midsummer brightness, and the harebell is on the banks, and the woodbine in the hedges, and the low furze, which the lambs cropped in the spring, has burst again into its golden blossoms. 58

All is beautiful that the eye can see; perhaps the more beautiful for being shut in with a forest-like closeness. We have no prospect in this labyrinth of lanes, cross-roads, mere cart-ways, leading to the innumerable little farms into which this part of the parish is divided. Uphill or down, these quiet woody lanes scarcely give us a peep at the world, except when, leaning over a gate, we look into one of the small enclosures, hemmed in with hedge-rows, so closely set with growing timber, that the meady opening looks almost like a glade in a wood; or when some cottage, planted at a corner of one of the little greens formed by the meeting of these crossways, almost startles us by the unexpected sight of the dwellings of men in such a solitude. But that we have more of hill and dale, and that our cross-roads are excellent in their kind, this side of our parish would resemble the description given of La Vendée, in Madame Laroche-Jacquelin's most interesting book.* I am sure if wood can entitle a country to be called Le Bocage, none can have a better right to the name. Even this pretty snug farm-house on the hillside, with its front covered with the rich vine, which goes wreathing up to the very top of the clustered chimney, and its sloping orchard full of fruit—even this pretty, quiet nest can hardly peep out of its leaves. Ah! they are gathering in the orchard harvest. Look at that young rogue in the old mossy apple-tree—that great tree, bending with the weight of its golden-rennets—see how he pelts his little sister beneath with apples as red and as round as her own cheeks, while she, with her outstretched frock, is trying to catch them, and laughing and offering to pelt again as often as one bobs against her; and look at that still younger imp, who, as grave as a

---

* An almost equally interesting account of that very peculiar and interesting scenery may be found in *The Maid of La Vendée*, an English novel, remarkable for its simplicity and truth of painting, written by Mrs. Le Noir, the daughter of Christopher Smart, an inheritrix of much of his talent. Her works deserve to be better known.

judge, is creeping on hands and knees under the tree, picking up the apples as they fall so deedily,* and depositing them so honestly in the great basket on the grass, already fixed so firmly and opened so widely, and filled almost to overflowing by the brown rough fruitage of the golden-rennet's next neighbour, the russeting; and see that smallest urchin of all, seated apart in infantine state on the turfy bank, with that toothsome piece of deformity, a crumpling, in each hand, now biting from one sweet, hard, juicy morsel, and now from another. Is not that a pretty English picture? And then, farther up the orchard, that bold, hardy lad, the eldest born, who has scaled (heaven knows how) the tall, straight upper branch of that great pear-tree, and is sitting there as securely and as fearlessly, in as much real safety and apparent danger, as a sailor on the top-mast. Now he shakes the tree with a mighty swing that brings down a pelting shower of stony bergamots, which the father gathers rapidly up, whilst the mother can hardly assist for her motherly fear—a fear which only spurs the spirited boy to bolder ventures. Is not that a pretty picture? And they are such a handsome family too, the Brookers. I do not know that there is any gipsy blood, but there is the true gipsy complexion, richly brown, with cheeks and lips so red, black hair curling close to their heads in short, crisp rings, white shining teeth—and such eyes!—That sort of beauty entirely eclipses your mere roses and lilies. Even Lizzy, the prettiest of fair children, would look poor and watery by the side of Willy Brooker, the sober little personage who is picking up the apples with his small chubby hands, and filling the basket so orderly, next

* "Deedily."—I am not quite sure that this word is good English; but it is genuine Hampshire, and is used by the most correct of female writers, Miss Austen. It means (and it is no small merit that it has no exact synonyme) anything done with a profound and plodding attention, an action which engrosses all the powers of mind and body.

to his father the most useful man in the field. "Willy!"
He hears without seeing; for we are quite hidden by the
high bank, and a spreading hawthorn bush that overtops
it, though between the lower branches and the grass
we have found a convenient peephole. "Willy!" The
voice sounds to him like some fairy dream, and the black
eyes are raised from the ground with sudden wonder, the
long silky eyelashes thrown back till they rest on the
delicate brow, and a deeper blush is burning on those dark
cheeks, and a smile is dimpling about those scarlet lips.
But the voice is silent now, and the little quiet boy, after
a moment's pause, is gone coolly to work again. He is,
indeed, a most lovely child. I think some day or another
he must marry Lizzy; I shall propose the match to their
respective mammas. At present the parties are rather
too young for a wedding—the intended bridegroom being,
as I should judge, six, or thereabout, and the fair bride
barely five—but at least we might have a betrothment
after the royal fashion—there could be no harm in that.
Miss Lizzy, I have no doubt, would be as demure and
coquettish as if ten winters more had gone over her head,
and poor Willy would open his innocent black eyes, and
wonder what was going forward. They would be the very
Oberon and Titania of the village—the fairy king and
queen.

Ah! here is the hedge along which the periwinkle
wreathes and twines so profusely, with its evergreen
leaves shining like the myrtle, and its starry blue flowers.
It is seldom found wild in this part of England; but,
when we do meet with it, it is so abundant and so welcome,—the very robin-redbreast of flowers, a winter
friend. Unless in those unfrequent frosts which destroy
all vegetation, it blossoms from September to June,
surviving the last lingering crane's-bill, forerunning the
earliest primrose, hardier even than the mountain daisy—
peeping out from beneath the snow, looking at itself in the

ice, smiling through the tempests of life, and yet welcoming and enjoying the sunbeams. Oh, to be like that flower!

The little spring that has been bubbling under the hedge all along the hillside, begins, now that we have mounted the eminence and are imperceptibly descending, to deviate into a capricious variety of clear, deep pools and channels, so narrow and so choked with weeds, that a child might overstep them. The hedge has also changed its character. It is no longer the close, compact vegetable wall of hawthorn, and maple, and brier-roses, intertwined with bramble and woodbine, and crowned with large elms or thickly set saplings. No! the pretty meadow which rises high above us, backed and almost surrounded by a tall coppice, needs no defence on our side but its own steep bank, garnished with tufts of broom, with pollard oaks wreathed with ivy, and here and there with long patches of hazel overhanging the water. "Ah, there are still nuts on that bough!" and in an instant my dear companion, active and eager and delighted as a boy, has hooked down with his walking-stick one of the lissome hazel stalks, and cleared it of its tawny clusters, and in another moment he has mounted the bank, and is in the midst of the nuttery, now transferring the spoil from the lower branches into that vast variety of pockets which gentlemen carry about them, now bending the tall tops into the lane, holding them down by main force, so that I might reach them and enjoy the pleasure of collecting some of the plunder myself. A very great pleasure he knew it would be. I doffed my shawl, tucked up my flounces, turned my straw bonnet into a basket, and began gathering and scrambling—for, manage it how you may, nutting is scrambling work—those boughs, however tightly you may grasp them by the young, fragrant twigs and the bright, green leaves, will recoil and burst away; but there is a pleasure even in that; so on we go, scrambling and gathering with all our might and all our glee. Oh what an enjoyment! All my life long I have had a passion for that sort of seeking which implies finding (the secret, I believe, of the love of field-sports, which is in man's mind a natural impulse)—therefore I love violeting—therefore, when we had a fine garden, I used to love to gather strawberries, and cut asparagus, and above all, to collect the filberts from the shrubberies : but this hedge-row nutting beats that sport all to nothing. That is a make-believe thing compared with this ; there was no surprise, no suspense, no unexpectedness—it was as inferior to this wild nutting as the turning out of a bag-fox is to unearthing the fellow, in the eyes of a staunch fox-hunter.

Oh what enjoyment this nut-gathering is ! They are in such abundance, that it seems as if there were not a boy in the parish, nor a young man, nor a young woman—for a basket of nuts is the universal tribute of country gallantry ; our pretty damsel Harriet has had at least half-a-dozen this season ; but no one has found out these. And they are so full, too, we lose half of them from over-ripeness ; they drop from the socket at the slightest motion. If we lose, there is one who finds. May is as fond of nuts as a squirrel, and cracks the shell and extracts the kernel with equal dexterity. Her white glossy head is upturned now to watch them as they fall. See how her neck is thrown back like that of a swan, and how her quick eye follows the rustling noise, and her light feet dance and pat the ground, and leap up with eagerness, seeming almost sustained in the air, just as I have seen her, when Brush is beating a hedge-row, and she knows from his questing that there is a hare afoot. See, she has caught that nut just before it touched the water ; but the water would have been no defence—she fishes them from the bottom, she delves after them amongst the matted grass — even my bonnet — how beggingly she looks at that! " Oh what a pleasure nutting is!—Is it not, May?" May tosses her graceful head as if she understood the question—" And we must go home now —must we not? But we will come nutting again some time or other—shall we not, my May?"

THE VISIT

OCTOBER 27th.—A lovely autumnal day; the air soft, balmy, genial; the sky of that softened and delicate blue upon which the eye loves to rest—the blue which gives such relief to the rich beauty of the earth, all around glowing in the ripe and mellow tints of the most gorgeous of the seasons. Really such an autumn may well compensate our English climate for the fine spring of the south, that spring of which the poets talk, but which we so seldom enjoy. Such an autumn glows upon us like a splendid evening; it is the very sunset of the year; and I have been tempted forth into a wider range of enjoyment than usual. This *walk* (if I may use the Irish figure of speech called a bull) will be a *ride*. A very dear friend has beguiled me into accompanying her in her pretty equipage to her beautiful home, four miles off; and having sent forward in the style of a running footman the servant who had driven her, she assumes the reins, and off we set.

My fair companion is a person whom nature and fortune would have spoiled if they could. She is one of those striking women whom a stranger cannot pass without turning to look at again; tall and finely proportioned, with a bold Roman contour of figure and feature, a delicate English complexion, and an air of distinction altogether her own. Her beauty is duchess-like. She seems born to wear feathers and diamonds, and to form the grace and ornament of a court; and the noble frankness and simplicity of her countenance and manner confirm the impression. Destiny has, however, dealt more kindly by her. She is the wife of a rich country gentleman of high descent and higher attainments, to whom she is most devotedly attached—the mother of a little girl as lovely as herself, and the delight of all who have the happiness of her acquaintance, to whom she is endeared not merely by her remarkable sweetness of temper and kindness of heart, but by the singular ingenuousness and openness of character, which communicate an indescribable charm to her conversation. She is as transparent as water. You may see every colour, every shade of a mind as lofty and beautiful as her person. Talking with her is like being in the Palace of Truth described by Madam de Genlis; and yet so kindly are her feelings, so great her indulgence to the little failings and foibles of our common nature, so intense her sympathy with the wants, the wishes, the sorrows, and the happiness of her fellow-creatures, that, with all her frank-speaking, I never knew her make an enemy or lose a friend.

But we must get on. What would she say if she knew I was putting her into print? We must get on up the hill. Ah! that is precisely what we are not likely to do! This horse, this beautiful and high-bred horse, well fed, and fat and glossy, who stood prancing at our gate like an Arabian, has suddenly turned sulky. He does not, indeed, stand quite still, but his way of moving is little better—the slowest and most sullen of all walks. Even they who ply the hearse at funerals, sad-looking beasts who totter under black feathers, go faster. It is of no use to admonish him by whip, or rein, or word. The rogue has found out that it is a weak and tender hand that guides him now. Oh, for one pull, one stroke of his old driver, the groom! how he would fly! But there is the groom half-a-mile before us, out of earshot, clearing the ground at a capital rate, beating us hollow. He has just turned the top of the hill; and in a moment—ay, now he is out of sight, and will undoubtedly so continue till he meets us at the lawn gate! Well! there is no great harm. It is only prolonging the pleasure of enjoying together this charming scenery in this fine weather. If once we make up our minds not to care how slowly our steed goes, not to fret ourselves by vain exertions, it is no matter what his pace may be. There is little doubt of his getting home by sunset, and that will content us. He is, after all, a fine, noble animal; and perhaps when he finds that we are determined to give him his way, he may relent and give us ours. All his sex are sticklers for dominion, though, when it is undisputed, some of them are generous enough to abandon it. Two or three of the most discreet wives of my acquaintance contrive to manage their husbands sufficiently with no better secret than this seeming submission; and in our case the example has the more weight, since we have no possible way of helping ourselves.

Thus philosophising, we reached the top of the hill, and viewed with " reverted eyes " the expansive and beautiful prospect that lay bathed in golden sunshine behind us. Cowper says, with that boldness of expressing in poetry the commonest and simplest feelings, which is perhaps the one great secret of his originality—

> " Scenes must be beautiful, which, daily seen,
> Please daily, and whose novelty survives
> Long knowledge and the scrutiny of years."

Every day I walk up this hill—every day I pause at the top to admire the broad winding road with the green waste on each side, uniting it with the thickly timbered hedge-rows; the two pretty cottages at unequal distances, placed so as to mark the bends; the village beyond, with its mass of roofs and clustered chimneys peeping through the trees; and the rich distance, where cottages, mansions, churches, towns, seem embowered in some wide forest, and shut in by blue shadowy hills. Every day I admire this most beautiful landscape; yet never did it seem to me so fine or so glowing as now. All the tints of the glorious autumn—orange, tawny, yellow, red—are poured in profusion among the bright greens of the meadows and turnip-fields, till the eyes are satiated with colour ; and then before us we have the common with its picturesque roughness of surface tufted with cottages, dappled with water, edging off on one side into fields and farms and orchards, and terminated on the other by the princely oak avenue. What a richness and variety the wild broken ground gives to the luxuriant cultivation of the rest of the landscape ! Cowper has described it for me. How perpetually, as we walk in the country, his vivid pictures recur to the memory ! Here is his common and mine !—

> " The common overgrown with fern, and rough
> With prickly gorse, that, shapeless and deform'd,
> And dangerous to the touch, has yet its bloom,
> And decks itself with ornaments of gold—
> ————————————————there the turf
> Smells fresh, and, rich in odoriferous herbs
> And fungous fruits of earth, regales the sense
> With luxury of unexpected sweets."

The description is exact. There, too, to the left, is my cricket-ground (Cowper's common wanted that finishing grace) ; and there stands one solitary urchin as if in contemplation of its past and future glories ; for, alas ! cricket is over for the season. Ah ! it is Ben Kirby, next brother to Joe, king of the youngsters, and probably his successor—for this Michaelmas has cost us Joe ! He is promoted from the farm to the mansion-house, two miles off ; there he cleans shoes, rubs knives, and runs on errands, and is, as his mother expresses it, " a sort of 'prentice to the footman." I should not wonder if Joe, some day or other, should overtop the footman, and rise to be butler ; and his splendid prospects must be our consolation for the loss of this great favourite. In the meantime we have Ben.

Ben Kirby is a year younger than Joe, and the school-

fellow and rival of Jem Eusden. To be sure, his abilities
lie in rather a different line ; Jem is a scholar, Ben is a wag ;
Jem is great in figures and writing, Ben in faces and mischief. His master says of him, that if there were two such
in the school he must resign his office ; and, as far as my
observation goes, the worthy pedagogue is right. Ben
is, it must be confessed, a great corrupter of gravity. He
hath an exceeding aversion to authority and decorum, and
a wonderful boldness and dexterity in overthrowing the
one and puzzling the other. His contortions of visage
are astounding. His " power over his own muscles and
those of other people " is almost equal to that of Liston ;
and, indeed, the original face, flat and square and Chinese
in its shape, of a fine tan complexion, with a snub nose,
and a slit for a mouth, is nearly as comical as that matchless
performer's. When aided by Ben's singular mobility of
feature, his knowing winks and grins and shrugs and nods,
together with a certain dry shrewdness, a habit of saying
sharp things, and a marvellous gift of impudence, it forms
as fine a specimen as possible of a humorous country boy,
an oddity in embryo. Everybody likes Ben except his
butts (which may perhaps comprise half his acquaintance) ;
and of them no one so thoroughly hates and dreads him
as our parish schoolmaster, a most worthy King Log,
whom Ben dumbfounds twenty times a-day. He is a
great ornament of the cricket-ground, has a real genius
for the game, and displays it after a very original manner,
under the disguise of awkwardness—as the clown shows off
his agility in a pantomime. Nothing comes amiss to him.
By-the-by, he would have been the very lad for us in our
present dilemma ; not a horse in England could master
Ben Kirby. But we are too far from him now—and
perhaps it is as well that we are so. I believe the rogue
has a kindness for me, in remembrance of certain apples
and nuts, which my usual companion, who delights in his
wit, is accustomed to dole out to him. But it is a Robin

Goodfellow nevertheless, a perfect Puck, that loves nothing on earth so well as mischief. Perhaps the horse may be the safer conductor of the two.

The avenue is quite alive to-day. Old women are picking up twigs and acorns, and pigs of all sizes doing their utmost to spare them the latter part of the trouble ; boys and girls groping for beech-nuts under yonder clump ; and a group of younger elves collecting as many dead leaves as they can find, to feed the bonfire which is smoking away so briskly amongst the trees—a sort of rehearsal of the grand bonfire nine days hence ; of the loyal conflagration of the arch-traitor Guy Fawkes, which is annually solemnised in the avenue, accompanied with as much squibbery and crackery as our boys can beg or borrow—not to say steal. Ben Kirby is a great man on the fifth of November. All the savings of a month, the hoarded halfpence, the new farthings, the very luck-penny, go off *in fumo* on that night. For my part, I like this day-light mockery better. There is no gunpowder— odious gunpowder ! no noise but the merry shouts of the small fry, so shrill and happy, and the cawing of the rooks, who are wheeling in large circles overhead, and wondering what is going forward in their territory— seeming, in their loud clamour, to ask what that light smoke may mean that curls so prettily amongst their old oaks, towering as if to meet the clouds. There is something very intelligent in the ways of these black people, the rooks, particularly in their wonder. I suppose it results from their numbers and their unity of purpose, a sort of collective and corporate wisdom. Yet geese con-gregate also ; and geese never by any chance look wise. But then geese are a domestic fowl ; we have spoiled them ; and rooks are free commoners of nature, who use the habitations we provide for them, tenant our groves and our avenues, but never dream of becoming our subjects.

What a labyrinth of a road this is ! I do not think there

are four turnings in the short half-mile between the avenue
and the mill.   And what a pity, as my companion observes
—not that our good and jolly miller, the very representative of the old English yeomanry, should be so rich, but
that one consequence of his riches should be the pulling
down of the prettiest old mill that ever looked at itself
in the Loddon, with the picturesque, low-browed, irregular
cottage, which stood with its light-pointed roof, its clustered
chimneys, and its ever-open door, looking like the real
abode of comfort and hospitality, to build this huge,
staring, frightful, red-brick mill, as ugly as a manufactory,
and this great, square house, ugly and red to match, just
behind.   The old buildings always used to remind me of
Wollet's beautiful engraving of a scene in the *Maid of the
Mill*.   It will be long before any artist will make a drawing of this.   Only think of this redness in a picture ! this
boiled lobster of a house !   Falstaff's description of Bar-
dolph's nose would look pale in the comparison.

Here is that monstrous machine of a tilted waggon,
with its load of flour, and its four fat horses.   I wonder
whether our horse will have the decency to get out of the
way.   If he does not, I am sure we cannot make him ;
and that enormous ship upon wheels, that ark on dry land,
would roll over us like the car of Juggernaut.   Really—
Oh, no ! there is no danger now. I should have remembered
that it is my friend Samuel Long who drives the mill-team.
He will take care of us. " Thank you, Samuel ! "   And
Samuel has put us on our way, steered us safely past his
waggon, escorted us over the bridge ; and now, having
seen us through our immediate difficulties, has parted
from us with a very civil bow and good-humoured smile,
as one who is always civil and good-humoured, but with a
certain triumphant masterful look in his eyes, which I have
noted in men, even the best of them, when a woman gets
into straits by attempting manly employments.   He has
done us great good, though, and may be allowed his little

feeling of superiority. The parting salute he bestowed on our steed, in the shape of an astounding crack of his huge whip, has put that refractory animal on his mettle. On we go ! past the glazier's pretty house, with its porch and its filbert walk ; along the narrow lane bordered with elms, whose fallen leaves have made the road one yellow carpet ; past that little farm-house with the horse-chestnut trees before, glowing like oranges ; past the whitewashed school on the other side, gay with October roses ; past the park, and the lodge, and the mansion, where once dwelt the great Earl of Clarendon—and now the rascal has began to discover that Samuel Long and his whip are a mile off, and that his mistress is driving him, and he slackens his pace accordingly. Perhaps he feels the beauty of the road just here, and goes slowly to enjoy it. Very beautiful it certainly is. The park paling forms the boundary on one side, with fine clumps of oak, and deer in all attitudes ; the water, tufted with alders, flowing along on the other. Another turn, and the water winds away, succeeded by a low hedge, and a sweep of green meadows ; whilst the park and its palings are replaced by a steep bank, on which stands a small, quiet, village alehouse ; and higher up, embosomed in wood, is the little country church, with its sloping churchyard and its low white steeple, peeping out from amongst magnificent yew trees :—

> " Huge trunks ! and each particular trunk a growth
> Of intertwisted fibres serpentine
> Up-coiling, and invet'rately convolved." *

No village church was ever more happily placed. It is the very image of the peace and humbleness inculcated within its walls.

Ah ! here is a higher hill rising before us, almost like a mountain. How grandly the view opens as we ascend over that wild bank, overgrown with fern, and heath,

* Wordsworth.

and gorse, and between those tall hollies, glowing with their
coral berries ! What an expanse ! But we have little time
to gaze at present ; for that piece of perversity, our horse,
who has walked over so much level ground, has now, in-
spired, I presume, by a desire to revisit his stable, taken
it into that unaccountable noddle of his to trot up this,
the very steepest hill in the county. Here we are on the
top ; and in five minutes we have reached the lawn gate,
and are in the very midst of that beautiful piece of art or
nature (I do not know to which it belongs), the pleasure-
ground of F. Hill. Never was the " prophetic eye of taste "
exerted with more magical skill than in these plantations.
Thirty years ago this place had no existence ; it was a mere
undistinguished tract of field and meadow and common
land ; now it is a mimic forest, delighting the eye with the
finest combinations of trees and shrubs, the rarest effects
of form and foliage, and bewildering the mind with its
green glades, and impervious recesses, and apparently
interminable extent. It is the triumph of landscape
gardening, and never more beautiful than in this autumn
sunset, lighting up the ruddy beech and the spotted
sycamore, and gilding the shining fir-cones that hang so
thickly amongst the dark pines. The robins are singing
around us, as if they too felt the magic of the hour. How
gracefully the road winds through the leafy labyrinth,
leading imperceptibly to the more ornamented sweep.
Here we are at the door amidst geraniums, and carnations,
and jasmines, still in flower. Ah ! here is a flower sweeter
than all, a bird gayer than the robin, the little bird that
chirps to the tune of " Mamma ! mamma ! " the bright-
faced fairy, whose tiny feet come pattering along, making
a merry music, mamma's own Frances ! And following
her guidance, here we are in the dear round room time
enough to catch the last rays of the sun, as they light
the noble landscape which lies like a panorama around us,
lingering longest on that long island of old thorns and

stunted oaks, the oasis of B. Heath, and then vanishing in a succession of gorgeous clouds.

October 28th.—Another soft and brilliant morning. But the pleasures of to-day must be written in shorthand. I have left myself no room for notes of admiration.

First we drove about the coppice, an extensive wood of oak, and elm, and beech, chiefly the former, which adjoins the park-paling of F. Hill, of which demesne, indeed, it forms one of the most delightful parts. The roads through the coppice are studiously wild ; so that they have the appearance of mere cart-tracks ; and the manner in which the ground is tumbled about, the steep declivities, the sunny slopes, the sudden swells and falls, now a close, narrow valley, then a sharp ascent to an eminence commanding an immense extent of prospect, have a striking air of natural beauty, developed and heightened by the perfection of art. All this, indeed, was familiar to me ; the colouring only was new. I had been there in early spring, when the fragrant palms were on the willow, and the yellow tassels on the hazel, and every twig was swelling with renewed life ; and I had been there again and again in the green leafiness of mid-summer ; but never as now, when the dark verdure of the fir-plantations, hanging over the picturesque and unequal paling, partly covered with moss and ivy, contrasts so remarkably with the shining orange-leaves of the beech, already half fallen, the pale yellow of the scattering elm, the deeper and richer tints of the oak, and the glossy stems of the " lady of the woods," the delicate weeping birch. The underwood is no less picturesque. The red-spotted leaves, and redder berries of the old thorns, the scarlet festoons of the bramble, the tall fern of every hue, seem to vie with the brilliant mosaic of the ground, now covered with dead leaves and strewn with fir-cones, now, where a little glade intervenes, gay with various mosses and splendid *fungi*. How beautiful is this coppice to-day ! especially where the little spring, as clear as crystal, comes bubbling out from the " old fantastic " beech root, and trickles over the grass, bright and silent as dew in a May morning. The wood-pigeons (who are just returned from their summer migration, and are cropping the ivy berries) add their low cooings, the very note of love, to the slight fluttering of the fallen leaves in the quiet air, giving a voice to the sunshine and the beauty. This coppice is a place to live and die in. But we must go. And how fine is the ascent which leads us again into the world, past those cottages hidden as in a pit, and by that hanging orchard and that rough, heathy bank ! The scenery in this one spot has a wildness, an abruptness of rise and fall rare in any part of England, rare above all in this rich and lovely but monotonous county. It is Switzerland in miniature.

And now we cross the hill to pay a morning visit to the family at the great house—another fine place, commanding another fine sweep of country. The park, studded with old trees, and sinking gently into a valley, rich in wood and water, is in the best style of ornamental landscape, though more according to the common routine of gentlemen's seats than the singularly original place which we have just left. There is, however, one distinctive beauty in the grounds of the great house—the magnificent firs which shade the terraces and surround the sweep, giving out in summer odours really Sabæan, and now in this low autumn sun producing an effect almost magical, as the huge red trunks, garlanded with ivy, stand out from the deep shadows like an army of giants. Indoors—Oh, I must not take my readers indoors, or we shall never get away !—Indoors the sunshine is brighter still ; for there, in a lofty, lightsome room, sat a damsel fair and arch and *piquante*, one whom Titian or Velasquez should be born again to paint, leaning over an instrument * as sparkling and fanciful as herself, singing pretty French romances,

* The dital harp.

and Scottish Jacobite songs, and all sorts of graceful and airy drolleries picked up I know not where—an English improvisatrice ! a gayer Annot Lyle ! whilst her sister, of a higher order of beauty, and with an earnest kindness in her smile that deepens its power, lends to the piano, as her father to the violin, an expression, a sensibility, a spirit, an eloquence almost superhuman—almost divine ! Oh, to hear these two instruments accompanying my dear companion (I forgot to say that she is a singer worthy to be so accompanied) in Haydn's exquisite canzonet, ' She never told her love "—to hear her voice, with all its power, its sweetness, its gush of sound, so sustained and assisted by modulations that rivalled its intensity of expression ; to hear at once such poetry, such music, such execution, is a pleasure never to be forgotten, or mixed with meaner things. I seem to hear it still.

As in the bursting springtime o'er the eye
   Of one who haunts the fields fair visions creep
   Beneath the closed lids (afore dull sleep
Dims the quick fancy) of sweet flowers that lie
On grassy banks, oxlip of orient dye,
   And palest primrose and blue violet,
   All in their fresh and dewy beauty set,
Pictured within the sense, and will not fly :
So in mine ear resounds and lives again
   One mingled melody—a voice, a pair
   Of instruments most voice-like ! Of the air
Rather than of the earth seems that high strain,
A spirit's song, and worthy of the train
   That soothed old Prospero with music rare.

THE COPSE

APRIL 18th.—Sad, wintry weather; a north-east wind; a sun that puts out one's eyes, without affording the slightest warmth; dryness that chaps lips and hands like a frost in December; rain that comes chilly and arrowy like hail in January; nature at a dead pause; no seeds up in the garden; no leaves out in the hedge-rows; no cowslips swinging their pretty bells in the fields; no nightingales in the dingles; no swallows skimming round the great pond; no cuckoos (that ever I should miss that rascally sonneteer!) in any part. Nevertheless, there is something of a charm in this wintry spring, this putting-back of the seasons. If the flower-clock must stand still for a month or two, could it choose a better time than that of the primroses and violets? I never remember (and for such gauds my memory, if not very good for aught of wise or useful, may be trusted) such an affluence of the one or such a duration of the other. Primrosy is the epithet which this year will retain in my recollection. Hedge, ditch, meadow, field, even the very paths and highways, are set with them; but their chief *habitat* is a certain copse, about a mile off, where they are spread like a carpet, and where I go to visit them rather oftener than quite comports with the dignity of a lady of mature age. I am going thither this very afternoon, and May and her company are going too.

This Mayflower of mine is a strange animal. Instinct and imitation make in her an approach to reason which is sometimes almost startling. She mimics all that she sees us do with the dexterity of a monkey, and far more of gravity and apparent purpose; cracks nuts and eats them;

gathers currants, and severs them from the stalk with the most delicate nicety; filches and munches apples and pears; is as dangerous in a orchard as a schoolboy; smells to flowers; smiles at meeting; answers in a pretty lively voice when spoken to (sad pity that the language should be unknown!) and has greatly the advantage of us in a conversation, inasmuch as our meaning is certainly clear to her—all this and a thousand amusing prettinesses (to say nothing of her canine feat of bringing her game straight to her master's feet, and refusing to resign it to any hand but his) does my beautiful greyhound perform untaught, by the mere effect of imitation and sagacity. Well, May, at the end of the coursing season, having lost Brush, our old spaniel, her great friend, and the blue greyhound, Mariette, her comrade and rival, both of which four-footed worthies were sent out to keep for the summer, began to find solitude a weary condition, and to look abroad for company. Now it so happened that the same suspension of sport which had reduced our little establishment from three dogs to one, had also dispersed the splendid kennel of a celebrated courser in our neighbourhood, three of whose finest young dogs came home to " their walk " (as the sporting phrase goes) at the collarmaker's in our village. May, accordingly, on the first morning of her solitude (she had never taken the slightest notice of her neighbours before, although they had sojourned in our street upwards of a fortnight), bethought herself of the timely resource offered to her by the vicinity of these canine *beaux,* and went up boldly and knocked at their stable-door, which was already very commodiously on the half-latch. The three dogs came out with much alertness and gallantry, and May, declining apparently to enter their territories, brought them off to her own. This manœuvre has been repeated every day, with one variation; of the three dogs, the first a brindle, the second a yellow, and the third a black, the two first only are now

allowed to walk or consort with her, and the last, poor
fellow, for no fault that I can discover except May's caprice,
is driven away not only by the fair lady, but even by his
old companions—is, so to say, sent to Coventry. Of her
two permitted followers, the yellow gentleman, Saladin
by name, is decidedly the favourite. He is, indeed, May's
shadow, and will walk with me whether I choose or not.
It is quite impossible to get rid of him unless by discarding
Miss May also—and to accomplish a walk in the country
without her would be like an adventure of Don Quixote
without his faithful squire Sancho.

So forth we set, May and I, and Saladin and the brindle ;
May and myself walking with the sedateness and decorum
befitting our sex and age (she is five years old this grass,
rising six)—the young things, for the soldan and the
brindle are (not meaning any disrespect) little better than
puppies, frisking and frolicking as best pleased them.

Our route lay for the first part along the sheltered,
quiet lanes which lead to our old habitation ; a way never
trodden by me without peculiar and home-like feelings,
full of the recollections, the pains and pleasures, of
other days. But we are not to talk sentiment now—even
May would not understand that maudlin language. We
must get on. What a wintry hedge-row this is for the
eighteenth of April ! Primrosy to be sure, abundantly
spangled with those stars of the earth—but so bare, so leaf-
less, so cold ! The wind whistles through the brown
boughs as in winter. Even the early elder shoots, which
do make an approach to springiness, look brown, and the
small leaves of the woodbine, which have also ventured to
peep forth, are of a sad purple, frost-bitten, like a dairy-
maid's elbows on a snowy morning. The very birds, in
the season of pairing and building, look chilly and uncomfortable, and their nests !——" Oh, Saladin ! come away
from the hedge ! Don't you see that what puzzles you and
makes you leap up in the air is a redbreast's nest ? Don't

you see the pretty speckled eggs ? Don't you hear the poor hen calling as it were for help ? Come here this moment, sir ! " And by good luck Saladin (who for a paynim has tolerable qualities) comes, before he has touched the nest, or before his playmate, the brindle, the less manageable of the two, has espied it.

Now we go round the corner and cross the bridge, where the common, with its clear stream winding between clumps of elms, assumes so park-like an appearance. Who is this approaching so slowly and majestically, this square bundle of petticoat and cloak, this road-waggon of a woman ? It is, it must be Mrs. Sally Mearing, the completest specimen within my knowledge of farmeresses (may I be allowed that innovation in language ?) as they were. It can be nobody else.

Mrs. Sally Mearing, when I first became acquainted with her, occupied, together with her father (a superannuated man of ninety), a large farm very near our former habitation. It had been anciently a great manor-farm or court-house, and was still a stately, substantial building, whose lofty halls and spacious chambers gave an air of grandeur to the common offices to which they were applied. Traces of gilding might yet be seen on the panels which covered the walls, and on the huge carved chimney-pieces which rose almost to the ceilings ; and the marble tables and the inlaid oak staircase still spoke of the former grandeur of the court. Mrs. Sally corresponded well with the date of her mansion, although she troubled herself little with its dignity. She was thoroughly of the old school, and had a most comfortable contempt for the new ; rose at four in winter and summer, breakfasted at six, dined at eleven in the forenoon, supped at five, and was regularly in bed before eight, except when the hay-time or the harvest imperiously required her to sit up till sunset—a necessity to which she submitted with no very good grace. To a deviation from these hours, and to the modern iniquities

THE COPSE

of white aprons, cotton stockings, and muslin handkerchiefs (Mrs. Sally herself always wore check, black worsted,
and a sort of yellow compound which she was wont to
call *susy*), together with the invention of drill plough
and thrashing machines, and other agricultural novelties,
she failed not to attribute all the mishaps or misdoings
of the whole parish. The last-mentioned discovery
especially aroused her indignation. Oh, to hear her
descant on the merits of the flail, wielded by a stout right
arm, such as she had known in her youth (for by her account
there was as great a deterioration in bones and sinews
as in the other implements of husbandry), was enough
to make the very inventor break his machine. She
would even take up her favourite instrument, and thrash
the air herself by way of illustrating her argument, and,
to say truth, few men in these degenerate days could have
matched the stout, brawny, muscular limb which Mrs.
Sally displayed at sixty-five.

In spite of this contumacious rejection of agricultural
improvements, the world went well with her at Court
Farm. A good landlord, an easy rent, incessant labour,
unremitting frugality, and excellent times, insured a
regular though moderate profit ; and she lived on, grumbling and prospering, flourishing and complaining, till two
misfortunes befell her at once—her father died and her
lease expired. The loss of her father, although a bed-
ridden man, turned off ninety, who could not in the
course of nature have been expected to live long, was a
terrible shock to a daughter, who was not so much younger
as to be without fears for her own life, and who had,
besides, been so used to nursing the good old man, and
looking to his little comforts, that she missed him as
a mother would miss an ailing child. The expiration
of the lease was a grievance and a puzzle of a different
nature. Her landlord would have willingly retained his
excellent tenant, but not on the terms on which she then

held the land, which had not varied for fifty years; so that poor Mrs. Sally had the misfortune to find rent rising and prices sinking both at the same moment—a terrible solecism in political economy. Even this, however, I believe she would have endured rather than have quitted the house where she was born, and to which all her ways and notions were adapted, had not a priggish steward, as much addicted to improvement and reform as she was to precedent and established usages, insisted on binding her by lease to spread a certain number of loads of chalk on every field. This tremendous innovation, for never had that novelty in manure whitened the crofts and pightles of Court Farm, decided her at once. She threw the proposals into the fire, and left the place in a week.

Her choice of a habitation occasioned some wonder, and much amusement in our village world. To be sure, upon the verge of seventy, an old maid may be permitted to dispense with the more rigid punctilio of her class, but Mrs. Sally had always been so tenacious on the score of character, so very a prude, so determined an avoider of the " men folk " (as she was wont contemptuously to call them), that we all were conscious of something like astonishment on finding that she and her little handmaid had taken up their abode in one end of a spacious farm-house belonging to the bluff old bachelor, George Robinson, of the Lea. Now farmer Robinson was quite as notorious for his aversion to petticoated things as Mrs. Sally for her hatred to the unfeathered bipeds who wear doublet and hose, so that there was a little astonishment in that quarter too, and plenty of jests, which the honest farmer speedily silenced, by telling all who joked on the subject that he had given his lodger fair warning, that, let the people say what they would, he was quite determined not to marry her; so that if she had any views that way, it would be better for her to go elsewhere. This declaration, which must be admitted to have been more remarkable for frankness than civility, made, however, no ill impression on Mrs. Sally. To the farmer's she went, and at his house she lives still, with her little maid, her tabby cat, a decrepit sheep-dog, and much of the lumber of Court Farm, which she could not find in her heart to part from. There she follows her old ways and her old hours, untempted by matrimony, and unassailed (as far as I hear) by love or by scandal, with no other grievance than an occasional dearth of employment for herself and her young lass (even pewter dishes do not always want scouring), and now and then a twinge of the rheumatism.

Here she is, that good relique of the olden time— for, in spite of her whims and prejudices, a better and a kinder woman never lived—here she is, with the hood of her red cloak pulled over her close black bonnet, of that silk which once (it may be presumed) was fashionable, since it is still called *mode*, and her whole stout figure huddled up in a miscellaneous and most substantial covering of thick petticoats, gowns, aprons, shawls, and cloaks—a weight which it requires the strength of a thrasher to walk under—here she is, with her square, honest visage, and her loud, frank voice—and we hold a pleasant, disjointed chat of rheumatisms and early chickens, bad weather and hats with feathers in them ; —the last exceedingly sore subject being introduced by poor Jane Davis (a cousin of Mrs. Sally), who, passing us in a beaver bonnet, on her road from school, stopped to drop her little curtsy, and was soundly scolded for her civility. Jane, who is a gentle, humble, smiling lass, about twelve years old, receives so many rebukes from her worthy relative, and bears them so meekly, that I should not wonder if they were to be followed by a legacy : I sincerely wish they may. Well, at last we said goodbye ; when, on inquiring my destination, and hearing that I was bent on the ten-acre copse (part of the farm which she ruled so long), she stopped me to tell a dismal story of two sheep-stealers who, sixty years ago, were found hidden in that copse, and only taken after great difficulty and resistance, and the maiming of a peace-officer. "Pray don't go there, Miss! For mercy's sake don't be so venturesome! Think if they should kill you!" were the last words of Mrs. Sally.

Many thanks for her care and kindness! But, without being at all fool-hardy in general, I have no great fear of the sheep-stealers of sixty years ago. Even if they escaped hanging for that exploit, I should greatly doubt their being in case to attempt another. So on we go; down the short, shady lane, and out on the pretty retired green, shut in by fields and hedge-rows, which we must cross to reach the copse. How lively this green nook is to-day, half covered with cows, and horses, and sheep! And how glad these frolicsome greyhounds are to exchange the hard gravel of the high road for this pleasant, short turf, which seems made for their gambols! How beautiful they are at play, chasing each other round and round in lessening circles, darting off at all kinds of angles, crossing and recrossing May, and trying to win her sedateness into a game at romps, turning round on each other with gay defiance, pursuing the cows and the colts, leaping up as if to catch the crows in their flight—all in their harmless and innocent——"Ah, wretches! villains! rascals! four-footed mischiefs! canine plagues! Saladin! Brindle!" They are after the sheep—"Saladin, I say!"—They have actually singled out that pretty spotted lamb—"Brutes, if I catch you! Saladin! Brindle!" We shall be taken up for sheep-stealing presently ourselves. They have chased the poor little lamb into a ditch, and are mounting guard over it, standing at bay. "Ah, wretches, I have you now! for shame, Saladin! Get away, Brindle! See how good May is. Off with you, brutes! For shame! For shame!" and brandishing a handkerchief, which could hardly be an efficient instrument of correction, I succeeded in driving away the two puppies, who after all meant nothing more than play, although it was somewhat rough, and rather too much in the style of the old fable of the boys and the frogs. May is gone after them, perhaps to scold them ; for she has been as grave as a judge during the whole proceeding, keeping ostentatiously close to me, and taking no part whatever in the mischief.

The poor little pretty lamb ! here it lies on the bank quite motionless, frightened I believe to death, for certainly those villains never touched it. It does not stir. Does it breathe ? Oh, yes, it does ! It is alive, safe enough. Look, it opens its eyes, and, finding the coast clear and its enemies far away, it springs up in a moment and gallops to its dam, who has stood bleating the whole time at a most respectful distance. Who would suspect a lamb of so much simple cunning ? I really thought the pretty thing was dead—and now how glad the ewe is to recover her curling spotted little one ! How fluttered they look ! Well ! this adventure has flurried me too ; between fright and running, I warrant you my heart beats as fast as the lamb's.

Ah ! here is the shameless villain, Saladin, the cause of the commotion, thrusting his slender nose into my hand to beg pardon and make up ! " Oh, wickedest of soldans ! Most iniquitous pagan ! Soul of a Turk ! " —but there is no resisting the good-humoured creature's penitence. I must pat him. " There ! there ! Now we will go to the copse ; I am sure we shall find no worse malefactors than ourselves—shall we, May ?—and the sooner we get out of sight of the sheep the better ; for Brindle seems meditating another attack. *Allons, messieurs,* over this gate, across this meadow, and here is the copse."

How boldly that superb ash-tree, with its fine silver bark, rises from the bank, and what a fine entrance it

makes with the holly beside it, which also deserves to
be called a tree ! But here we are in the copse. Ah !
only one-half of the underwood was cut last year, and
the other is at its full growth ; hazel, briar, woodbine,
bramble, forming one impenetrable thicket, and almost
uniting with the lower branches of the elms, and oaks,
and beeches, which rise at regular distances overhead.
No foot can penetrate that dense and thorny entangle-
ment ; but there is a walk all round by the side of the
wide sloping bank, walk and bank and copse carpeted
with primroses, whose fresh and balmy odour impregnates
the very air. Oh, how exquisitely beautiful ; and it is
not the primroses only, those gems of flowers, but the
natural mosaic of which they form a part : that net-
work of ground ivy with its lilac blossoms and the subdued
tint of its purplish leaves, those rich mosses, those
enamelled wild hyacinths, those spotted arums, and
above all, those wreaths of ivy linking all those flowers
together with chains of leaves more beautiful than blossoms, whose white veins seem swelling amidst the deep
green or splendid brown—it is the whole earth that is so
beautiful ! Never surely were primroses so richly set,
and never did primroses better deserve such a setting.
There they are of their own lovely yellow, the hue to
which they have given a name, the exact tint of the
butterfly that overhangs them (the first I have seen
this year ! can spring really be coming at last ?)—sprinkled
here and there with tufts of a reddish purple, and others
of the purest white, as some accident of soil affects that
strange and inscrutable operation of nature, the colouring
of flowers. Oh, how fragrant they are, and how pleasant
it is to sit in this sheltered copse, listening to the fine
creaking of the wind among the branches, the most
unearthly of sounds, with this gay tapestry under our
feet, and the wood-pigeons flitting from tree to tree, and
mixing the deep note of love with the elemental music.

Yes! spring is coming. Wood-pigeons, butterflies, and sweet flowers, all give tokens of the sweetest of the seasons. Spring is coming. The hazel stalks are swelling and putting forth their pale tassels, the satin palms with their honeyed odours are out on the willow, and the last lingering winter berries are dropping from the hawthorn, and making way for the bright and blossomy leaves.

THE WOOD

APRIL 20th.—Spring is actually come now, with the fulness and almost the suddenness of a northern summer. To-day is completely April—clouds and sunshine, wind and showers ; blossoms on the trees, grass in the fields, swallows by the ponds, snakes in the hedge-rows, nightingales in the thickets, and cuckoos everywhere. My young friend Ellen G. is going with me this evening to gather wood-sorrel. She never saw that most elegant plant, and is so delicate an artist that the introduction will be a mutual benefit ; Ellen will gain a subject worthy of her pencil, and the pretty weed will live—no small favour to a flower almost as transitory as the gum cistus ; duration is the only charm which it wants, and that Ellen will give it. The weather is, to be sure, a little threatening, but we are not people to mind the weather when we have an object in view ; we shall certainly go in quest of the wood-sorrel, and will take May, provided we can escape May's followers ; for since the adventure of the lamb, Saladin has had an affair with a gander, furious in defence of his goslings, in which rencontre the gander came off conqueror ; and as geese abound in the wood to which we are going (called by the country people the Pinge), and the victory may not always incline to the right side, I should be very sorry to lead the soldan to fight his battles over again. We will take nobody but May.

So saying, we proceeded on our way through winding lanes, between hedge-rows tenderly green, till we reached the hatch-gate, with the white cottage beside it, em-

bosomed in fruit trees, which forms the entrance to the
Pinge, and in a moment the whole scene was before our
eyes.

" Is not this beautiful, Ellen ? " The answer could
hardly be other than a glowing, rapid, " Yes ! " A wood
is generally a pretty place ; but this wood—imagine a
smaller forest, full of glades and sheep-walks, surrounded
by irregular cottages with their blooming orchards, a
clear stream winding about the brakes, and a road intersecting it, and giving life and light to the picture ; and
you will have a faint idea of the Pinge. Every step was
opening a new point of view, a fresh combination of glade,
and path, and thicket. The accessories, too, were chang-
ing every moment. Ducks, geese, pigs, and children,
giving way, as we advanced into the wood, to sheep and
forest ponies ; and they again disappearing as we became
more entangled in its mazes, till we heard nothing but
the song of the nightingale, and saw only the silent
flowers.

What a piece of fairy-land ! The tall elms overhead
just bursting into tender, vivid leaf, with here and there
a hoary oak, or a silver-barked beech, every twig swelling
with the brown buds, and yet not quite stripped of the
tawny foliage of autumn ; tall hollies and hawthorn
beneath, with their crisp, brilliant leaves, mixed with the
white blossoms of the sloe, and woven together with
garlands of woodbines and wild-briers—what a fairy-land !

Primroses, cowslips, pansies, and the regular open-
eyed white blossom of the wood anemone (or to use
the more elegant Hampshire name, the windflower),
were set under our feet as thick as daisies in a meadow ;
but the pretty weed that we came to seek was coyer ;
and Ellen began to fear that we had mistaken the place
or the season. At last she had herself the pleasure of
finding it under a brake of holly—" Oh, look ! look ! I
am sure that this is the wood - sorrel ! Look at the

pendent white flower, shaped like a snow-drop, and veined
with purple streaks, and the beautiful trefoil leaves
folded like a heart—some, the young ones, so vividly,
yet tenderly green, that the foliage of the elm and the
hawthorn would show dully at their side—others of a
deeper tint, and lined, as it were, with a rich and changeful
purple !—Don't you see them ? " pursued my dear young
friend, who is a delightful piece of life and sunshine,
and was half inclined to scold me for the calmness with
which, amused by her enthusiasm, I stood listening to
her ardent exclamations—" Don't you see them ? Oh,
how beautiful ! and in what quantity ! what profusion !
See how the dark shade of the holly sets off the light
and delicate colouring of the flower !—And see that
other bed of them springing from the rich moss in the
roots of that old beech tree ! Pray let us gather some.
Here are baskets." So, quickly and carefully we began
gathering leaves, blossoms, roots and all, for the plant
is so fragile that it will not brook separation—quickly
and carefully we gathered, encountering divers petty
misfortunes in spite of all our care, now caught by the
veil in a holly bush, now hitching our shawls in a bramble,
still gathering on, in spite of scratched fingers, till we had
nearly filled our baskets and began to talk of our departure.

" But where is May ? May ! May ! No going home
without her. May ! Here she comes galloping, the
beauty ! "—(Ellen is almost as fond of May as I am.)
" What has she got in her mouth ? that rough, round,
brown substance which she touches so tenderly ? What
can it be ? A bird's nest ? Naughty May ! "

" No ! as I live, a hedgehog ! Look, Ellen, how it
has coiled itself into a thorny ball ! Off with it, May !
Don't bring it to me ! "——And May, somewhat reluctant to part with her prickly prize, however trouble-
some of carriage, whose change of shape seemed to me

to have puzzled her sagacity more than any event I ever witnessed, for in general she has perfectly the air of understanding all that is going forward—May, at last, dropt the hedgehog ; continuing, however, to pat it with her delicate, cat-like paw, cautious and daintily applied, and caught back suddenly and rapidly after every touch, as if her poor captive had been a red-hot coal. Finding that these pats entirely failed in solving the riddle (for the hedgehog shammed dead, like the lamb the other day, and appeared entirely motionless), she gave him so spirited a nudge with her pretty black nose, that she not only turned him over, but sent him rolling some little way along the turfy path—an operation which that sagacious quadruped endured with the most perfect passiveness, the most admirable non-resistance. No wonder that May's discernment was at fault. I myself, if I had not been aware of the trick, should have said that the ugly rough thing which she was trundling along, like a bowl or a cricket-ball, was an inanimate substance, something devoid of sensation and of will. At last my poor pet, thoroughly perplexed and tired out, fairly relinquished the contest, and came slowly away, turning back once or twice to look at the object of her curiosity, as if half inclined to return and try the event of another shove. The sudden flight of a wood-pigeon effectually diverted her attention ; and Ellen amused herself by fancying how the hedgehog was scuttling away, till our notice was also attracted by a very different object.

We had nearly threaded the wood, and were approaching an open grove of magnificent oaks on the other side, when sounds other than of nightingales burst on our ear, the deep and frequent strokes of the woodman's axe, and emerging from the Pinge we saw the havoc which that axe had committed. Above twenty of the finest trees lay stretched on the velvet turf. There they lay in every shape and form of devastation :

some bare trunks, stripped ready for the timber carriage, with the bark built up in long piles at the side ; some with the spoilers busy about them, stripping, hacking, hewing ; others with their noble branches, their brown and fragrant shoots, all fresh as if they were alive— majestic corses, the slain of to-day. The grove was like a field of battle. The young lads who were stripping the bark, the very children who were picking up the chips, seemed awed and silent, as if conscious that death was around them. The nightingales sang faintly and interruptedly—a few low frightened notes like a requiem.

Ah ! here we are at the very scene of murder, the very tree that they are felling ; they have just hewn round the trunk with those slaughtering axes, and are about to saw it asunder. After all, it is a fine and thrilling operation, as the work of death usually is. Into how grand an attitude was that young man thrown as he gave the final strokes round the root ; and how wonderful is the effect of that supple and apparently powerless saw, bending like a riband, and yet overmastering that giant of the woods, conquering and overthrowing that thing of life ! Now it has passed half through the trunk, and the woodman has begun to calculate which way the tree will fall ; he drives a wedge to direct its course ; now a few more movements of the noiseless saw, and then a larger wedge. See how the branches tremble ! Hark, how the trunk begins to crack ! Another stroke of the huge hammer on the wedge, and the tree quivers, as with a mortal agony, shakes, reels, and falls. How slow, and solemn, and awful it is ! How like to death, to human death in its grandest form ! Cæsar in the Capitol, Seneca in the bath, could not fall more sublimely than that oak.

Even the heavens seem to sympathise with the devasta- tion. The clouds have gathered into one thick, low canopy, dark and vapoury as the smoke which overhangs

London; the setting sun is just gleaming underneath with a dim and bloody glare, and the crimson rays spreading upward with a lurid and portentous grandeur, a subdued and dusky glow, like the light reflected on the sky from some vast conflagration. The deep flush fades away, and the rain begins to descend; and we hurry homeward rapidly, yet sadly, forgetful alike of the flowers, the hedgehog, and the wetting, thinking and talking only of the fallen tree.

THE DELL

MAY 2nd.—A delicious evening; bright sunshine; light summer air; a sky almost cloudless; and a fresh yet delicate verdure on the hedges and in the fields; an evening that seems made for a visit to my newly-discovered haunt, the mossy dell, one of the most beautiful spots in the neighbourhood, which, after passing, times out of number, the field which it terminates, we found out about two months ago from the accident of May's killing a rabbit there. May has had a fancy for the place ever since; and so have I.

Thither accordingly we bend our way—through the village—up the hill—along the common—past the avenue —across the bridge; and by the hill. How deserted the road is to-night! We have not seen a single acquaintance, except poor blind Robert, laden with his sack of grass plucked from the hedges, and the little boy that leads him. A singular division of labour! Little Jem guides Robert to the spots where the long grass grows, and tells him where it is most plentiful; and then the old man cuts it close to the roots, and between them they fill the sack, and sell the contents in the village. Half the cows in the street—for our baker, our wheelwright, and our shoemaker has each his Alderney—owe the best part of their maintenance to blind Robert's industry.

Here we are at the entrance of the cornfield which leads to the dell, and which commands so fine a view of the Loddon, the mill, the great farm, with its picturesque outbuildings, and the range of woody hills beyond. It

is impossible not to pause a moment at that gate, the
landscape, always beautiful, is so suited to the season
and the hour—so bright, and gay, and spring-like. But
May, who has the chance of another rabbit in her pretty
head, has galloped forward to the dingle, and poor May,
who follows me so faithfully in all my wanderings, has
a right to a little indulgence in hers. So to the dingle
we go.

At the end of the field, which, when seen from the
road, seems terminated by a thick, dark coppice, we
come suddenly to the edge of a ravine, on one side fringed
with a low growth of alder, birch, and willow, on the
other mossy, turfy, and bare, or only broken by bright
tufts of blossomed broom. One or two old pollards
almost conceal the winding road that leads down the
descent, by the side of which a spring as bright as crystal
runs gurgling along. The dell itself is an irregular piece
of broken ground, in some parts very deep, intersected
by two or three high banks of equal irregularity, now
abrupt and bare, and rock-like, now crowned with tufts
of the feathery willow or magnificent old thorns. Everywhere the earth is covered by short, fine turf, mixed with
mosses, soft, beautiful, and various, and embossed with
the speckled leaves and lilac flowers of the arum, the paler
blossoms of the common orchis, the enamelled blue of
the wild hyacinth, so splendid in this evening light, and
large tufts of oxslips and cowslips rising like nosegays
from the short turf.

The ground on the other side of the dell is much lower
than the field through which we came, so that it is mainly
to the labyrinthine intricacy of these high banks that
it owes its singular character of wildness and variety.
Now we seem hemmed in by those green cliffs, shut out
from all the world, with nothing visible but those verdant
mounds and the deep blue sky ; now by some sudden
turn we get a peep at an adjoining meadow, where the

sheep are lying, dappling its sloping surface like the small clouds on the summer heaven. Poor harmless, quiet creatures, how still they are! Some socially lying side by side; some grouped in threes and fours; some quite apart. Ah! there are lambs amongst them—pretty, pretty lambs—nestled in by their mothers. Soft, quiet, sleepy things! Not all so quiet, though! There is a party of these young lambs as wide-awake as heart can desire; half-a-dozen of them playing together, frisking, dancing, leaping, butting, and crying in the young voice, which is so pretty a diminutive of the full-grown bleat. How beautiful they are with their innocent spotted faces, their mottled feet, their long curly tails, and their light flexible forms, frolicing like so many kittens, but with a gentleness, an assurance of sweetness and innocence, which no kitten, nothing that ever is to be a cat, can have. How complete and perfect is their enjoyment of existence! Ah! little rogues! your play has been too noisy; you have awakened your mammas; and two or three of the old ewes are getting up; and one of them marching gravely to the troop of lambs has selected her own, given her a gentle butt, and trotted off; the poor rebuked lamb following meekly, but every now and then stopping and casting a longing look at its playmates; who, after a moment's awed pause, had resumed their gambols; whilst the stately dame every now and then looked back in her turn, to see that her little one was following. At last she lay down, and the lamb by her side. I never saw so pretty a pastoral scene in my life.*

* I have seen one which affected me much more. Walking in the Church-lane with one of the young ladies of the vicarage, we met a large flock of sheep, with the usual retinue of shepherds and dogs. Lingering after them and almost out of sight, we encountered a straggling ewe, now trotting along, now walking, and every now and then stopping to look back, and bleating. A little behind her came a lame lamb, bleating occasionally, as if in answer to its dam, and doing its very best to keep up with her. It was a lameness of both

Another turning of the dell gives a glimpse of the dark coppice by which it is backed, and from which we are separated by some marshy, rushy ground, where the springs have formed into a pool, and where the moor-hen loves to build her nest. Ay, there is one scudding away now—I can hear her plash into the water, and the rustling of her wings amongst the rushes. This is the deepest part of the wild dingle. How uneven the ground is ! Surely these excavations, now so thoroughly clothed with vegetation, must originally have been huge gravel pits ; there is no other way of accounting for the labyrinth, for they do dig gravel in such capricious meanders ; but the quantity seems incredible. Well ! there is no end of guessing ! We are getting amongst the springs, and must turn back. Round this corner, where on ledges like fairy terraces the orchises and arums grow, and we emerge suddenly on a new side of the dell, just fronting the small homestead of our good neighbour, farmer Allen.

This rustic dwelling belongs to what used to be called in this part of the country " a little bargain ; " thirty or forty acres, perhaps, of arable land, which the owner and his sons cultivated themselves, whilst the wife and daughters assisted in the husbandry, and eked out the slender earnings by the produce of the dairy, the poultry-

the fore feet ; the knees were bent, and it seemed to walk on the very edge of the hoof—on tip-toe, if I may venture such an expression. My young friend thought that the lameness proceeded from original malformation ; I am rather of opinion that it was accidental, and that the poor creature was wretchedly foot-sore. However that might be, the pain and difficulty with which it took every step were not to be mistaken ; and the distress and fondness of the mother, her perplexity as the flock passed gradually out of sight, the effort with which the poor lamb contrived to keep up a sort of trot, and their mutual calls and lamentations, were really so affecting, that Ellen and I, although not at all lachrymose sort of people, had much ado not to cry. We could not find a boy to carry the lamb, which was too big for us to manage—but I was quite sure that the ewe would not desert it, and as the dark was coming on, we both trusted that the shepherds, on folding their flock, would miss them and return for them—and so I am happy to say it proved.

yard, and the orchard—an order of cultivators now passing rapidly away, but in which much of the best part of the English character, its industry, its frugality, its sound sense, and its kindness might be found. Farmer Allen himself is an excellent specimen, the cheerful, venerable old man, with his long white hair, and his bright grey eye, and his wife is a still finer. They have had a hard struggle to win through the world and keep their little property undivided ; but good management and good principles, and the assistance afforded them by an admirable son, who left our village a poor 'prentice boy, and is now a partner in a great house in London, have enabled them to overcome all the difficulties of these trying times, and they are now enjoying the peaceful evenings of a well-spent life as free from care and anxiety as their best friends could desire.

Ah ! there is Mr. Allen in the orchard, the beautiful orchard, with its glorious gardens of pink and white, its pearly pear-blossoms and coral apple-buds. What a flush of bloom it is ! how brightly delicate it appears, thrown into strong relief by the dark house and the weather-stained barn, in this soft evening light ! The very grass is strewed with the snowy petals of the pear and the cherry. And there sits Mrs. Allen feeding her poultry, with her three little granddaughters from London, pretty fairies, from three years old to five (only two-and-twenty months elapsed between the birth of the eldest and the youngest), playing round her feet.

Mrs. Allen, my dear Mrs. Allen, has been that rare thing, a beauty ; and although she be now an old woman, I had almost said that she is so still. Why should I not say so ? Nobleness of feature and sweetness of expression are surely as delightful in age as in youth. Her face and figure are much like those which are stamped indelibly on the memory of every one who ever saw that grand specimen of woman—Mrs. Siddons. The outline of Mrs. Allen's face is exactly the same; but there is more softness, more gentleness, a more feminine composure in the eye and in the smile. Mrs. Allen never played Lady Macbeth. Her hair, almost as black as at twenty, is parted on her large, fair forehead, and combed under her exquisitely neat and snowy cap; a muslin neckerchief, a grey stuff gown, and a white apron complete the picture.

There she sits under an old elder tree which flings its branches over her like a canopy, whilst the setting sun illumines her venerable figure, and touches the leaves with an emerald light; there she sits, placid and smiling, with her spectacles in her hand and a measure of barley on her lap, into which the little girls are dipping their chubby hands and scattering the corn amongst the ducks and chickens with unspeakable glee. But those ingrates, the poultry, don't seem so pleased and thankful as they ought to be; they mistrust their young feeders. All domestic animals dislike children, partly from an instinctive fear of their tricks and their thoughtlessness; partly, I suspect, from jealousy. Jealousy seems a strange tragic passion to attribute to the inmates of the *basse cour*,—but only look at that strutting fellow of a bantam cock (evidently a favourite), who sidles up to his old mistress with an air half affronted and half tender, turning so scornfully from the barley-corns which Annie is flinging towards him, and say if he be not as jealous as Othello? Nothing can pacify him but Mrs. Allen's notice and a dole from her hand. See, she is calling to him and feeding him, and now how he swells out his feathers, and flutters his wings, and erects his glossy neck, and struts and crows and pecks, proudest and happiest of bantams, the pet and glory of the poultry-yard!

In the meantime my own pet, May, who has all this while been peeping into every hole, and penetrating every nook and winding of the dell, in hopes of finding another rabbit, has returned to my side and is sliding her snake-like head into my hand, at once to invite the caress which she likes so well, and to intimate, with all due respect, that it is time to go home. The setting sun gives the same warning; and in a moment we are through the dell, the field, and the gate, past the farm and the mill, and hanging over the bridge that crosses the Loddon river.

What a sunset! how golden! how beautiful! The sun just disappearing, and the narrow liny clouds, which a few minutes ago lay like soft vapoury streaks along the horizon, lightened up with a golden splendour that the eye can scarcely endure, and those still softer clouds which floated above them wreathing and curling into a thousand fantastic forms, as thin and changeful as summer smoke, now defined and deepened into grandeur, and edged with ineffable, insufferable light! Another minute and the brilliant orb totally disappears, and the sky above grows every moment more varied and more beautiful as the dazzling golden lines are mixed with glowing red and gorgeous purple, dappled with small, dark specks, and mingled with such a blue as the egg of the hedge-sparrow. To look up at that glorious sky, and then to see that magnificent picture reflected in the clear and lovely Loddon water, is a pleasure never to be described and never forgotten. My heart swells and my eyes fill as I write of it, and think of the immeasurable majesty of nature, and the unspeakable goodness of God, who has spread an enjoyment so pure, so peaceful, and so intense before the meanest and the lowliest of His creatures.

THE OLD HOUSE AT ABERLEIGH

JUNE 25th.—What a glowing, glorious day! Summer in
its richest prime, noon in its most sparkling brightness,
little white clouds dappling the deep blue sky, and the
sun, now partially veiled, and now bursting through them
with an intensity of light! It would not do to walk
to-day, professedly to walk—we should be frightened at
the very sound! and yet it is probable that we may be
beguiled into a pretty long stroll before we return home.
We are going to drive to the old house at Aberleigh, to
spend the morning under the shade of those balmy firs,
and amongst those luxuriant rose trees, and by the side
of that brimming Loddon river. "Do not expect us
before six o'clock," said I, as I left the house; "Six
at soonest!" added my charming companion; and off
we drove in our little pony chaise, drawn by our old
mare, and with the good-humoured urchin, Henry's
successor, a sort of younger Scrub, who takes care of
horse and chaise, and cow, and garden, for our charioteer.

My comrade in this homely equipage was a young
lady of high family and high endowments, to whom the
novelty of the thing, and her own naturalness of character
and simplicity of taste, gave an unspeakable enjoyment.
She danced the little chaise up and down as she got into
it, and laughed for very glee like a child. Lizzy herself
could not have been more delighted. She praised the
horse and the driver, and the roads and the scenery, and
gave herself fully up to the enchantment of a rural excur-
sion in the sweetest weather of this sweet season. I
enjoyed all this too; for the road was pleasant to every
sense, winding through narrow lanes, under high elms,

and between hedges garlanded with woodbine and rose trees, whilst the air was scented with the delicious fragrance of blossomed beans. I enjoyed it all—but, I believe, my principal pleasure was derived from my companion herself.

Emily I. is a person whom it is a privilege to know. She is quite like a creation of the older poets, and might pass for one of Shakespeare's or Fletcher's women stepped into life ; just as tender, as playful, as gentle, and as kind. She is clever too, and has all the knowledge and accomplishments that a carefully-conducted education, acting on a mind of singular clearness and ductility, matured and improved by the very best company, can bestow. But one never thinks of her acquirements. It is the charming artless character, the bewitching sweetness of manner, the real and universal sympathy, the quick taste and the ardent feeling, that one loves in Emily. She is Irish by birth, and has in perfection the melting voice and soft caressing accent by which her fair country-women are distinguished. Moreover, she is pretty—I think her beautiful, and so do all who have heard as well as seen her—but pretty, very pretty, all the world must confess ; and perhaps that is a distinction more enviable, because less envied, than the " palmy state " of beauty. Her prettiness is of the prettiest kind—that of which the chief character is youthfulness. A short but pleasing figure, all grace and symmetry, a fair blooming face, beaming with intelligence and good-humour ; the prettiest little feet and the whitest hands in the world—such is Emily I.

She resides with her maternal grandmother, a venerable old lady, slightly shaken with the palsy ; and when together (and they are so fondly attached to each other that they are seldom parted), it is one of the loveliest combinations of youth and age ever witnessed. There is no seeing them without feeling an increase of respect and affection for both grandmother and granddaughter—

always one of the tenderest and most beautiful of natural connections—as Richardson knew when he made such exquisite use of it in his matchless book. I fancy that grandmamma Shirley must have been just such another venerable lady as Mrs. S., and our sweet Emily—Oh, no! Harriet Byron is not half good enough for her! There is nothing like her in the whole seven volumes.

But here we are at the bridge! Here we must alight! "This is the Loddon, Emily. Is it not a beautiful river? rising level with its banks, so clear, and smooth, and peaceful, giving back the verdant landscape and the bright blue sky, and bearing on its pellucid stream the snowy water-lily, the purest of flowers, which sits enthroned on its own cool leaves, looking chastity itself, like the lady in Comus. That queenly flower becomes the water, and so do the stately swans who are sailing so majestically down the stream, like those who—

> " ' On St. Mary's lake
> Float double, swan and shadow.' "

We must dismount here, and leave Richard to take care of our equipage under the shade of these trees, whilst we walk up to the house—See, there it is! We must cross this stile; there is no other way now."

And crossing the stile, we were immediately in what had been a drive round a spacious park, and still retained something of the character, though the park itself had long been broken into arable fields—and in full view of the Great House, a beautiful structure of James the First's time, whose glassless windows and dilapidated doors form a melancholy contrast with the strength and entireness of the rich and massive front.

The story of that ruin—for such it is—is always to me singularly affecting: It is that of the decay of an ancient and distinguished family, gradually reduced from the highest wealth and station to actual poverty. The

house and park, and a small estate around it, were entailed
on a distant cousin, and could not be alienated; and the
late owner, the last of his name and lineage, after long
struggling with debt and difficulty, farming his own
lands, and clinging to his magnificent home with a love
of place almost as tenacious as that of the younger Foscari,
was at last forced to abandon it, retired to a paltry
lodging in a paltry town, and died there about twenty
years ago, broken-hearted. His successor, bound by
no ties of association to the spot, and rightly judging
the residence to be much too large for the diminished
estate, immediately sold the superb fixtures, and would
have entirely taken down the house, if, on making the
attempt, the masonry had not been found so solid that
the materials were not worth the labour. A great part,
however, of one side is laid open, and the splendid
chambers, with their carving and gilding, are exposed to
wind and rain—sad memorials of past grandeur! The
grounds have been left in a merciful neglect; the park,
indeed, is broken up, the lawn mown twice a-year like a
common hay-field, the grotto mouldering into ruin, and
the fish-ponds choked with rushes and aquatic plants;
but the shrubs and flowering trees are undestroyed, and
have grown into a magnificence of size and wildness of
beauty, such as we may imagine them to attain in their
native forests. Nothing can exceed their luxuriance,
especially in the spring, when the lilac, and laburnum,
and double-cherry put forth their gorgeous blossoms.
There is a sweet sadness in the sight of such floweriness
amidst such desolation; it seems the triumph of nature
over the destructive power of man. The whole place,
in that season more particularly, is full of a soft and
soothing melancholy, reminding me, I scarcely know
why, of some of the descriptions of natural scenery in
the novels of Charlotte Smith, which I read when a girl,
and which, perhaps, for that reason hang on my memory.

But here we are, in the smooth, grassy ride, on the top of a steep turfy slope descending to the river, crowned with enormous firs and limes of equal growth, looking across the winding waters into a sweet, peaceful landscape of quiet meadows, shut in by distant woods. What a fragrance is in the air from the balmy fir trees and the blossomed limes! What an intensity of odour! And what a murmur of bees in the lime trees! What a coil those little winged people make over our heads! And what a pleasant sound it is! the pleasantest of busy sounds, that which comes associated with all that is good and beautiful—industry and forecast, and sunshine and flowers. Surely these lime trees might store a hundred hives; the very odour is of a honeyed richness, cloying, satiating.

Emily exclaimed in admiration as we stood under deep, strong, leafy shadow, and still more when honey-suckles trailed their profusion in our path, and roses, really trees, almost intercepted our passage.

"On, Emily! farther yet! Force your way by that jessamine—it will yield; I will take care of this stubborn white rose bough."—"Take care of yourself! Pray take care," said my fairest friend; "let me hold back the branches."—After we had won our way through the strait, at some expense of veils and flounces, she stopped to contemplate and admire the tall, graceful shrub, whose long, thorny stems, spreading in every direction, had opposed our progress, and now waved their delicate clusters over our heads. "Did I ever think," exclaimed she, "of standing under the shadow of a white rose tree! What an exquisite fragrance! And what a beautiful flower! so pale, and white, and tender, and the petals thin and smooth as silk! What rose is it?"—"Don't you know? Did you never see it before? It is rare now, I believe, and seems rarer than it is, because it only blossoms in very hot summers; but this, Emily, is the musk rose,—that very musk rose of which Titania talks,

and which is worthy of Shakespeare and of her. Is it
not ?—No ! do not smell it ; it is less sweet so than
other roses ; but one cluster in a vase, or even that bunch
in your bosom, will perfume a large room, as it does
the summer air."—" Oh ! we will take twenty clusters,"
said Emily—" I wish grandmamma were here ! She talks
so often of a musk rose tree that grew against one end of
her father's house. I wish she were here to see this ! "

Echoing her wish, and well laden with musk roses,
planted, perhaps, in the days of Shakespeare, we reached
the steps that led to a square summer-house or banqueting-
room, overhanging the river : the under part was a
boat-house, whose projecting roof, as well as the walls
and the very top of the little tower was covered with
ivy and woodbine, and surmounted by tufted barberries,
bird cherries, acacias, covered with their snowy chains,
and other pendant and flowering trees. Beyond rose
two poplars of unrivalled magnitude, towering like
stately columns over the dark tall firs, and giving a sort
of pillared and architectural grandeur to the scene.

We were now close to the mansion ; but it looked sad
and desolate, and the entrance, choked with brambles
and nettles, seemed almost to repel our steps. The
beautiful summer-house was free, and open, and inviting,
commanding from the unglazed windows, which hung
high above the water, a reach of the river terminated by
a rustic mill.

There we sat, emptying our little basket of fruit and
country cakes, till Emily was seized with a desire of
viewing, from the other side of the Loddon, the scenery
which had so much enchanted her. " I must," said she,
" take a sketch of the ivied boat-house, and of this sweet
room, and this pleasant window—Grandmamma would
never be able to walk from the road to see the place itself,
but she must see its likeness." So forth we sallied, not
forgetting the dear musk roses.

We had no way of reaching the desired spot but by
retracing our steps a mile, during the heat of the hottest
hour of the day, and then following the course of the
river to an equal distance on the other side ; nor had
we any materials for sketching, except the rumpled
paper which had contained our repast, and a pencil
without a point which I happened to have about me.
But these small difficulties are pleasures to gay and
happy youth. Regardless of such obstacles, the sweet
Emily bounded on like a fawn, and I followed, delighting
in her delight. The sun went in, and the walk was
delicious ; a reviving coolness seemed to breathe over
the water, wafting the balmy scent of the firs and limes ;
we found a point of view presenting the boat-house, the
water, the poplars, and the mill, in a most felicitous
combination ; the little straw fruit basket made a capital
table ; and refreshed and sharpened and pointed by our
trusty lackey's excellent knife (your country boy is never
without a good knife, it is his prime treasure), the pencil
did double duty—first in the skilful hands of Emily,
whose faithful and spirited sketch does equal honour to
the scene and to the artist, and then in the humbler
office of attempting a faint transcript of my own impres-
sions in the following sonnet :—

> It was an hour of calmest noon, at day
>   Of ripest summer : o'er the deep blue sky
>   White speckled clouds came sailing peacefully,
> Half-shrouding in a chequer'd veil the ray
> Of the sun, too ardent else—what time we lay
>   By the smooth Loddon, opposite the high,
>   Steep bank, which as a coronet gloriously
> Wore its rich crest of firs and lime trees, gay
>   With their pale tassels ; while from out a bower
> Of ivy (where those column'd poplars rear
>   Their heads) the ruin'd boat-house, like a tower,
> Flung its deep shadow on the waters clear
>   My Emily ! forget not that calm hour,
>   Nor that fair scene, by thee made doubly dear !

THE SHAW

SEPTEMBER 9th.—A bright, sunshiny afternoon. What a comfort it is to get out again—to see once more that rarity of rarities, a fine day! We English people are accused of talking over much of the weather; but the weather, this summer, has forced people to talk of it. Summer! did I say? Oh! season most unworthy of that sweet, sunny name! Season of coldness and cloudiness, of gloom and rain! A worse November!—for in November the days are short; and shut up in a warm room, lighted by that household sun, a lamp, one feels through the long evenings comfortably independent of the out-of-door tempests. But though we may have, and did have, fires all through the dog-days, there is no shutting out daylight; and sixteen hours of rain, pattering against the windows and dripping from the eaves—sixteen hours of rain, not merely audible, but visible for seven days in the week—would be enough to exhaust the patience of Job or Grizzel; especially if Job were a farmer, and Grizzel a country gentlewoman. Never was known such a season! Hay swimming, cattle drowning, fruit rotting, corn spoiling! and that naughty river, the Loddon, who never can take Puff's advice, and "keep between its banks," running about the country, fields, roads, gardens, and houses, like mad! The weather would be talked of. Indeed, it was not easy to talk of anything else. A friend of mine having occasion to write me a letter, thought it worth abusing in rhyme, and bepommelled it through three pages of Bathguide verse; of which I subjoin a specimen :—

" Aquarius surely *reigns* over the world,
  And of late he his water-pot strangely has twirl'd ;
Or he's taken a cullender up by mistake,
  And unceasingly dips it in some mighty lake ;
Though it is not in Lethe—for who can forget
  The annoyance of getting most thoroughly wet ?
It must be in the river called Styx, I declare,
  For the moment it drizzles it makes the men swear.
' It did rain to-morrow,' is growing good grammar ;
  Vauxhall and camp-stools have been brought to the
      hammer ;
A pony-gondola is all I can keep,
  And I use my umbrella and pattens in sleep :
Row out of my window, whene'er 'tis my whim
  To visit a friend, and just ask, ' Can you swim ? ' "

So far my friend.* In short, whether in prose or in
verse, everybody railed at the weather. But this is
over now. The sun has come to dry the world ; mud
is turned into dust ; rivers have retreated to their proper
limits ; farmers have left off grumbling ; and we are
about to take a walk, as usual, as far as the Shaw, a
pretty wood about a mile off. But one of our companions
being a stranger to the gentle reader, we must do him
the honour of an introduction.

Dogs, when they are sure of having their own way,
have sometimes ways as odd as those of the unfurred,
unfeathered animals, who walk on two legs, and talk,

* This friend of mine is a person of great quickness and talent,
who, if she were not a beauty and a woman of fortune—that is to
say, if she were prompted by either of those two powerful *stimuli*,
want of money or want of admiration, to take due pains—would
inevitably become a clever writer. As it is, her notes and *jeux
d'esprit* struck off *à trait de plume*, have great point and neatness.
Take the following billet, which formed the label to a closed basket,
containing the ponderous present alluded to, last Michaelmas day :—

" *To Miss M.*

' When this you see,
    Remember me,'
Was long a phrase in use ;
    And so I send
    To you, dear friend,
My proxy, ' What ? '—A goose ! "

and are called rational. My beautiful white greyhound, Mayflower,* for instance, is as whimsical as the finest lady in the land. Amongst her other fancies, she has taken a violent affection for a most hideous stray dog, who made his appearance here about six months ago, and contrived to pick up a living in the village, one can hardly tell how. Now appealing to the charity of old Rachel Strong, the laundress—a dog-lover by profession; now winning a meal from the light-footed and open-hearted lasses at the Rose; now standing on his hind-legs, to extort by sheer beggary a scanty morsel from some pair of " drouthy cronies," or solitary drover, discussing his dinner or supper on the alehouse bench; now catching a mouthful, flung to him in pure contempt by some scornful gentleman of the shoulder-knot, mounted on his throne, the coach-box, whose notice he had attracted by dint of ugliness; now sharing the commons of Master Keep the shoemaker's pigs; now succeeding to the reversion of the well-gnawed bone of Master Brown the shopkeeper's fierce house-dog; now filching the skim-milk of Dame Wheeler's cat—spit at by the cat; worried by the mastiff; chased by the pigs; screamed at by the dame; stormed at by the shoemaker; flogged by the shopkeeper; teased by all the children, and scouted by all the animals of the parish—but yet living through his griefs, and bearing them patiently, " for sufferance is the badge of all his tribe "—and even seeming to find, in an occasional full meal, or a gleam of sunshine, or a wisp of dry straw on which to repose his sorry carcass, some comfort in his disconsolate condition.

In this plight was he found by May, the most high-blooded and aristocratic of greyhounds; and from this plight did May rescue him; invited him into her territory, the stable; resisted all attempts to turn him out; reinstated him there, in spite of maid and boy, and

* Dead, alas, since this was written.

mistress and master; wore out everybody's opposition by the activity of her protection, and the pertinacity of her self-will; made him sharer of her bed and of her mess; and, finally, established him as one of the family as firmly as herself.

Dash—for he has even won himself a name amongst us; before he was anonymous—Dash is a sort of a kind of a spaniel; at least there is in his mongrel composition some sign of that beautiful race. Besides his ugliness, which is of the worst sort—that is to say, the shabbiest —he has a limp on one leg that gives a peculiar one-sided awkwardness to his gait; but independently of his great merit in being May's pet, he has other merits which serve to account for that phenomenon—being, beyond all comparison, the most faithful, attached, and affectionate animal that I have ever known; and that is saying much. He seems to think it necessary to atone for his ugliness by extra good conduct, and does so dance on his lame leg, and so wag his scrubby tail, that it does any one who has a taste for happiness good to look at him—so that he may now be said to stand on his own footing. We are all rather ashamed of him when strangers come in the way, and think it necessary to explain that he is May's pet; but amongst ourselves, and those who are used to his appearance, he has reached the point of favouritism in his own person. I have, in common with wiser women, the feminine weakness of loving whatever loves me—and, therefore, I like Dash. His master has found out that he is a capital finder, and in spite of his lameness will hunt a field or beat a cover with any spaniel in England — and, therefore, *he* likes Dash. The boy has fought a battle, in defence of his beauty, with another boy bigger than himself, and beat his opponent most handsomely—and, therefore, *he* likes Dash; and the maids like him, or pretend to like him, because we do— as is the fashion of that pliant and imitative class. And now Dash and May follow us everywhere, and are going with us to the Shaw, as I said before—or rather to the cottage by the Shaw, to bespeak milk and butter of our little dairy-woman, Hannah Bint—a housewifely occupation, to which we owe some of our pleasantest rambles.

And now we pass the sunny, dusty village street—who would have thought, a month ago, that we should complain of sun and dust again!—and turn the corner where the two great oaks hang so beautifully over the clear, deep pond, mixing their cool green shadows with the bright blue sky, and the white clouds that flit over it ; and loiter at the wheeler's shop, always picturesque, with its tools, and its work, and its materials, all so various in form, and so harmonious in colour ; and its noisy, merry workmen, hammering and singing, and making a various harmony also. The shop is rather empty to-day, for its usual inmates are busy on the green beyond the pond—one set building a cart, another painting a waggon. And then we leave the village quite behind, and proceed slowly up the cool, quiet lane, between tall hedge-rows of the darkest verdure, overshadowing banks green and fresh as an emerald.

Not so quick as I expected, though—for they are shooting here to-day, as Dash and I have both discovered : he with great delight, for a gun to him is as a trumpet to a war-horse ; I with no less annoyance, for I don't think a partridge itself, barring the accident of being killed, can be more startled than I at that abominable explosion. Dash has certainly better blood in his veins than any one would guess to look at him. He even shows some inclination to elope into the fields, in pursuit of those noisy iniquities. But he is an orderly person after all, and a word has checked him.

Ah ! here is a shriller din mingling with the small artillery—a shriller and more continuous. We are not yet arrived within sight of Master Weston's cottage, snugly hidden behind a clump of elms; but we are in full hearing of Dame Weston's tongue, raised, as usual, to scolding pitch. The Westons are new arrivals in our neighbourhood, and the first thing heard of them was a complaint from the wife to our magistrate of her husband's beating her: it was a regular charge of assault —an information in full form. A most piteous case did Dame Weston make of it, softening her voice for the nonce into a shrill, tremulous whine, and exciting the mingled pity and anger—pity towards herself, anger towards her husband—of the whole female world, pitiful and indignant as the female world is wont to be on such occasions. Every woman in the parish railed at Master Weston; and poor Master Weston was summoned to attend the bench on the ensuing Saturday, and answer the charge; and such was the clamour abroad and at home, that the unlucky culprit, terrified at the sound of a warrant and a constable, ran away, and was not heard of for a fortnight.

At the end of that time he was discovered, and brought to the bench; and Dame Weston again told her story, and, as before, on the full cry. She had no witnesses, and the bruises of which she had made complaint had disappeared, and there were no women present to make common cause with the sex. Still, however, the general feeling was against Master Weston; and it would have gone hard with him when he was called in, if a most unexpected witness had not risen up in his favour. His wife had brought in her arms a little girl about eighteen months old, partly, perhaps, to move compassion in her favour; for a woman with a child in her arms is always an object that excites kind feelings. The little girl had looked shy and frightened, and had been as quiet as a lamb during her mother's examination; but she no sooner saw her father, from whom she had been a fortnight separated, than she clapped her hands, and laughed, and cried, " Daddy ! daddy ! " and sprang into his arms, and hung round his neck, and covered him with kisses—again shouting, " Daddy, come home ! daddy ! daddy ! "—and finally nestled her little head in his bosom, with a fulness of contentment, an assurance of tenderness and protection, such as no wife-beating tyrant ever did inspire, or ever could inspire, since the days of King Solomon. Our magistrates acted in the very spirit of the Jewish monarch : they accepted the evidence of nature, and dismissed the complaint. And subsequent events have fully justified their decision ; Mistress Weston proving not only renowned for the feminine accomplishment of scolding (tongue-banging, it is called in our parts, a compound word which deserves to be Greek), but is actually herself addicted to administering the conjugal discipline, the infliction of which she was pleased to impute to her luckless husband.

Now we cross the stile, and walk up the fields to the Shaw. How beautifully green this pasture looks ! and how finely the evening sun glances between the boles of that clump of trees, beech, and ash, and aspen ! and how sweet the hedge-rows are with woodbine and wild scabious, or, as the country people call it, the gipsy-rose ! Here is little Dolly Weston, the unconscious witness, with cheeks as red as a real rose, tottering up the path to meet her father. And here is the carrotty polled urchin, George Coper, returning from work, and singing, " Home ! sweet home ! " at the top of his voice ; and then, when the notes prove too high for him, continuing the air in a whistle, until he has turned the impassable corner ; then taking up again the song and the words, " Home ! sweet home ! " and looking as if he felt their full import, ploughboy though he be. And so he does ; for he is one of a large, an honest, a kind, and an industrious family, where all goes well, and where the poor ploughboy is sure of finding cheerful faces and coarse comforts—all that he has learned to desire. Oh, to be as cheaply and as thoroughly contented as George Coper! All his luxuries, a cricket-match!—all his wants satisfied in "Home! sweet home!"

Nothing but noises to-day! They are clearing Farmer Brooke's great bean-field, and crying the "Harvest Home!" in a chorus, before which all other sounds—the song, the scolding, the gunnery—fade away, and become faint echoes. A pleasant noise is that! though, for one's ears' sake, one makes some haste to get away from it. And here, in happy time, is that pretty wood, the Shaw, with its broad pathway, its tangled dingles, its nuts and its honeysuckles—and, carrying away a fagot of those sweetest flowers, we reach Hannah Bint's; of whom we shall say more another time.

NOTE.—Poor Dash is also dead. We did not keep him long; indeed, I believe that he died of the transition from starvation to good feed, as dangerous to a dog's stomach and to most stomachs, as the less agreeable change from good feed to starvation. He has been succeeded in place and favour by another Dash, not less amiable in demeanour and far more creditable in appearance, bearing no small resemblance to the pet spaniel of my friend Master Dinely, he who stole the bone from the magpies, and who figures as the first Dash of this volume. Let not the unwary reader opine that, in assigning the same name to three several individuals, I am acting as an humble imitator of the inimitable writer who has given immortality to the Peppers and the Mustards, on the one hand; or showing a poverty of invention, or a want of acquaintance with the bead-roll of canine appellations, on the other. I merely, with my usual scrupulous fidelity, take the names as I find them. The fact is, that half the handsome spaniels in England are called Dash, just as half the tall footmen are called Thomas. The name belongs to the species. Sitting in an open carriage one day last summer at the door of a farm-house where my father had some business, I saw a noble and beautiful animal of this kind lying in great state and laziness on the steps, and felt an immediate desire to make acquaintance with him. My father, who had had the same fancy, had patted him and called him "poor fellow" in passing, without eliciting the smallest notice in return. "Dash!" cried I, at a venture, "good Dash! noble Dash!" and up he started in a moment, making but one spring from the door into the gig. Of course I was right in my guess. The gentleman's name was Dash.

HANNAH BINT

THE Shaw, leading to Hannah Bint's habitation, is, as I perhaps have said before, a very pretty mixture of wood and coppice; that is to say, a tract of thirty or forty acres covered with fine growing timber—ash, and oak, and elm, very regularly planted; and interspersed here and there with large patches of underwood, hazel, maple, birch, holly, and hawthorn, woven into almost impenetrable thickets by long wreathes of the bramble, the briony, and the brier-rose, or by the pliant and twisting garlands of the wild honeysuckle. In other parts the Shaw is quite clear of its bosky undergrowth, and clothed only with large beds of feathery fern, or carpets of flowers, primroses, orchises, cowslips, ground-ivy, crane's bill, cotton-grass, Solomon's seal, and forget-me-not, crowded together with a profusion and brilliancy of colour such as I have rarely seen equalled even in a garden. Here, so soft to the eye, the wild hyacinth really enamels the ground with its fresh and lovely purple; there,

> " On aged roots, with bright green mosses clad,
> Dwells the wood-sorrel, with its bright thin leaves
> Heart-shaped and triply folded, and its root
> Creeping like beaded coral; whilst around
> Flourish the copse's pride, anemones,
> With rays like golden studs on ivory laid
> Most delicate; but touch'd with purple clouds,
> Fit crown for April's fair but changeful brow."

The variety is much greater than I have enumerated; for the ground is so unequal, now swelling in gentle accents, now dimpling into dells and hollows, and the soil so different in many parts, that the sylvan Flora is unusually extensive and complete.

The season is, however, now too late for this floweriness ; and except the tufted woodbines, which have continued in bloom during the whole of this lovely autumn, and some lingering garlands of the purple wild veitch, wreathing round the thickets, and uniting with the ruddy leaves of the bramble, and the pale festoons of the briony, there is little to call one's attention from the grander beauties of the trees — the sycamore, its broad leaves already spotted—the oak, heavy with acorns—and the delicate shining rind of the weeping birch, " the lady of the woods," thrown out in strong relief from a background of holly and hawthorn, each studded with coral berries, and backed with old beeches, beginning to assume the rich tawny hue which makes them, perhaps, the most picturesque of autumnal trees, as the transparent freshness of their young foliage is undoubtedly the choicest ornament of the forest in spring.

A sudden turn round one of these magnificent beeches brings us to the boundary of the Shaw, and leaning upon a rude gate, we look over an open space of about ten acres of ground, still more varied and broken than that which we have passed, and surrounded on all sides by thick woodland. As a piece of colour, nothing can be finer. The ruddy glow of the heath-flower, contrasting, on the one hand, with the golden-blossomed furze— on the other, with a patch of buck-wheat, of which the bloom is not past, although the grain be ripening, the beautiful buck-wheat, whose transparent leaves and stalks are so brightly tinged with vermilion, while the delicate pink-white of the flower, a paler persicaria, has a feathery fall, at once so rich and so graceful, and a fresh and reviving odour, like that of birch trees in the dew of a May evening. The bank that surmounts this attempt at cultivation is crowned with the late foxglove

and the stately mullein ; the pasture of which so great
a part of the waste consists, looks as green as an emerald ;
a clear pond, with the bright sky reflected in it, lets
light into the picture ; the white cottage of the keeper
peeps from the opposite coppice ; and the vine-covered
dwelling of Hannah Bint rises from amidst the pretty
garden, which lies bathed in the sunshine around it.

The living and moving accessories are all in keeping
with the cheerfulness and repose of the landscape.
Hannah's cow grazing quietly beside the keeper's pony ;
a brace of fat pointer puppies holding amicable intercourse with a litter of young pigs ; ducks, geese, cocks,
hens, and chickens scattered over the turf ; Hannah
herself sallying forth from the cottage-door, with her
milk-bucket in her hand, and her little brother following
with the milking-stool.

My friend Hannah Bint is by no means an ordinary
person. Her father, Jack Bint (for in all his life he
never arrived at the dignity of being called John—indeed,
in our parts he was commonly known by the cognomen
of London Jack), was a drover of high repute in his
profession. No man between Salisbury Plain and Smith-
field was thought to conduct a flock of sheep so skilfully
through all the difficulties of lanes and commons, streets
and high-roads, as Jack Bint, aided by Jack Bint's famous
dog Watch ; for Watch's rough, honest face, black, with
a little white about the muzzle, and one white ear, was as
well known at fairs and markets as his master's equally
honest and weather-beaten visage. Lucky was the
dealer that could secure their services ; Watch being
renowned for keeping a flock together better than any
shepherd's dog on the road—Jack, for delivering them
more punctually, and in better condition. No man had
a more thorough knowledge of the proper night stations
where good feed might be produced for his charge, and
good liquor for Watch and himself, Watch, like other

sheep dogs, being accustomed to live chiefly on bread and beer. His master, though not averse to a pot of good double X, preferred gin ; and they who plod slowly along, through wet and weary ways, in frost and in fog, have undoubtedly a stronger temptation to indulge in that cordial and reviving stimulus than we water-drinkers, sitting in warm and comfortable rooms, can readily imagine. For certain, our drover could never resist the gentle seduction of the gin-bottle, and being of a free, merry, jovial temperament, one of those persons commonly called good fellows, who like to see others happy in the same way with themselves, he was apt to circulate it at his own expense, to the great improvement of his popularity and the great detriment of his finances.

All this did vastly well whilst his earnings continued proportionate to his spendings, and the little family at home were comfortably supported by his industry : but when a rheumatic fever came on, one hard winter, and finally settled in his limbs, reducing the most active and hardy man in the parish to the state of a confirmed cripple, then his reckless improvidence stared him in the face ; and poor Jack, a thoughtless but kind creature, and a most affectionate father, looked at his three motherless children with the acute misery of a parent who has brought those whom he loves best in the world to abject destitution. He found help where he probably least expected it, in the sense and spirit of his young daughter, a girl of twelve years old.

Hannah was the eldest of the family, and had, ever since her mother's death, which event had occurred two or three years before, been accustomed to take the direction of their domestic concerns, to manage her two brothers, to feed the pigs and the poultry, and to keep house during the almost constant absence of her father. She was a quick, clever lass, of a high spirit, a firm temper, some pride, and a horror of accepting parochial relief,

which is every day becoming rarer amongst the peasantry ;
but which forms the surest safeguard to the sturdy
independence of the English character. Our little damsel
possessed this quality in perfection ; and when her father
talked of giving up their comfortable cottage, and removing
to the workhouse, whilst she and her brothers must go
to service, Hannah formed a bold resolution, and without
disturbing the sick man by any participation of her hopes
and fears, proceeded, after settling their trifling affairs,
to act at once on her own plans and designs.

Careless of the future as the poor drover had seemed,
he had yet kept clear of debt, and by subscribing constantly to a benefit club, had secured a pittance that
might at least assist in supporting him during the long
years of sickness and helplessness to which he was doomed
to look forward. This his daughter knew. She knew
also that the employer in whose service his health had
suffered so severely was a rich and liberal cattle-dealer
in the neighbourhood, who would willingly aid an
old and faithful servant, and had, indeed, come forward
with offers of money. To assistance from such a quarter
Hannah saw no objection. Farmer Oakley and the
parish were quite distinct things. Of him, accordingly,
she asked, not money, but something much more in his
own way—" A cow ! any cow ! old or lame, or what
not, so that it were a cow ! she would be bound to keep
it well ; if she did not, he might take it back again. She
even hoped to pay for it by-and-by, by instalments, but
that she would not promise ! " and, partly amused,
partly interested by the child's earnestness, the wealthy
yeoman gave her, not as a purchase, but as a present, a
very fine young Alderney. She then went to the lord
of the manor, and, with equal knowledge of character,
begged his permisson to keep her cow on the Shaw
common. " Farmer Oakley had given her a fine Alderney,
and she would be bound to pay the rent, and keep her

father off the parish, if he would only let it graze on the waste ; " and he, too, half from real good-nature—half, not to be outdone in liberality by his tenant, not only granted the requested permission, but reduced the rent so much, that the produce of the vine seldoms fails to satisfy their kind landlord.

Now Hannah showed great judgment in setting up as a dairy-woman. She could not have chosen an occupation more completely unoccupied, or more loudly called for. One of the most provoking of the petty difficulties which beset people with a small establishment in this neighbourhood, is the trouble, almost the impossibility, of procuring the pastoral luxuries of milk, eggs, and butter, which rank, unfortunately, amongst the indispensable necessaries of housekeeping. To your thorough-bred Londoner, who, whilst grumbling over his own breakfast, is apt to fancy that thick cream, and fresh butter, and new-laid eggs grow, so to say, in the country —form an actual part of its natural produce—it may be some comfort to learn, that in this great grazing district, however the calves and the farmers may be the better for cows, nobody else is ; that farmers' wives have ceased to keep poultry ; and that we unlucky villagers sit down often to our first meal in a state of destitution, which may well make him content with his thin milk and his Cambridge butter, when compared to our imputed pastoralities.

Hannah's Alderney restored us to one rural privilege. Never was so cleanly a little milkmaid. She changed away some of the cottage finery, which, in his prosperous days, poor Jack had pleased himself with bringing home, the China tea-service, the gilded mugs, and the painted waiters, for the useful utensils of the dairy, and speedily established a regular and gainful trade in milk, eggs, butter, honey, and poultry—for poultry they had always kept.

Her domestic management prospered equally. Her

father, who retained the perfect use of his hands, began a manufacture of mats and baskets, which he constructed with great nicety and adroitness ; the eldest boy, a sharp and clever lad, cut for him his rushes and osiers ; erected, under his sister's direction, a shed for the cow, and enlarged and cultivated the garden (always with the good leave of her kind patron, the lord of the manor) until it became so ample that the produce not only kept the pig, and half kept the family, but afforded another branch of merchandise to the indefatigable directress of the establishment. For the younger boy, less quick and active, Hannah contrived to obtain an admission to the charity-school, where he made great progress—retaining him at home, however, in the hay-making and leasing season, or whenever his services could be made available, to the great annoyance of the schoolmaster, whose favourite he is, and who piques himself so much on George's scholarship (your heavy, sluggish boy at country work often turns out quick at his book), that it is the general opinion that this much-vaunted pupil will, in process of time, be promoted to the post of assistant, and may, possibly, in course of years, rise to the dignity of a parish pedagogue in his own person ; so that his sister, although still making him useful at odd times, now considers George as pretty well off her hands, whilst her elder brother Tom could take an under-gardener's place directly, if he were not too important at home to be spared even for a day.

In short, during the five years that she has ruled at the Shaw cottage, the world has gone well with Hannah Bint. Her cow, her calves, her pigs, her bees, her poultry, have each in their several ways thriven and prospered. She has even brought Watch to like buttermilk as well as strong beer, and has nearly persuaded her father (to whose wants and wishes she is most anxiously attentive) to accept of milk as a substitute for gin. Not but Hannah hath had her enemies as well as her betters. Why should she not? The old woman at the lodge, who always piqued herself on being spiteful, and crying down new ways, foretold from the first she would come to no good, and could not forgive her for falsifying her prediction; and Betty Barnes, the slatternly widow of a tippling farmer, who rented a field, and set up a cow herself, and was universally discarded for insufferable dirt, said all that the wit of an envious woman could devise against Hannah and her Alderney; nay, even Ned Miles, the keeper, her next neighbour, who had whilom held entire sway over the Shaw common, as well as its coppices, grumbled as much as so good-natured and genial a person could grumble, when he found a little girl sharing his dominion, a cow grazing beside his pony, and vulgar cocks and hens hovering around the buck-wheat destined to feed his noble pheasants. Nobody that had been accustomed to see that paragon of keepers, so tall, and manly, and pleasant looking, with his merry eye, and his knowing smile, striding gaily along, in his green coat and his gold laced hat, with Neptune, his noble Newfoundland dog (a retriever is the sporting word), and his beautiful spaniel, Flirt, at his heels, could conceive how askew he looked when he first found Hannah and Watch holding equal reign over his old territory, the Shaw common.

Yes! Hannah hath had her enemies; but they are passing away. The old woman at the lodge is dead, poor creature; and Betty Barnes, having herself taken to tippling, has lost the few friends she once possessed, and looks, luckless wretch, as if she would soon die too!— and the keeper?—why, he is not dead, or like to die; but the change that has taken place there is the most astonishing of all—except, perhaps, the change in Hannah herself.

Few damsels of twelve years old, generally a very pretty age, were less pretty than Hannah Bint. Short and stunted in her figure, thin in face, sharp in feature, with

a muddled complexion, wild sun-burnt hair, and eyes
whose very brightness had in them something startling,
over-informed, super-subtle, too clever for her age—
at twelve years old she had quite the airs of a little old
fairy. Now, at seventeen, matters are mended. Her
complexion has cleared ; her countenance has developed
itself ; her figure has shot up into height and lightness,
and a sort of rustic grace ; her bright, acute eye is softened
and sweetened by the womanly wish to please ; her hair
is trimmed, and curled, and brushed, with exquisite
neatness ; and her whole dress arranged with that nice
attention to the becoming, the suitable both in form and
texture, which would be called the highest degree of
coquetry, if it did not deserve the better name of propriety. Never was such a transmogrification beheld.
The lass is really pretty, and Ned Miles has discovered
that she is so.   There he stands, the rogue, close at
her side (for he hath joined her whilst we have been
telling her little story, and the milking is over !)—there
he stands—holding her milk-pail in one hand, and stroking
Watch with the other ; while she is returning the compliment by patting Neptune's magnificent head.   There
they stand, as much like lovers as may be ; he smiling,
and she blushing—he never looking so handsome nor she
so pretty in all their lives.   There they stand, in blessed
forgetfulness of all except each other ; as happy a couple
as ever trod the earth.   There they stand, and one would
not disturb them for all the milk and butter in Christen-
dom.   I should not wonder if they were fixing the
wedding-day.

THE FALL OF THE LEAF

NOVEMBER 6th.—The weather is as peaceful to-day, as calm, and as mild, as in early April; and, perhaps, an autumn afternoon and a spring morning do resemble each other more in feeling, and even in appearance, than in any two periods of the year. There is in both the same freshness and dewiness of the herbage; the same balmy softness in the air; and the same pure and lovely blue sky, with white fleecy clouds floating across it. The chief difference lies in the absence of flowers and the presence of leaves. But then the foliage of November is so rich, and glowing, and varied, that it may well supply the place of the gay blossoms of the spring; whilst all the flowers of the field or the garden could never make amends for the want of leaves—that beautiful and graceful attire in which nature has clothed the rugged forms of trees—the verdant drapery to which the landscape owes its loveliness and the forests their glory.

If choice must be between two seasons, each so full of charm, it is at least no bad philosophy to prefer the present good, even whilst looking gratefully back, and hopefully forward, to the past and the future. And of a surety, no fairer specimen of a November day could well be found than this—a day made to wander

"By yellow commons and birch-shaded hollows,
   And hedge-rows bordering unfrequented lanes;"

nor could a prettier country be found for our walk than this shady and yet sunny Berkshire, where the scenery, without rising into grandeur or breaking into wildness,

125

is so peaceful, so cheerful, so varied, and so thoroughly English.

We must bend our steps towards the water side, for I have a message to leave at Farmer Riley's : and sooth to say, it is no unpleasant necessity ; for the road thither is smooth and dry, retired, as one likes a country walk to be, but not too lonely, which women never like ; leading past the Loddon—the bright, brimming, transparent Loddon—a fitting mirror for this bright blue sky, and terminating at one of the prettiest and most comfortable farm-houses in the neighbourhood.

How beautiful the lane is to-day, decorated with a thousand colours ! The brown road, and the rich verdure that borders it, strewed with the pale yellow leaves of the elm, just beginning to fall ; hedge-rows glowing with long wreaths of the bramble in every variety of purplish red ; and overhead the unchanged green of the fir, contrasting with the spotted sycamore, the tawny beech, and the dry sere leaves of the oak, which rustle as the light wind passes through them ; a few common hardy yellow flowers (for yellow is the common colour of flowers, whether wild or cultivated, as blue is the rare one), flowers of many sorts, but almost of one tint, still blowing in spite of the season, and ruddy berries glowing through all. How very beautiful is the lane !

And how pleasant is this hill where the road widens, with the group of cattle by the wayside, and George Hearn, the little post-boy, trundling his hoop at full speed, making all the better haste in his work because he cheats himself into thinking it play ! And how beautiful again is this patch of common at the hill-top with the clear pool, where Martha Pither's children —elves of three, and four, and five years old—without any distinction of sex in their sunburnt faces and tattered drapery, are dipping up water in their little homely cups shining with cleanliness, and a small brown pitcher

with the lip broken, to fill that great kettle, which, when
it is filled, their united strength will never be able to
lift ! They are quite a group for a painter, with their
rosy cheeks, and chubby hands, and round merry faces ;
and the low cottage in the background, peeping out of its
vine leaves and china roses, with Martha at the door,
tidy, and comely, and smiling, preparing the potatoes
for the pot, and watching the progress of dipping and
filling that useful utensil, completes the picture.

But we must go on. No time for more sketches in
those short days. It is getting cold too. We must
proceed in our walk. Dash is showing us the way, and
beating the thick double hedge-row that runs along the
side of the meadow, at a rate that indicates game astir,
and causes the leaves to fly as fast as an east wind after
a hard frost. Ah ! a pheasant ! a superb cock pheasant !
Nothing is more certain than Dash's questing, whether
in a hedge-row or covert, for a better spaniel never went
into the field; but I fancied that it was a hare afoot,
and was also as much startled to hear the whirring of
those splendid wings as the princely bird himself would
have been at the report of a gun. Indeed, I believe
that the way in which a pheasant goes off does sometimes
make young sportsmen a little nervous (they don't own
it very readily, but the observation may be relied on
nevertheless), until they get, as it were, broken-in to the
sound ; and then that grand and sudden burst of wing
becomes as pleasant to them as it seems to be to Dash, who
is beating the hedge-row with might and main, and giving
tongue louder, and sending the leaves about faster than
ever—very proud of finding the pheasant, and perhaps
a little angry with me for not shooting it ; at least looking
as if he would be angry if I were a man ; for Dash is a
dog of great sagacity, and has doubtless not lived four
years in the sporting world without making the discovery,
that although gentlemen do shoot, ladies do not.

The Loddon at last! the beautiful Loddon! and the bridge, where every one stops, as by instinct, to lean over the rails, and gaze a moment on a landscape of surpassing loveliness—the fine grounds of the Great House, with their magnificent groups of limes, and firs, and poplars grander than ever poplars were; the green meadows opposite, studded with oaks and elms; the clear winding river; the mill with its picturesque old buildings bounding the scene; all glowing with the rich colouring of autumn, and harmonised by the soft beauty of the clear blue sky, and the delicious calmness of the hour. The very peasant whose daily path it is cannot cross the bridge without a pause.

But the day is wearing fast, and it grows colder and colder. I really think it will be a frost. After all, spring is the pleasantest season, beautiful as this scenery is. We must get on. Down that broad yet shadowy lane, between the park, dark with evergreens and dappled with deer, and the meadows where sheep, and cows, and horses are grazing under the tall elms; that lane, where the wild bank, clothed with fern and tufted with furze, and crowned by rich berried thorn and thick shining holly, on the one side, seems to vie in beauty with the picturesque old paling, the bright laurels, and the plumy cedars, on the other; down that shady lane, until the sudden turn brings us to an opening where four roads meet, where a noble avenue turns down to the Great House; where the village church rears its modest spire from amidst its venerable yew trees: and where, embosomed in orchards and gardens, and backed by barns and ricks, and all the wealth of the farm-yard, stands the spacious and comfortable abode of good Farmer Riley—the end and object of our walk.

And in happy time the message is said and the answer given, for this beautiful mild day is edging off into a dense frosty evening; the leaves of the elm and the linden in the old avenue are quivering and vibrating and fluttering in the air, and at length falling crisply on the earth, as if Dash were beating for pheasants in the tree-tops; the sun gleams dimly through the fog, giving little more of light and heat than his fair sister the lady moon—I don't know a more disappointing person than a cold sun; and I am beginning to wrap my cloak closely round me, and to calculate the distance to my own fireside, recanting all the way my praises of November, and longing for the showery, flowery April, as much as if I were a half-chilled butterfly, or a dahlia knocked down by the frost.

Ah, dear me! what a climate this is, that one cannot keep in the same mind about it for half-an-hour together! I wonder, by-the-way, whether the fault is in the weather, which Dash does not seem to care for, or in me? If I should happen to be wet through in a shower next spring, and should catch myself longing for autumn, that would settle the question.

HANNAH

THE prettiest cottage on our village-green is the little dwelling of Dame Wilson. It stands in a corner of the common, where the hedge-rows go curving off into a sort of bay round a clear bright pond, the earliest haunt of the swallow. A deep woody, green lane, such as Hobbema or Ruysdael might have painted, a lane that hints of nightingales, forms one boundary of the garden, and a sloping meadow the other; whilst the cottage itself, a low thatched irregular building, backed by a blooming orchard, and covered with honeysuckle and jessamine, looks like the chosen abode of snugness and comfort. And so it is.

Dame Wilson was a respected servant in a most respectable family, where she passed all the early part of her life, and which she quitted only on her marriage with a man of character and industry, and of that peculiar universality of genius which forms, what is called in country phrase, a handy fellow. He could do any sort of work; was thatcher, carpenter, bricklayer, painter, gardener, gamekeeper, "everything by turns, and nothing long." No job came amiss to him. He killed pigs, mended shoes, cleaned clocks, doctored cows, dogs, and horses, and even went as far as bleeding and drawing teeth in his experiments on the human subject. In addition to these multifarious talents, he was ready, obliging, and unfearing; jovial withal, and fond of good fellowship; and endowed with a promptness of resource which made him the general adviser of the stupid, the puzzled, and the timid. He was universally admitted to be the cleverest man in the parish ; and his death, which happened about ten years ago, in consequence of standing in the water, drawing a pond for one neighbour, at a time when he was overheated by loading hay for another, made quite a gap in our village commonwealth. John Wilson had no rival, and has had no successor :—for the Robert Ellis, whom certain youngsters would fain exalt to a co-partnery of fame, is simply nobody—a bell-ringer, a ballad-singer, a troller of profane catches—a fiddler—a bruiser—a loller on alehouse benches —a teller of good stories—a mimic—a poet ! What is all this to compare with the solid parts of John Wilson ? —Whose clock hath Robert Ellis cleaned ?—whose windows hath he mended ?—whose dog hath he broken ? —whose pigs hath he ringed ?—whose pond hath he fished ?—whose hay hath he saved ?—whose cow hath he cured ?—whose calf hath he killed ?—whose teeth hath he drawn ?—whom hath he bled ? Tell me that, irreverent whipsters ! No ! John Wilson is not to be replaced. He was missed by the whole parish ; and most of all he was missed at home. His excellent wife was left the sole guardian and protector of two fatherless girls ; one an infant at her knee, the other a pretty handy lass about nine years old. Cast thus upon the world, there must have been much to endure, much to suffer ; but it was borne with a smiling patience, a hopeful cheeriness of spirit, and a decent pride, which seemed to command success as well as respect in their struggle for independence. Without assistance of any sort, by needle-work, by washing and mending lace and fine linen, and other skilful and profitable labours, and by the produce of her orchard and poultry, Dame Wilson contrived to maintain herself and her children in their old comfortable home. There was no visible change ; she and the little girls were as neat as ever ; the house had still within and without the same sunshiny cleanliness, and the garden was still famous over all other gardens for its cloves, and stocks, and double wall-flowers. But the sweetest flower of the garden, and the joy and pride of her mother's heart, was her daughter Hannah. Well might she be proud of her! At sixteen Hannah Wilson was, beyond a doubt, the prettiest girl in the village, and the best. Her beauty was quite in a different style from the common country rosebud — far more choice and rare. Its chief characteristic was modesty. A light youthful figure, exquisitely graceful and rapid in all its movements; springy, elastic, and buoyant as a bird, and almost as shy; a fair innocent face, with downcast blue eyes, and smiles and blushes coming and going almost with her thoughts; a low soft voice, sweet even in its monosyllables; a dress remarkable for neatness and propriety, and borrowing from her delicate beauty an air of superiority not its own;—such was the outward woman of Hannah. Her mind was very like her person; modest, graceful, gentle, affectionate, grateful, and generous above all. The generosity of the poor is always a very real and fine thing; they give what they want; and Hannah was of all poor people the most generous. She loved to give; it was her pleasure, her luxury. Rosy-cheeked apples, plums with the bloom on them, nosegays of cloves and blossomed myrtle; these were offerings which Hannah delighted to bring to those whom she loved, or those who had shown her kindness; whilst to such of her neighbours as needed other attentions than fruit and flowers, she would give her time, her assistance, her skill; for Hannah inherited her mother's dexterity in feminine employments, with something of her father's versatile power. Besides being an excellent laundress, she was accomplished in all the arts of the needle, millinery, dressmaking, and plain work; a capital cutter-out, an incomparable mender, and endowed with a gift of altering, which made old things better than new. She had no rival at a *rifaci-mento*, as half the turned gowns on the common can witness. As a dairy-woman, and a rearer of pigs and poultry, she was equally successful; none of her ducks and turkeys ever died of neglect or carelessness, or to use the phrase of the poultry-yard on such occasions, of "ill-luck." Hannah's fowls never dreamed of sliding out of the world in such an ignoble way; they all lived to be killed, to make a noise at their deaths, as chickens should do. She was also a famous "scholar"; kept accounts, wrote bills, read letters, and answered them; was a trusty accomptant, and a safe confidante. There was no end to Hannah's usefulness or Hannah's kindness; and her prudence was equal to either. Except to be kind or useful, she never left her home; attended no fairs, or revels, or mayings; went nowhere but to church; and seldom made a nearer approach to rustic revelry than by standing at her own garden-gate on a Sunday evening, with her little sister in her hand, to look at the lads and lasses on the green. In short, our village beauty had fairly reached her twentieth year without a sweet-heart, without the slightest suspicion of her having ever written a love-letter on her own account; when, all on a sudden, appearances changed. She was missing at the "accustomed gate"; and one had seen a young man go into Dame Wilson's; and another had descried a trim, elastic figure walking, not unaccompanied, down the shady lane. Matters were quite clear. Hannah had gotten a lover; and, when poor little Susan, who, deserted by her sister, ventured to peep rather nearer to the gay group, was laughingly questioned on the subject, the hesitating No, and the half Yes, of the smiling child, were equally conclusive.

Since the new marriage act,* we, who belong to country

* It is almost unnecessary to observe, that this little story was written during the short life of that whimsical experiment in legislation.

magistrates, have gained a priority over the rest of the parish in matrimonial news. We (the privileged) see on a work-day the names which the sabbath announces to the generality. Many a blushing, awkward pair hath our little lame clerk (a sorry Cupid!) ushered in between dark and light to stammer and hacker, to bow and curtesy, to sign or make a mark, as it pleases Heaven. One Saturday, at the usual hour, the limping clerk made his appearance; and walking through our little hall, I saw a fine athletic young man, the very image of health and vigour, mental and bodily, holding the hand of a young woman, who, with her head half buried in a geranium in the window, was turning bashfully away, listening, and yet not seeming to listen, to his tender whispers. The shrinking grace of that bending figure was not to be mistaken. "Hannah!" and she went aside with me, and a rapid series of questions and answers conveyed the story of the courtship. "William was," said Hannah, "a journeyman hatter in B. He had walked over one Sunday evening to see the cricketing, and then he came again. Her mother liked him. Everybody liked her William—and she had promised—she was going—was it wrong?"—"Oh no! and where are you to live?"—"William has got a room in B. He works for Mr. Smith, the rich hatter in the market-place and Mr. Smith speaks of him—oh, so well! But William will not tell me where our room is. I suppose in some narrow street or lane, which he is afraid I shall not like, as our common is so pleasant. He little thinks —anywhere."—She stopped suddenly; but her blush and her clasped hands finished the sentence, "anywhere with him!"—"And when is the happy day?"— "On Monday fortnight, Madam," said the bridegroom-elect, advancing with the little clerk to summon Hannah to the parlour, "the earliest day possible." He drew her arm through his, and we parted.

The Monday fortnight was a glorious morning; one of those rare November days when the sky and the air are soft and bright as in April. "What a beautiful day for Hannah!" was the first exclamation of the breakfast table. "Did she tell you where they should dine?"—"No, Ma'am; I forgot to ask."—"I can tell you," said the master of the house, with somewhat of good-humoured importance in his air, somewhat of the look of a man, who having kept a secret as long as it was necessary, is not sorry to get rid of the burthen. "I can tell you: in London."—"In London!"—"Yes. Your little favourite has been in high luck. She has married the only son of one of the best and richest men in B., Mr. Smith, the great hatter. It is quite a romance," continued he: "William Smith walked over one Sunday evening to see a match at cricket. He saw our pretty Hannah, and forgot to look at the cricketers. After having gazed his fill, he approached to address her, and the little damsel was off like a bird. William did not like her the less for that, and thought of her the more. He came again and again; and at last contrived to tame this wild dove, and even to get the *entrée* of the cottage. Hearing Hannah talk is not the way to fall out of love with her. So William, at last finding his case serious, laid the matter before his father, and requested his consent to the marriage. Mr. Smith was at first a little startled; but William is an only son, and an excellent son; and, after talking with me, and looking at Hannah (I believe her sweet face was the more eloquent advocate of the two), he relented; and having a spice of his son's romance, finding that he had not mentioned his situation in life, he made a point of its being kept secret till the wedding-day. We have managed the business of settlements; and William, having discovered that his fair bride has some curiosity to see London (a curiosity, by-the-bye, which I suspect she owes to you or poor Lucy), intends taking her thither for a fortnight. He will then bring her home to one of the best houses in B., a fine garden, fine furniture, fine clothes, fine servants, and more money than she will know what to do with. Really the surprise of Lord E.'s farmer's daughter, when, thinking she had married his steward, he brought her to Burleigh, and installed her as its mistress, could hardly have been greater. I hope the shock will not kill Hannah though, as is said to have been the case with that poor lady."—" Oh no! Hannah loves her husband too well. Anywhere with him."

And I was right. Hannah has survived the shock. She is returned to B., and I have been to call on her. I never saw anything so delicate and bride-like as she looked in her white gown and her lace mob, in a room light and simple, and tasteful and elegant, with nothing fine except some beautiful greenhouse plants. Her reception was a charming mixture of sweetness and modesty, a little more respectful than usual, and far more shamefaced! Poor thing! her cheeks must have pained her! But this was the only difference. In everything else she is still the same Hannah, and has lost none of her old habits of kindness and gratitude. She was making a handsome matronly cap, evidently for her mother and spoke, even with tears, of her new father's goodness to her and to Susan. She would fetch the cake and wine herself, and would gather, in spite of all remonstrance, some of her choicest flowers as a parting nosegay. She did, indeed, just hint at her troubles with visitors and servants—how strange and sad it was! seemed distressed at ringing the bell, and visibly shrank from the sound of a double knock. But, in spite of these calamities, Hannah is a happy woman. The double rap was her husband's; and the glow on her cheek, and the smile of her lips and eyes when he appeared, spoke more plainly than ever, " Anywhere with him ! '

A GREAT FARM-HOUSE

THESE are bad times for farmers. I am sorry for it. Independently of all questions of policy, as a mere matter of taste and of old association, it is a fine thing to witness the hospitality and to think of the social happiness of a great farm-house. No situation in life seemed so richly privileged; none had so much power for good and so little for evil; it seemed a place where pride could not live and poverty could not enter. These thoughts pressed on my mind the other day in passing the green sheltered lane, overhung with trees like an avenue, that leads to the great farm at M., where ten or twelve years ago I used to spend so many pleasant days. I could not help advancing a few paces up the lane, and then turning to lean over the gate, seemingly gazing on the rich undulating valley crowned with woody hills, which, as I stood under the dark and shady arch, lay bathed in the sunshine before me, but really absorbed in thoughts of other times, in recollections of the old delights of that delightful place, and of the admirable qualities of its owners. How often had I opened the gate, and how gaily—certain of meeting a smiling welcome—and what a picture of comfort it was!

Passing up the lane we used first to encounter a thick solid suburb of ricks of all sorts, shapes, and dimensions. Then came the farm, like a town; a magnificent series of buildings, stables, cart-houses, cow-houses, granaries, and barns, that might hold half the corn of the parish, placed at all angles towards each other, and mixed with smaller habitations for pigs, dogs, and poultry They

formed, together with the old substantial farm-house, a
sort of amphitheatre, looking over a beautiful meadow,
which swept greenly and abruptly down into fertile
enclosures, richly set with hedge-row timber, oak, and
ash, and elm. Both the meadow and farm-yard swarmed
with inhabitants of the earth and of the air ; horses,
oxen, cows, calves, heifers, sheep, and pigs ; beautiful
greyhounds, all manner of poultry, a tame goat, and a
pet donkey.

The master of this land of plenty was well fitted to pre-
side over it ; a thick, stout man of middle height, and
middle aged, with a healthy, ruddy, square face, all
alive with intelligence and good-humour. There was a
lurking jest in his eye, and a smile about the corners of
his firmly closed lips, that gave assurance of good-fellowship. His voice was loud enough to have hailed a ship
at sea, without the assistance of a speaking-trumpet,
wonderfully rich and round in its tones, and harmonising
admirably with his bluff, jovial visage. He wore his dark
shining hair combed straight over his forehead, and had
a trick, when particularly merry, of stroking it down
with his hand. The moment his hand approached his
head, out flew a jest.

Besides his own great farm, the business of which
seemed to go on like machinery, always regular, prosperous, and unfailing—besides this, and two or three
constant stewardships, and a perpetual succession of
arbitrations, in which, such was the influence of his
acuteness, his temper, and his sturdy justice, that he was
often named by both parties, and left to decide alone—
in addition to those occupations he was a sort of standing
overseer and churchwarden ; he ruled his own hamlet
like a despotic monarch, and took a prime minister's
share in the government of the large parish to which it was
attached ; and one of the gentlemen whose estates he
managed, being the independent member of an inde-

pendent borough, he had every now and then a contested election on his shoulders. Even that did not discompose him. He had always leisure to receive his friends at home, or to visit them abroad ; to take journeys to London, or make excursions to the seaside ; was as punctual in pleasure as in business, and thought being happy and making happy as much the purpose of his life as getting rich. His great amusement was coursing. He kept several brace of capital greyhounds, so high-blooded, that I remember when five of them were confined in five different kennels on account of their ferocity. The greatest of living painters once called a greyhound, " the line of beauty in perpetual motion." Our friend's large dogs, were a fine illustration of this remark. His old dog, Hector, for instance, for whom he refused a hundred guineas—what a suberb dog was Hector !—a model of grace and symmetry, necked and crested like an Arabian, and bearing himself with a stateliness and gallantry which showed some " conscience of his worth." He was the largest dog I ever saw ; but so finely proportioned, that the most determined fault-finder could call him neither too long nor too heavy. There was not an inch too much of him. His colour was the purest white, entirely unspotted, except that his head was very regularly and richly marked with black. Hector was certainly a perfect beauty. But the little bitches, on which his master piqued himself still more, were not in my poor judgment so admirable. They were pretty little round, graceful things, sleek and glossy, and for the most part milk-white, with the smallest heads and the most dove-like eyes that were ever seen. There was a peculiar sort of innocent beauty about them, like that of a rolly-poly child. They were as gentle as lambs too : all the evil spirit of the family evaporated in the gentlemen. But, to my thinking, these pretty creatures were fitter for the parlour than the field. They were

strong, certainly, excellently loined, cat-footed, and
chested like a war-horse; but there was a want of length
about them—a want of room, as the coursers say; something a little, a very little, inclined to the clumsy; a
dumpiness, a pointer-look. They went off like an arrow
from a bow; for the first hundred yards nothing could
stand against them; then they began to flag, to find
their weight too much for their speed, and to lose ground
from the shortness of the stroke. Up-hill, however,
they were capital. There their compactness told. They
turned with the hare, and lost neither wind nor way in
the sharpest ascent. I shall never forget one single-
handed course of our good friend's favourite little bitch
Helen, on W. hill. All the coursers were in the valley
below, looking up the hillside as on a moving picture.
I suppose she turned the hare twenty times on a piece
of greensward not much bigger than an acre, and as steep
as the roof of a house It was an old hare, a famous
hare, one that had baffled half the dogs in the country;
but she killed him; and then, though almost as large
as herself, took it up in her mouth, brought it to her
master, and laid it down at his feet. Oh, how pleased
he was! and what a pleasure it was to see his triumph!
He did not always find W. hill so fortunate. It is a high
steep hill, of a conical shape, encircled by a mountain
road winding up to the summit like a corkscrew—a deep
road dug out of the chalk, and fenced by high mounds
on either side. The hares always make for this hollow
way, as it is called, because it is too wide for a leap, and
the dogs lose much time in mounting and descending
the sharp acclivities. Very eager dogs, however, will
sometimes dare the leap, and two of our good friend's
favourite greyhounds perished in the attempt in two
following years. They were found dead in the hollow
way. After this he took a dislike to coursing meetings,
and sported chiefly on his own beautiful farm.

His wife was like her husband, with a difference, as they say in heraldry. Like him in looks, only thinner and paler ; like him in voice and phrase, only not so loud ; like him in merriment and good-humour ; like him in her talent of welcoming and making happy, and being kind ; like him in cherishing an abundance of pets, and in getting through with marvellous facility an astounding quantity of business and pleasure. Perhaps the quality in which they resembled each other most completely was the happy ease and serenity of behaviour, so seldom found amongst people of the middle rank, who have usually a best manner and a worst, and whose best (that is, the studied, the company manner) is so very much the worst. She was frankness itself ; entirely free from prickly defiance or bristling self-love. She never took offence or gave it ; never thought of herself or of what others would think of her ; had never been afflicted with the besetting sins of her station, a dread of the vulgar, or an aspiration of the genteel. Those " words of fear " had never disturbed her delightful heartiness.

Her pets were her cows, her poultry, her bees, and her flowers ; chiefly her poultry, almost as numerous as the bees, and as various as the flowers. The farm-yard swarmed with peacocks, turkeys, geese, tame and wild ducks, fowls, guinea-hens, and pigeons ; besides a brood or two of favourite bantams in the green court before the door, with a little ridiculous strutter of a cock at their head, who imitated the magnificent demeanour of the great Tom of the barn-yard, just as Tom in his turn copied the fierce bearing of that warlike and terrible biped, the he-turkey, I am the least in the world afraid of a turkey-cock, and used to steer clear of the turkery as often as I could. Commend me to the peaceable vanity of that jewel of a bird, the peacock, sweeping his gorgeous tail along the grass, or dropping it gracefully from some low-boughed tree, whilst he turns round his crested head with the air of a birthday belle, to see who admires him. What a glorious creature it is! How thoroughly content with himself, and with all the world!

Next to her poultry our good farmer's wife loved her flower-garden; and, indeed, it was of the very first water, the only thing about the place that was fine. She was a real, genuine florist; valued pinks, tulips, and auriculas, for certain qualities of shape and colour, with which beauty has nothing to do; preferred black ranunculuses, and gave in to all those obliquities of a triple-refined taste by which the professed florist contrives to keep pace with the vagaries of the Bibliomaniac. Of all odd fashions, that of dark, gloomy, dingy flowers, appears to me the oddest. Your true *connoisseurs* now shall prefer a deep puce hollyhock to the gay pink blossoms which cluster round that splendid plant like a pyramid of roses. So did she. The nomenclature of her garden was more distressing still. One is never thoroughly sociable with flowers till they are naturalised, as it were, christened, provided with decent, homely, well-wearing English names. Now her plants had all sorts of heathenish appellations, which—no offence to her learning—always sounded wrong. I liked the bees' garden best; the plot of ground immediately round their hives, filled with common flowers for their use, and literally " redolent of sweets." Bees are insects of great taste in every way, and seem often to select for beauty as much as for flavour. They have a better eye for colour than the florist. The butterfly is also a *dilettante.* Rover though he be, he generally prefers the blossoms that become him best. What a pretty picture it is, in a sunshiny autumn day, to see a bright spotted butterfly, made up of gold and purple and splendid brown, swinging on the rich flower of the china-aster!

To come back to our farm. Within doors everything went as well as without. There were no fine misses sitting before the piano, and mixing the alloy with their new-fangled tinsel with the old sterling metal; nothing but an only son, excellently brought up, a fair, slim youth, whose extraordinary and somewhat pensive elegance of mind and manner was thrown into fine relief by his father's loud hilarity, and harmonised delightfully with the smiling kindness of his mother. His Spensers and Thomsons, too, looked well amongst the hyacinths and geraniums that filled the windows of the little snug room in which they usually sat; a sort of after-thought, built at an angle from the house, and looking into the farm-yard. It was closely packed with favourite arm-chairs, favourite sofas, favourite tables, and a side-board decorated with the prize-cups and collars of the grey-hounds, and generally loaded with substantial work-baskets, jars of flowers, great pyramids of home-made cakes, and sparkling bottles of gooseberry wine, famous all over the country. The walls were covered with portraits of half-a-dozen greyhounds, a brace of spaniels as large as life, an old pony, and the master and mistress of the house in half-length. She as unlike as possible, prim, mincing, delicate, in lace and satin; he so staringly and ridiculously like, that when the picture fixed its good-humoured eyes upon you as you entered the room, you were almost tempted to say—How d'ye do !—— Alas ! the portraits are now gone, and the originals. Death and distance have despoiled that pleasant home. The garden has lost its smiling mistress ; the greyhounds their kind master; and new people, new manners, and new cares, have taken possession of the old abode of peace and plenty—the great farm-house.

BRAMLEY MAYING

Mr. Geoffrey Crayon has, in his delightful but some-what fanciful writings, brought into general view many old sports and customs, some of which, indeed, still linger about the remote counties, familiar as local peculiarities to their inhabitants, whilst the greater part lie buried in books of the Elizabethan age, known only to the curious in English literature. One rural custom which would have enchanted him, and which prevails in the north of Hampshire, he has not noticed, and probably does not know. Did any of my readers ever hear of a Maying? Let not any notions of chimney-sweeps soil the imagination of the gay Londoner! A country Maying is altogether a different affair from the street exhibitions which mix so much pity with our mirth, and do the heart good, perhaps, but not by gladdening it. A country Maying is a meeting of the lads and lasses of two or three parishes, who assemble in certain erections of green boughs called May-houses, to dance and—but I am going to tell all about it in due order, and must not forestall my description.

Last year we went to Bramley Maying. There had been two or three such merry-makings before in that inaccessible neighbourhood, where the distance from large towns, the absence of great houses, and the consequent want of all decent roads, together with a country of peculiar wildness and beauty, combined to produce a sort of modern Arcadia. We had intended to assist at a Maying in the forest of Pamber, thinking that the deep glades of that fine woodland scenery would be more congenial to the spirit of our English merriment, as it

breathed more of Robin Hood and Maid Marian than
a mere village green—to say nothing of its being of the
two more accessible by four-footed and two-wheeled
conveyances. But the Pamber day had been suffered to
pass, and Bramley was the last Maying of the season.
So to Bramley we went.

As we had a considerable distance to go, we set out
about noon, intending to return to dinner at six. Never
was a day more congenial to a happy purpose. It was
a day made for country weddings and dances on the
green—a day of dazzling light, of ardent sunshine falling
on hedge-rows and meadows fresh with spring showers.
You might almost see the grass grow and the leaves
expand under the influence of that vivifying warmth ;
and we passed through the well-known and beautiful
scenery of W. Park, and the pretty village of M., with a
feeling of new admiration, as if we had never before
felt their charms ; so gloriously did the trees in their
young leaves, the grass springing beneath them, the
patches of golden broom and deeper furze, the cottages
covered with roses, the blooming orchards, and the light
snowy sprays of the cherry trees tossing their fair blossoms
across the deep blue sky, pour upon the eye the full magic
of colour. On we passed gaily and happily as far as we
knew our way—perhaps a little further, for the place
of our destination was new to both of us, when we had
the luck, good or bad, to meet with a director in the
person of the butcher of M. My companion is known
to most people within a circuit of ten miles ; so we had
ready attention and most civil guidance from the man
of beef and mutton—a prodigious person, almost as big
as a prize ox, as rosy and jovial-looking as Falstaff
himself, who was standing in the road with a slender
shrewd-looking boy, apt and ready enough to have passed
for the page. He soon gave us the proper, customary,
and unintelligible directions as to the lanes and turnings

—first to the right, then to the left, then round Farmer Jennings' close, then across the Holy Brook, then to the right again—till at last, seeing us completely bewildered, he offered to send the boy, who was going our way for half-a-mile to carry out a shoulder of veal, to attend us to that distance as a guide; an offer gratefully accepted by all parties, especially the lad, whom we relieved of his burden and took up behind, where he swung in an odd but apparently satisfactory posture, between running and riding. While he continued with us we fell into no mistakes; but at last he and the shoulder of veal reached their place of destination; and after listening to a repetition, or perhaps a variation, of the turns right and left which were to conduct us to Bramley-green, we and our little guide parted.

On we went, twisting and turning through a labyrinth of lanes, getting deeper and deeper every moment, till at last, after many doubtings, we became fairly convinced that we had lost our way. Not a soul was in the fields; not a passenger in the road; not a cottage by the road-side: so on we went—I am afraid to say how far (for when people have lost their way they are not the most accurate measurers of distance)—till we came suddenly on a small farm-house, and saw at once that the road we had trodden led to that farm, and thither only. The solitary farm-house had one solitary inmate, a smiling middle-aged woman, who came to us and offered her services with the most alert civility :—" All her boys and girls were gone to the Maying," she said, " and she remained to keep house."—" The Maying ! We are near Bramley, then ? "—" Only two miles the nearest way across the field—were we going ?—she would see to the horse—we should soon be there, only over that stile, and then across that field, and then turn to the right, and then take the next turning—no ! the next but one to the left."—Right and left again for two miles over

those deserted fields !—Right and left ! we shuddered
at the words. " Is there no carriage road ?—Where
are we ? "—" At Silchester, close to the walls, only half-
a-mile from the church."—" At Silchester ! " and in
ten minutes we had said a thankful farewell to our kind
informant, had retraced our steps a little, had turned
up another lane, and found ourselves at the foot of that
commanding spot which antiquaries call the amphitheatre,
close under the walls of the Roman city, and in full view
of an old acquaintance, the schoolmaster of Silchester,
who happened to be there in his full glory, playing the
part of Cicerone to a party of ladies, and explaining far
more than he knows, or than any one knows, of streets,
and gates, and sites of temples, which, by-the-by, the
worthy pedagogue usually calls parish churches. I never
was so glad to see him in my life, never thought he could
have spoken with so much sense and eloquence as were
comprised in the two words, "straight forward," by which
he answered our inquiry as to the road to Bramley.

And forward we went by a way beautiful beyond
description : a road bounded on one side by every variety
of meadow, and corn-field, and rich woodland ; on the
other, by the rock-like walls of the old city, crowning an
abrupt, magnificent bank of turf, broken by fragments,
crags, as it were, detached from the ruin, and young
trees, principally ash, with silver stems standing out in
picturesque relief from the green slope, and itself crowned
with every sort of vegetation, from the rich festoons of
briar and ivy which garlanded its side to the venerable
oaks and beeches which nodded on its summit. I never
saw anything so fine in my life. To be sure, we nearly
broke our necks. Even I, who, having been overset
astonishingly often, without any harm happening, have
acquired, from frequency of escape, the confidence of escaping, and the habit of not caring for that particular danger,
which is, I suppose, what in a man, and in battle, would

be called courage; even I was glad enough to get out,
and do all I could towards wriggling the gig round the
rock-like stones, or sometimes helping to lift the wheel
over the smaller impediments. We escaped that danger,
and left the venerable walls behind us.—But I am losing
my way here, too; I must loiter on the road no longer.
Our other delays of a broken bridge—a bog—another
wrong turning—and a meeting with a loaded waggon,
in a lane too narrow to pass—all this must remain untold.

At last we reached a large farm-house at Bramley;
another mile remained to the green, but that was impassable. Nobody thinks of riding at Bramley. The late
lady of the manor, when at rare and uncertain intervals
she resided for a few weeks at her house of B. R., used,
in visiting her only neighbour, to drive her coach and
four through her farmer's ploughed fields. We must
walk: but the appearance of gay crowds of rustics,
all passing along one path, gave assurance that this time
we should not lose our way. Oh, what a pretty path
it was! along one sunny sloping field, up and down,
dotted with trees like a park; then across a deep shady
lane, with cows loitering and cropping grass from the
banks; then up a long narrow meadow, in the very
pride and vigour of its greenness, richly bordered by
hedge-row timber, and terminating in the churchyard and
a little country church.

Bramley church is well worth seeing. It contains
that rare thing, a monument fine in itself, and finer in
its situation. We had heard of it, and in spite of the
many delays we had experienced, could not resist the
temptation of sending one of the loiterers, who seemed
to stand in the churchyard as a sort of out-guard to the
Maying, to the vicar's house for the key. Prepared as
we had been to see something unusual, we were very much
struck. The church is small, simple, decaying, almost
ruinous; but as you turn from the entrance into the

centre aisle, and advance up to the altar, your eye falls on a lofty recess, branching out like a chapel on one side, and seen through a Gothic arch. It is almost paved with monumental brasses of the proud family of B., who have possessed the surrounding property from the time of the Conqueror; and in the centre of the large open space stands a large monument, surrounded by steps, on which reclines the figure of a dying man, with a beautiful woman leaning over him, full of a lovely look of anxiety and tenderness. The figures are very fine; but that which makes the grace and glory of this remarkable piece of sculpture, is its being backed by an immense Gothic window, nearly the whole size of the recess, entirely composed of old stained glass. I do not know the story which the artist, in the series of pictures, intended to represent; but there they are, the gorgeous, glorious colours—reds, and purples, and greens, glowing like an anemone bed in the sunshine, or like one of the windows made of amethysts and rubies in the Arabian Tales, and throwing out the monumental figures with an effect almost magical The parish clerk was at the Maying, and we had only an unlettered rustic to conduct us, so that I do not even know the name of the sculptor—he must have a strange mingled feeling if ever he saw his work in its present home—delight that it looks so well, and regret that there is no one to look at it. That monument alone was worth losing our way for.

But across two fields more, and up a quiet lane, and we are at the Maying, announced afar off by the merry sound of music, and the merrier clatter of childish voices. Here we are at the green—a little turfy spot, where three roads meet, close shut in by hedge-rows, with a pretty white cottage, and its long slip of garden at one angle. I had no expectation of scenery so compact, so like a glade in a forest; it is quite a cabinet picture, with green trees for the frame. In the midst grows a superb horse-chestnut, in the full glory of its flowery pyramids, and from the trunk of the chestnut the May-houses commence. They are covered alleys built of green boughs, decorated with garlands and great bunches of flowers, the gayest that blow—lilacs, Guelder-roses, peonies, tulips, stocks—hanging down like chandeliers among the dancers; for of dancers, gay, dark-eyed young girls in straw bonnets and white gowns, and their lovers in their Sunday attire, the May-houses were full. The girls had mostly the look of extreme youth, and danced well and quietly like ladies —too much so: I should have been glad to see less elegance and more enjoyment; and their partners, though not altogether so graceful, were as decorous and as indifferent as real gentlemen. It was quite like a ball-room, as pretty and almost as dull. Outside was the fun. It is the outside, the upper gallery of the world, that has that good thing. There were children laughing, eating, trying to cheat, and being cheated, round an ancient and practised vendor of oranges and ginger-bread; and on the other side of the tree lay a merry group of old men, in coats almost as old as themselves, and young ones in no coats at all, excluded from the dance by the disgrace of a smock-frock. Who would have thought of etiquette finding its way into the May-houses! That group would have suited Teniers; it smoked and drank a little, but it laughed a great deal more. There were a few decent, matronly-looking women, too, sitting in a cluster; and young mothers strolling about with infants in their arms; and ragged boys peeping through the boughs at the dancers. Oh, what a pretty sight it was! worth losing our way for—worth losing our dinner—both which events happened; whilst a party of friends, who were to have joined us, were far more unlucky; for they not only lost their way and their dinner, but rambled all day about the country, and never reached Bramley Maying.

ANOTHER GLANCE AT OUR VILLAGE

IT is now many months since our village first sat for its
picture, and I cannot say farewell to my courteous readers
without giving them a little intelligence of our goings on
—a sort of parting glance at us and our condition. In
outward appearance it hath, I suppose, undergone less
alteration than any place of its inches in the kingdom.
There it stands, the same long straggling street of pretty
cottages, divided by pretty gardens, wholly unchanged
in size or appearance, unincreased and undiminished by
a single brick. To be sure, yesterday evening a slight
misfortune happened to our goodly tenement, occasioned
by the unlucky diligence mentioned in my first notice,
which, under the conduct of a sleepy coachman and a
restive horse, contrived to knock down and demolish
the wall of our court, and fairly to drive through the
front garden, thereby destroying in its course sundry
curious stocks, carnations, and geraniums. The three
insides (ladies) squalling from the interior of that commodious vehicle; the outsides (gentlemen) swearing on
the roof; the coachman, still half asleep, but unconsciously blowing his horn; we in the house screaming
and scolding; the passers-by shouting and hallooing;
and May, who little brooked such an invasion of her
territories, barking in her tremendous lion-note, and
putting down the other noises like a clap of thunder. But
passengers, coachman, horses, and spectators all righted
at last; and there is no harm done but to my flowers
and to the wall. May, however, stands bewailing the
ruins, for that low wall was her favourite haunt; she

used to parade backwards and forwards on the top of it,
as if to show herself, just after the manner of a peacock
on the top of a house ; and would sit or lie for hours on
the corner next the gate, basking in the sunshine like a
marble statue.   Really she has quite the air of one who
laments the destruction of personal property ; but the
wall is to be rebuilt to-morrow, with old weather-stained
bricks—no patchwork ! and exactly in the same form ;
May herself will not find the difference ; so that in the
way of alteration this little misfortune will pass for
nothing.   Neither have we any improvements worth
calling such.   Except that the wheeler's green door hath
been retouched, out of the same pot (as I judge from the
tint) with which he furbished up our new-old pony-chaise ;
that the shop-window of our neighbour, the universal
dealer, hath been beautified, and his name and calling
splendidly set forth in yellow letters on a black ground ;
and that our landlord of the Rose hath hoisted a new sign
of unparalleled splendour ; one side consisting of a full-
faced damask rose, of the size and hue of a peony, the
other of a maiden blush in profile, which looks exactly
like a carnation, so that both flowers are considerably
indebted to the modesty of the " out-of-door artist,"
who has warily written The Rose under each—except
these trifling ornaments, which nothing but the jealous
eye of a lover could detect, the dear place is altogether
unchanged.

The only real improvement with which we have been
visited for our sins—(I hate all innovations, whether for
better or worse, as if I was a furious Tory, or a woman
of threescore and ten)—the only misfortune of that sort
which has befallen us is under foot.   The road has been
adjusted on the plan of Mr. Macadam ; and a tremendous
operation it is.   I do not know what good may ensue ;
but for the last six months some part or other of the highway has been impassable for any feet, except such as are

shod by the blacksmith; and even the four-footed people
who wear iron shoes make wry faces, poor things! at
those stones, enemies to man and beast. However, the
business is nearly done now: we are covered with sharp
flints every inch of us, except a "bad step" up the hill,
which, indeed, looks like a bit cut out of the deserts of
Arabia, fitter for camels and caravans than for Christian
horses and coaches; a point which, in spite of my dislike
of alteration, I was forced to acknowledge to our surveyor,
a portly gentleman, who, in a smart gig, drawn by a
prancing steed, was kicking up a prodigious dust at that
very moment. He and I ought to be great enemies; for,
besides the Macadamite enormity of the stony road, he
hath actually been guilty of tree murder, having been
accessory before the fact in the death of three limes
along the rope-walk—dear, sweet, innocent limes, that
did no harm on earth except shading the path! I
never should have forgiven that offence, had not
their removal, by opening a beautiful view from
the village up the hill, reconciled even my tree-
loving eye to their abstraction. And, to say the
truth, though we have had twenty little squabbles,
there is no bearing malice with our surveyor; he is so
civil and good-humoured, has such a bustling and happy
self-importance, such an honest earnestness in his vocation
(which is gratuitous, by-the-by), and such an intense
conviction that the state of the turnpike road between
B. and K. is the principal affair of this life, that I would
not undeceive him for the world. How often have I
seen him in a cold winter morning, with a face all frost
and business, great-coated up to the eyes, driving from
post to post, from one gang of labourers to another,
praising, scolding, ordering, cheated, laughed at, and
liked by them all! Well, when once the hill is finished,
we shall have done with him for ever, as he used to tell
me by way of consolation, when I shook my head at him,

as he went jolting along over his dear new roads, at the
imminent risk of his springs and his bones; we shall see
no more of him; for the Macadam ways are warranted
not to wear out. So be it; I never wish to see a road-
mender again.

But if the form of outward things be all unchanged
around us, if the dwellings of man remain the same to
the sight and the touch, the little world within hath
undergone its usual mutations—the hive is the same,
but of the bees some are dead and some are flown away,
and some that we left insects in the shell are already
putting forth their young wings. Children in our village
really sprout up like mushrooms; the air is so promotive
of growth, that the rogues spring into men and women,
as if touched by Harlequin's wand, and are quite offended
if one happens to say or do anything which has a reference
to their previous condition. My father grievously affronted
Sally L. only yesterday, by bestowing upon her a great
lump of ginger-bread, with which he had stuffed his pockets
at a fair. She immediately, as she said, gave it to the
"children." Now Sally cannot be above twelve, to my
certain knowledge, though taller than I am. Lizzy
herself is growing womanly. I actually caught that
little lady stuck on a chest of drawers, contemplating
herself in the glass, and striving with all her might to
gather the rich curls that hung about her neck, and turn
them under a comb. Well! If Sally and Lizzy live to
be old maids, they may probably make the *amende
honorable* to time, and wish to be thought young again.
In the meanwhile, shall we walk up the street?

The first cottage is that of Mr. H., the patriot, the
illuminator, the independent and sturdy yet friendly
member of our little state, who, stout and comely, with
a handsome chaise-cart, a strong mare, and a neat garden,
might have passed for a portrait of that enviable class of
Englishman, who, after a youth of frugal industry, sit

down in some retired place, to "live upon their means."
He and his wife seemed the happiest couple on earth:
except a little too much leisure, I never suspected that
they had one trouble or one care. But Care, the witch,
will come everywhere, even to that happiest station,
and this prettiest place. She came in one of her most
terrific forms—blindness—or (which is perhaps still
more tremendous) the faint glimmering light and gradual
darkness which precede the total eclipse. For a long
time we had missed the pleasant bustling officiousness,
the little services, the voluntary tasks which our good
neighbour loved so well. Fruit-trees were blighted, and
escaped his grand specific, fumigation ; wasps multiplied,
and their nests remained untraced ; the cheerful modest
knock with which, just at the very hour when he knew
it could be spared, he presented himself to ask for the
newspaper, was heard no more ; he no longer hung over
his gate to waylay passengers, and entice them into chat ;
at last he even left off driving his little chaise, and was
only seen moping up and down the garden-walk, or
stealing gropingly from the wood-pile to the house. He
evidently shunned conversation or questions, forbade his
wife to tell what ailed him, and even when he put a green
shade over his darkened eyes, fled from human sympathy
with a stern pride that seemed almost ashamed of the
humbling infirmity. That strange (but to a vigorous
and healthy man perhaps natural) feeling soon softened.
The disease increased hourly, and he became dependent
on his excellent wife for every comfort and relief. She
had many willing assistants in her labour of love ; all
his neighbours strove to return, according to their several
means, the kindness which all had received from him
in some shape or other. The country boys, to whose
service he had devoted so much time, in shaping bats,
constructing bows and arrows, and other quips and
trickeries of the same nature, vied with each other in

performing little offices about the yard and stable; and
John Evens, the half-witted gardener, to whom he had
been a constant friend, repaid his goodness by the most
unwearied attention. Gratitude even seemed to sharpen
poor John's perception and faculties. There is an old
man in our parish workhouse who occasionally walks
through the streets, led by a little boy holding the end
of a long stick. The idea of this man, who had lived in
utter blindness for thirty years, was always singularly
distressing to Mr. H. I shall never forget the address
with which our simple gardener used to try to divert
his attention from this miserable fellow-sufferer. He
would get between them to prevent the possibility of
recognition by the dim and uncertain vision; would
talk loudly to drown the peculiar noise, the sort of duet
of feet, caused by the quick short steps of the child, and
the slow irregular tread of the old man; and, if any one
ventured to allude to blind Robert, he would turn the
conversation with an adroitness and acuteness which
might put to shame the proudest intellect. So passed
many months. At last Mr. H. was persuaded to consult
a celebrated oculist, and the result was most comforting.
The disease was ascertained to be a cataract; and now
with the increase of darkness came an increase of
hope. The film spread, thickened, ripened, speedily and
heathily; and to-day the requisite operation has been
performed with equal skill and success. You may still
see some of the country boys lingering round the gate
with looks of strong and wondering interest; poor John
is going to and fro, he knows not for what, unable to
rest a moment; Mrs. H., too, is walking in the garden,
shedding tears of thankfulness; and he who came to
support their spirit, the stout strong-hearted farmer A.,
seems trembling and overcome. The most tranquil
person in the house is probably the patient: he bore the
operation with resolute firmness, and *he has seen again.*

Think of the bliss bound up in those four words! He is in darkness now, and must remain so for some weeks; but he has seen, and he will see; and that humble cottage is again a happy dwelling.

Next we come to the shoemaker's abode. All is unchanged there, except that its master becomes more industrious and more pale-faced, and that his fair daughter is a notable exemplification of the development which I have already noticed amongst our young things. But she is in the real transition state, just emerging from the chrysalis, and the eighteen months, between fourteen and a half and sixteen, would metamorphose a child into a woman all the world over. She is still pretty, but not so elegant as when she wore frocks and pinafores, and unconsciously classical, parted her long brown locks in the middle of her forehead, and twisted them up in a knot behind, giving to her finely shaped head and throat the air of a Grecian statue. Then she was stirring all day in her small housewifery, or her busy idleness, delving and digging in her flower-border, tossing and dandling every infant that came within her reach, feeding pigs and poultry, playing with May, and prattling with an open-hearted frankness to the country lads, who assemble at evening in the shop to enjoy a little gentle gossiping; for be it known to my London readers, that the shoemaker's in a country village is now what (according to tradition and the old novels) the barber's used to be—the resort of all the male newsmongers, especially the young. Then she talked to these visitors gaily and openly, sang, and laughed, and ran in and out, and took no more thought of a young man than of a gosling. Then she was only fourteen. Now she wears gowns and aprons—puts her hair in paper—has left off singing, talks—has left off running, walks—nurses the infants with a grave solemn grace—has entirely cut her former playmate, Mayflower, who tosses her pretty head as much as to say—who cares?

—and has nearly renounced all acquaintance with the visitors to the shop, who are by no means disposed to take matters so quietly. There she stands on the threshold, shy and demure, just vouchsafing a formal nod or a faint smile as they pass, and if she in her turn be compelled to pass the open door of their newsroom (for the working apartment is separate from the house), edging along as slyly and mincingly as if there were no such beings as young men in the world. Exquisite coquette! I think (she is my opposite neighbour, and I have a right to watch her doings—the right of retaliation) there is one youth particularly distinguished by her non-notice, one whom she never will see nor speak to, who stands a very fair chance to carry her off. He is called Jem Tanner, and is a fine lad, with an open ruddy countenance, a clear blue eye, and curling hair of that tint which the poets are pleased to denominate golden. Though not one of our eleven, he was a promising cricketer. We have missed him lately on the green at the Sunday evening game, and I find on inquiry that he now frequents a chapel about a mile off, where he is the best male-singer, as our nymph of the shoe-shop is incomparably the first female. I am not fond of betting; but I would venture the lowest stake of gentility, a silver threepence, that, before the winter ends, a wedding will be the result of these weekly meetings at the chapel. In the long dark evenings, when the father has enough to do in piloting the mother with conjugal gallantry through the dirty lanes, think of the opportunity that Jem will have to escort the daughter! A little difficulty he may have to encounter: the lass will be coy for a while; the mother will talk of their youth, the father of their finances; but the marriage, I doubt not, will ensue.

Next in order, on the other side of the street, is the blacksmith's house. Change has been busy here in a different and more awful form. Our sometime constable, the tipsiest of parish officers, of blacksmiths, and of men, is dead. Returning from a revel with a companion as full of beer as himself, one or the other, or both, contrived to overset the cart in a ditch (the living scapegrace is pleased to lay the blame of the mishap on the horse, but that is contrary to all probability, this respectable quadruped being a water-drinker); and inward bruises, acting on inflamed blood and an impaired constitution, carried him off in a very short time, leaving an ailing wife and eight children, the eldest of whom is only fourteen years of age. This sounds like a very tragical story; yet, perhaps, because the loss of a drunken husband is not quite so great a calamity as the loss of a sober one, the effect of this event is not altogether so melancholy as might be expected. The widow, when she was a wife, had a complaining, broken-spirited air, a peevish manner, a whining voice, a dismal countenance, and a person so neglected and slovenly, that it was difficult to believe that she had once been remarkably handsome. She is now quite another woman. The very first Sunday she put on her weeds, we all observed how tidy and comfortable she looked, how much her countenance, in spite of a decent show of tears, was improved, and how completely through all her sighings her tone had lost its peevishness. I have never seen her out of spirits or out of humour since. She talks and laughs and bustles about, managing her journeymen and scolding her children as notably as any dame in the parish. The very house looks more cheerful; she has cut down the old willow trees that stood in the court and let in the light; and now the sun glances brightly from the casement windows, and plays amidst the vine-leaves and the clusters of grapes which cover the walls; the door is newly painted, and shines like the face of its mistress; even the forge has lost half its dinginess. Everything smiles. She indeed talks by fits of "poor George," especially when any allusion to her old enemy, mine host of the Rose, brings the deceased to her memory : then she bewails (as is proper) her dear husband and her desolate condition ; calls herself a lone widow ; sighs over her eight children ; complains of the troubles of business, and tries to persuade herself and others that she is as wretched as a good wife ought to be. But this will not do. She is a happier woman than she has been any time these fifteen years, and she knows it. My dear village husbands, if you have a mind that your wives should be really sorry when you die, whether by a fall from a cart or otherwise, keep from the ale-house !

Next comes the tall thin red house, that ought to boast genteeler inmates than its short fat mistress, its children, its pigs, and its quantity of noise, happiness, and vulgarity. The din is greater than ever. The husband, a merry jolly tar, with a voice that sounds as if issuing from a speaking-trumpet, is returned from a voyage to India ; and another little one, a chubby roaring boy, has added his lusty cries to the family concert.

This door, blockaded by huge bales of goods, and half darkened by that moving mountain, the tilted waggon of the S. mill, which stands before it, belongs to the village shop. Increase has been here too in every shape. Within fourteen months two little pretty quiet girls have come into the world. Before Fanny could well manage to totter across the road to her good friend the nymph of the shoe-shop, Margaret made her appearance ; and poor Fanny, discarded at once from the maid's arms and her mother's knee, degraded from the rank and privileges of " the baby " (for at that age precedence is strangely reversed), would have had a premature foretaste of the instability of human felicity, had she not taken refuge with that best of nurses, a fond father. Everything thrives about the shop, from the rosy children to the neat maid and the smart apprentice. No room now for lodgers, and no need! The young mantua-making schoolmistresses, the old inmates, are gone; one of them not very far. She grew tired of scolding little boys and girls about their A B C, and of being scolded in her turn by their sisters and mothers about pelisses and gowns; so she gave up both trades almost a year ago, and has been ever since our pretty Harriet. I do not think she has ever repented of the exchange, though it might not perhaps have been made so soon, had not her elder sister, who had been long engaged to an attendant at one of the colleges of Oxford, thought herself on the point of marriage just as the housemaid left us. Poor Betsy! She had shared the fate of many a prouder maiden, wearing out her youth in expectation of the promotion that was to authorise her union with the man of her heart. Many a year had she waited in smiling constancy, fond of William in no common measure, and proud of him, as well she might be; for, when the vacation so far lessened his duties as to render a short absence practicable, and he stole up here for a few days to enjoy her company, it was difficult to distinguish him in air and manner, as he sauntered about in elegant indolence with his fishing rod and his flute, from the young Oxonians, his masters. At last promotion came; and Betsy, apprised of it by an affectionate and congratulatory letter from his sister, prepared her wedding-clothes, and looked hourly for the bridegroom. No bridegroom came. A second letter announced, with regret and indignation, that William had made another choice, and was to be married early in the ensuing month. Poor Betsy! We were alarmed for her health, almost for her life. She wept incessantly, took no food, wandered recklessly about from morning till night, lost her natural rest, her flesh, her colour; and in less than a week she was so altered that no one would have known her. Consolation and remonstrance were alike rejected, till at last

Harriet happened to strike the right chord by telling her that "she wondered at her want of spirit." This was touching her on the point of honour; she had always been remarkably high-spirited, and could as little brook the imputation as a soldier or a gentleman. This lucky suggestion gave an immediate turn to her feelings : anger and scorn succeeded to grief ; she wiped her eyes, " hemmed away a sigh," and began to scold most manfully. She did still better. She recalled an old admirer, who, in spite of repeated objections, had remained constant in his attachment, and made such good speed that she was actually married the day before her faithless lover, and is now the happy wife of a very respectable tradesman.

Ah ! the in-and-out cottage ! the dear, dear home ! No weddings there ! No changes ! except that the white kitten, who sits purring at a window under the great myrtle, has succeeded to his lamented grandfather, our beautiful Persian cat, I cannot find one alteration to talk about. The wall of the court indeed—but that will be mended to-morrow.

Here is the new sign, the well-frequented Rose inn. Plenty of changes there ! Our landlord is always improving, if it be only a pig-sty or a watering trough— plenty of changes and one splendid wedding. Miss Phœbe is married, not to her old lover the recruiting sergeant (for he had one wife already, probably more), but to a patten-maker, as arrant a dandy as ever wore mustachios. How Phœbe could " abase her eyes " from the stately sergeant to this youth, half a foot shorter than herself, whose " waist would go into any alderman's thumb-ring," might, if the final choice of a coquette had ever been matter of wonder, have occasioned some speculation. But our patten-maker is a man of spirit ; and the wedding was of extraordinary splendour. Three gigs, each containing four persons, graced the procession, besides numerous carts and innumerable pedestrians. The bride was equipped in muslin and satin, and really looked very pretty with her black sparkling eyes, her clear brown complexion, her blushes and her smiles ; the bridemaidens were only less smart than the bride ; and the bridegroom was " point device in his accoutrements," and as munificent as a nabob. Cake flew about the village ; plumpuddings were abundant ; and strong beer, ay, even mine host's best double X, was profusely distributed. There was all manner of eating and drinking, with singing, fiddling, and dancing between ; and in the evening, to crown all, there was Mr. Moon, the conjuror. Think of that stroke of good fortune—Mr. Moon, the very pearl of all conjurors, who had the honour of puzzling and delighting their late Majesties with his " wonderful and pleasing exhibition of Thaumaturgics, Tachygraphy, mathematical operations, and magical deceptions," happened to arrive about an hour before dinner, and commenced his ingenious deceptions very unintentionally at our house. Calling to apply for permission to perform in the village, being equipped in a gay scarlet coat, and having something smart and sportsman-like in his appearance, he was announced by Harriet as one of the gentlemen of the C. hunt, and taken (mistaken I should have said) by the whole family for a certain captain newly arrived in the neighbourhood. That misunderstanding, which must, I think, have retaliated on Mr. Moon a little of the puzzlement that he inflicts on others, vanished of course at the production of his bill of fare ; and the requested permission was instantly given. Never could he have arrived in a happier hour ! Never were spectators more gratified or more scared. All the tricks prospered. The cock crew after his head was cut off ; and half-crowns and sovereigns flew about as if winged ; and the very wedding-ring could not escape Mr. Moon's incantations. We heard of nothing else for a week. From the bridegroom, *un esprit fort*, who defied all manner of conjuration and *diablerie*, down to my Lizzy, whose boundless faith swallows the Arabian Tales, all believed and trembled. So thoroughly were men, women, and children impressed with the idea of the worthy conjuror's dealings with the devil, that when he had occasion to go to B., not a soul would give him a cart, from pure awe ; and if it had not been for our pony-chaise, poor Mr. Moon must have walked. I hope he is really a prophet ; for he foretold all happiness to the new-married pair.

So this pretty white house with the lime-trees before it, which has been under repair for these three years, is on the point of being finished. The vicar has taken it, as the vicarage-house is not yet fit for his reception. He has sent before him a neat modest maid-servant, whose respectable appearance gives a character to her master and mistress — a hamper full of flower-roots, sundry boxes of books, a pianoforte, and some simple and useful furniture. Well, we shall certainly have neighbours, and I have a presentiment that we shall find friends.

Lizzy, you may now come along with me round the corner and up the lane, just to the end of the wheeler's shop, and then we shall go home, it is high time. What is this *affiche* in the parlour window ? "Apartments to let—inquire within." These are certainly the curate's lodgings—Is he going away ? Oh, I suppose the new vicar will do his own duty—yet, however well he may do it, rich and poor will regret the departure of Mr. B. Well, I hope that he may soon get a good living. "Lodgings to let"—whoever thought of seeing such a placard hereabouts ? The lodgings, indeed, are very convenient for "a single gentleman, a man and his wife, or two sisters," as the newspapers say — comfortable apartments, neat and tasty withal, and the civilest of all civil treatment from the host and hostess. But who would ever have dreamt of such a notice ? Lodgings to let in our village !

A COUNTRY CRICKET-MATCH

I DOUBT if there be any scene in the world more animating or delightful than a cricket-match—I do not mean a set match at Lord's Ground, for money, hard money, between a certain number of gentlemen and players, as they are called—people who make a trade of that noble sport, and degrade it into an affair of bettings, and hedgings, and cheatings, it may be, like boxing or horse-racing; nor do I mean a pretty *fête* in a gentleman's park, where one club of cricketing dandies encounter another such club, and where they show off in graceful costume to a gay marquee of admiring belles, who condescend so to purchase admiration, and while away a long summer morning in partaking cold collations, conversing occasionally, and seeming to understand the game—the whole being conducted according to ball-room etiquette, so as to be exceedingly elegant and exceedingly dull. No! the cricket that I mean is a real solid old-fashioned match between neighbouring parishes, where each attacks the other for honour and a supper, glory and half-a-crown a man. If there be any gentlemen amongst them, it is well —if not, it is so much the better. Your gentleman cricketer is in general rather an anomalous character. Elderly gentlemen are obviously good for nothing; and your beaux are, for the most part, hampered and trammelled by dress and habit; the stiff cravat, the pinched-in-waist, the dandy-walk—oh, they will never do for cricket! Now, our country lads, accustomed to the flail or the hammer (your blacksmiths are capital hitters) have the free use of their arms; they know how to move their shoulders;

and they can move their feet too—they can run; then they are so much better made, so much more athletic, and yet so much lissomer—to use a Hampshire phrase, which deserves at least to be good English. Here and there, indeed, one meets with an old Etonian, who retains his boyish love for that game which formed so considerable a branch of his education; some even preserve their boyish proficiency, but in general it wears away like the Greek, quite as certainly, and almost as fast; a few years of Oxford, or Cambridge, or the continent, are sufficient to annihilate both the power and the inclination. No! a village match is the thing—where our highest officer—our conductor (to borrow a musical term) is but a little farmer's second son; where a day-labourer is our bowler, and a blacksmith our long-stop; where the spectators consist of the retired cricketers, the veterans of the green, the careful mothers, the girls, and all the boys of two parishes, together with a few amateurs, little above them in rank, and not at all in pretension; where laughing and shouting, and the very ecstasy of merriment and good-humour prevail: such a match, in short, as I attended yesterday, at the expense of getting twice wet through, and as I would attend to-morrow, at the certainty of having that ducking doubled.

For the last three weeks our village has been in a state of great excitement, occasioned by a challenge from our north-western neighbours, the men of B., to contend with us at cricket. Now, we have not been much in the habit of playing matches. Three or four years ago, indeed, we encountered the men of S., our neighbours south-by-east, with a sort of doubtful success, beating them on our own ground, whilst they in the second match returned the compliment on theirs. This discouraged us. Then an unnatural coalition between a high-church curate and an evangelical gentleman-farmer drove our lads from the Sunday-evening practice,

which, as it did not begin before both services were con-
cluded, and as it tended to keep the young men from
the ale-house, our magistrates had winked at if not
encouraged. The sport, therefore, had languished until
the present season, when under another change of
circumstances the spirit began to revive. Half-a-dozen
fine active lads, of influence amongst their comrades, grew
into men and yearned for cricket; an enterprising
publican gave a set of ribands : his rival, mine host of
the Rose, and out-doer by profession, gave two ; and
the clergyman and his lay ally, both well-disposed and
good-natured men, gratified by the submission to their
authority, and finding, perhaps, that no great good re-
sulted from the substitution of public-houses for out-of-
door diversions, relaxed. In short, the practice recom-
menced, and the hill was again alive with men and boys,
and innocent merriment; but farther than the riband
matches amongst ourselves nobody dreamed of going,
till this challenge—we were modest, and doubted our
own strength. The B. people, on the other hand, must
have been braggers born, a whole parish of gasconaders.
Never was such boasting ! such crowing ! such ostenta-
tious display of practice ! such mutual compliments from
man to man—bowler to batter, batter to bowler ! It was
a wonder they did not challenge all England. It must
be confessed that we were a little astounded ; yet we
firmly resolved not to decline the combat ; and one of
the most spirited of the new growth, William Grey by
name, took up the glove in a style of manly courtesy,
that would have done honour to a knight in the days of
chivalry.—" We were not professed players," he said,
" being little better than school-boys, and scarcely older ;
but, since they have done us the honour to challenge us,
we would try our strength. It would be no discredit
to be beaten by such a field."

Having accepted the wager of battle, our champion

began forthwith to collect his forces. William Grey is
himself one of the finest youths that one shall see—tall,
active, slender and yet strong, with a piercing eye full
of sagacity, and a smile full of good humour—a farmer's
son by station, and used to hard work as farmers' sons are
now, liked by everybody, and admitted to be an excellent
cricketer. He immediately set forth to muster his men,
remembering with great complacency that Samuel Long,
a bowler *comme il y en a peu*, the very man who had
knocked down nine wickets, had beaten us, bowled us
out at the fatal return match some years ago at S., had
luckily, in a remove of a quarter of a mile last Ladyday,
crossed the boundaries of his old parish, and actually
belonged to us. Here was a stroke of good fortune!
Our captain applied to him instantly; and he agreed at
a word. Indeed, Samuel Long is a very civilised person.
He is a middle-aged man, who looks rather old amongst
our young lads, and whose thickness and breadth gave
no token of remarkable activity; but he is very active,
and so steady a player! so safe! We had half gained
the match when we had secured him. He is a man of
substance, too, in every way; owns one cow, two donkeys,
six pigs, and geese and ducks beyond count—dresses like
a farmer, and owes no man a shilling—and all this from
pure industry, sheer day-labour. Note that your good
cricketer is commonly the most industrious man in the
parish; the habits that make him such are precisely
those which make a good workman—steadiness, sobriety,
and activity—Samuel Long might pass for the *beau ideal*
of the two characters. Happy were we to possess him!
Then we had another piece of good luck. James Brown,
a journeyman blacksmith and a native, who, being of a
rambling disposition, had roamed from place to place
for half-a-dozen years, had just returned to settle with
his brother at another corner of our village, bringing
with him a prodigious reputation in cricket and in

gallantry—the gay Lothario of the neighbourhood. He is
said to have made more conquests in love and in cricket
than any blacksmith in the county. To him also went
the indefatigable William Grey, and he also consented
to play. No end to our good fortune! Another celebrated batter, called Joseph Hearne, had likewise recently
married into the parish. He worked, it is true, at the
A. mills, but slept at the house of his wife's father in our
territories. He also was sought and found by our leader.
But he was grand and shy; made an immense favour of
the thing; courted courting and then hung back—
"Did not know that he could be spared; had partly
resolved not to play again—at least not this season;
thought it rash to accept the challenge; thought they
might do without him——" "Truly I think so too,"
said our spirited champion; "we will not trouble you,
Mr. Hearne."

Having thus secured two powerful auxiliaries, and rejected a third, we began to reckon and select the regular
native forces. Thus ran our list:—William Grey, 1.—
Samuel Long, 2.—James Brown, 3.—George and John
Simmons, one capital, the other so-so—an uncertain
hitter, but a good fieldsman, 5.—Joel Brent, excellent,
6.—Ben Appleton—here was a little pause—Ben's abilities
at cricket were not completely ascertained; but then
he was so good a fellow, so full of fun and waggery! no
doing without Ben. So he figured in the list, 7.—George
Harris—a short halt there too! Slowish—slow but
sure. I think the proverb brought him in, 8.—Tom
Coper—oh, beyond the world, Tom Coper! the red-
headed gardening lad, whose left-handed strokes send
her (a cricket-ball, like that other moving thing, a ship,
is always of the feminine gender), send her spinning a
mile, 9.—Harry Willis, another blacksmith, 10.

We had now ten of our eleven, but the choice of the
last occasioned some demur. Three young Martins, rich

farmers of the neighbourhood, successively presented themselves, and were all rejected by our independent and impartial general for want of merit—*cricketal* merit. " Not good enough," was his pithy answer. Then our worthy neighbour, the half-pay lieutenant, offered his services—he, too, though with some hesitation and modesty, was refused—" Not quite young enough " was his sentence. John Strong, the exceeding long son of our dwarfish mason, was the next candidate—a nice youth— everybody likes John Strong—and a willing, but so tall and so limp, bent in the middle—a thread-paper, six- feet high! We were all afraid that, in spite of his name, his strength would never hold out. " Wait till next year, John," quoth William Grey, with all the dignified seniority of twenty speaking to eighteen. " Coper's a year younger," said John. " Coper's a foot shorter," replied William : so John retired : and the eleventh man remained unchosen, almost to the eleventh hour. The eve of the match arrived, and the post was still vacant, when a little boy of fifteen, David Willis, brother to Harry, admitted by accident to the last practice, saw eight of them out, and was voted in by acclamation.

That Sunday evening's practice (for Monday was the important day) was a period of great anxiety, and, to say the truth, of great pleasure. There is something strangely delightful in the innocent spirit of party. To be one of a numerous body, to be authorised to say *we*, to have a rightful interest in triumph or defeat, is gratifying at once to social feeling and to personal pride. There was not a ten-year old urchin, or a septuagenary woman in the parish who did not feel an additional importance, a reflected consequence, in speaking of " our side." An election interests in the same way ; but that feeling is less pure. Money is there, and hatred, and politics, and lies. Oh, to be a voter, or a voter's wife, comes nothing near the genuine and hearty sympathy of belonging to a parish, breathing the same air, looking on the same trees, listening to the same nightingales! Talk of a patriotic elector! Give me a parochial patriot, a man who loves his parish! Even we, the female partisans, may partake the common ardour. I am sure I did. I never, though tolerably eager and enthusiastic at all times, remember being in a more delicious state of excitement than on the eve of that battle. Our hopes waxed stronger and stronger. Those of our players who were present were excellent. William Grey got forty notches off his own bat; and that brilliant hitter, Tom Coper, gained eight from two successive balls. As the evening advanced, too, we had encouragement of another sort. A spy, who had been despatched to reconnoitre the enemy's quarters, returned from their practising ground with a most consolatory report. "Really," said Charles Grover, our intelligence—a fine old steady judge, one who had played well in his day— "they are no better than so many old women. Any five of ours would beat their eleven." This sent us to bed in high spirits.

Morning dawned less favourably. The sky promised a series of deluging showers, and kept its word as English skies are wont to do on such occasions; and a lamentable message arrived at the head-quarters from our trusty comrade Joel Brent. His master, a great farmer, had begun the hay-harvest that very morning, and Joel, being as eminent in one field as in another, could not be spared. Imagine Joel's plight! the most ardent of all our eleven! a knight held back from the tourney! a soldier from the battle! The poor swain was inconsolable. At last, one who is always ready to do a good-natured action, great or little, set forth to back his petition; and, by dint of appealing to the public spirit of our worthy neighbour and the state of the barometer, talking alternately of the parish honour and thunder showers, of lost matches and sopped hay, he carried his point, and returned triumphantly with the delighted Joel.

In the meantime, we became sensible of another defalcation. On calling over our roll, Brown was missing; and the spy of the preceding night, Charles Grover—the universal scout and messenger of the village, a man who will run half-a-dozen miles for a pint of beer, who does errands for the very love of the trade, who, if he had been a lord, would have been an ambassador—was instantly despatched to summon the truant. His report spread general consternation. Brown had set off at four o'clock in the morning to play in a cricket-match at M., a little town twelve miles off, which had been his last residence. Here was desertion ! Here was treachery ! Here was treachery against that goodly state, our parish ! To send James Brown to Coventry was the immediate resolution ; but even that seemed too light a punishment for such delinquency. Then how we cried him down ! At ten on Sunday night (for the rascal had actually practised with us, and never said a word of his intended disloyalty) he was our faithful mate, and the best player (take him all in all) of the eleven. At ten in the morning he had run away, and we were well rid of him ; he was no batter compared with William Grey or Tom Coper ; not fit to wipe the shoes of Samuel Long, as a bowler ; nothing of a scout to John Simmons ; the boy David Willis was worth fifty of him—

> " I trust we have within our realm,
>   Five hundred good as he,"

was the universal sentiment. So we took tall John Strong, who, with an incurable hankering after the honour of being admitted, had kept constantly with the players, to take the chance of some such accident—we took John for our *pis-aller*. I never saw any one prouder than the

good-humoured lad was of this not very flattering piece
of preferment.

John Strong was elected, and Brown sent to Coventry ;
and when I first heard of his delinquency, I thought the
punishment only too mild for the crime. But I have
since learned the secret history of the offence (if we could
know the secret histories of all offences, how much better
the world would seem than it does now !) and really my
wrath is much abated. It was a piece of gallantry, of
devotion to the sex, or rather a chivalrous obedience to
one chosen fair. I must tell my readers the story. Mary
Allen, the prettiest girl of M., had, it seems, revenged
upon our blacksmith the numberless inconsistencies of
which he stood accused. He was in love over head and
ears, but the nymph was cruel. She said no, and no,
and no, and poor Brown, three times rejected, at last
resolved to leave the place, partly in despair, and partly
in the hope which often mingles strangely with a lover's
despair, the hope that when he was gone he should be
missed.   He came home to his brother's accordingly ;
but for five weeks he heard nothing from or of the in-
exorable Mary, and was glad to beguile his own " vexing
thoughts " by endeavouring to create in his mind an
artificial and factitious interest in our cricket-match—
all unimportant as such a trifle must have seemed to a
man in love. Poor James, however, is a social and
warm-hearted person, not likely to resist a contagious
sympathy. As the time for the play advanced, the
interest which he had at first affected became genuine and
sincere : and he was really, when he left the ground
on Sunday night, almost as enthusiastically absorbed
in the event of the next day, as Joel Brent himself. He
little foresaw the new and delightful interest which
awaited him at home, where, on the moment of his arrival,
his sister-in-law and confidante presented him with a
billet from the lady of his heart. It had, with the usual

delay of letters sent by private hands in that rank of life, loitered on the road, in a degree inconceivable to those who are accustomed to the punctual speed of the post, and had taken ten days for its twelve miles' journey. Have my readers any wish to see this *billet-doux*? I can show them (but in strict confidence) a literal copy. It was addressed,

"For mistur jem browne
"blaxmith by
"S."

The inside ran thus:—"Mistur browne this is to Inform you that oure parish plays bramley men next monday is a week, i think we shall lose without yew. from your humbell servant to command
"MARY ALLEN."

Was there ever a prettier relenting? a summons more flattering, more delicate, more irresistible? The precious epistle was undated; but, having ascertained who brought it, and found, by cross-examining the messenger, that the Monday in question was the very next day, we were not surprised to find that *Mistur browne* forgot his engagement to us, forgot all but Mary and Mary's letter, and set off at four o'clock the next morning to walk twelve miles, and to play for her parish, and in her sight. Really we must not send James Brown to Coventry— must we? Though if, as his sister-in-law tells our damsel Harriet he hopes to do, he should bring the fair Mary home as his bride, he will not greatly care how little we say to him. But he must not be sent to Coventry— True-love forbid!

At last we were all assembled, and marched down to H. common, the appointed ground, which, though in our dominions according to the maps, was the constant practising place of our opponents, and *terra incognita* to us. We found our adversaries on the ground as we expected, for our various delays had hindered us from taking the field so early as we wished; and, as soon as we had settled all preliminaries, the match began.

But, alas! I have been so long settling my preliminaries, that I have left myself no room for the detail of our victory, and must squeeze the account of our grand achievements into as little compass as Cowley, when he crammed the names of eleven of his mistresses into the narrow space of four eight-syllable lines. *They* began the warfare — those boastful men of B. And what think you, gentle reader, was the amount of their innings! These challengers—the famous eleven—how many did they get? Think! imagine! guess!—You cannot?—Well!—they got twenty-two, or, rather, they got twenty; for two of theirs were short notches, and would never have been allowed, only that, seeing what they were made of, we and our umpires were not particular. —They should have had twenty more if they had chosen to claim them. Oh, how well we fielded! and how well we bowled! our good play had quite as much to do with their miserable failure as their bad. Samuel Long is a slow bowler, George Simmons a fast one, and the change from Long's lobbing to Simmons's fast balls posed them completely. Poor simpletons! they were always wrong, expecting the slow for the quick, and the quick for the slow. Well, we went in. And what were our innings? Guess again!—guess! A hundred and sixty-nine! in spite of soaking showers, and wretched ground, where the ball would not run a yard, we headed them by a hundred and forty-seven; and then they gave in, as well they might. William Grey pressed them much to try another innings. "There was so much chance," as he courteously observed, "in cricket, that advantageous as our position seemed, we might, very possibly, be overtaken. The B. men had better try." But they were beaten sulky, and would not move—to my great disappointment ; I wanted to prolong the pleasure of success. What a glorious sensation it is to be for five hours together — winning — winning ! always feeling what a whistplayer feels when he takes up four honours, seven trumps ! Who would think that a little bit of leather, and two pieces of wood, had such a delightful and delighting power !

The only drawback on my enjoyment was the failure of the pretty boy, David Willis, who, injudiciously put in first, and playing for the first time in a match amongst men and strangers, who talked to him, and stared at him, was seized with such a fit of shamefaced shyness, that he could scarcely hold his bat, and was bowled out without a stroke, from actual nervousness. " He will come off that," Tom Coper says—I am afraid he will. I wonder whether Tom had ever any modesty to lose. Our other modest lad, John Strong, did very well ; his length told in fielding, and he got good fame. Joel Brent, the rescued mower, got into a scrape, and out of it again ; his fortune for the day. He ran out his mate, Samuel Long ; who, I do believe, but for the excess of Joel's eagerness, would have stayed in till this time, by which exploit he got into sad disgrace ; and then he himself got thirty-seven runs, which redeemed his reputation. William Grey made a hit which actually lost the cricket-ball. We think she lodged in a hedge, a quarter of a mile off, but nobody could find her. And George Simmons had nearly lost his shoe, which he tossed away in a passion, for having been caught out, owing to the ball glancing against it. These, together with a very complete somerset of Ben Appleton, our long-stop, who floundered about in the mud, making faces and attitudes as laughable as Grimaldi, none could tell whether by accident or design, were the chief incidents of the scene of action. Amongst the spectators nothing remarkable occurred, beyond the general calamity of two or three drenchings, except that a form, placed by the side of a hedge, under a very insufficient shelter, was knocked into the ditch, in a sudden rush of the cricketers to escape a pelting shower, by which means all parties shared the fate of Ben Appleton, some on land and some by water; and that, amidst the scramble, a saucy gipsy of a girl contrived to steal from the knee of the demure and well-appareled Samuel Long, a smart handkerchief which his careful dame had tied round it to preserve his new (what is the mincing feminine word?) —his new—inexpressibles, thus reversing the story of Desdemona, and causing the new Othello to call aloud for his handkerchief, to the great diversion of the company. And so we parted; the players retired to their supper, and we to our homes; all wet through, all good-humoured and happy—except the losers.

To-day we are happy too. Hats, with ribands in them, go glancing up and down; and William Grey says, with a proud humility, "We do not challenge any parish; but if we be challenged, we are ready."

WHEAT-HOEING

May the 3rd.—Cold, bright weather. All within doors sunny and chilly; all without windy and dusty. It is quite tantalising to see that brilliant sun careering through so beautiful a sky, and to feel little more warmth from his presence than one does from that of his fair but cold sister, the moon. Even the sky, beautiful as it is, has the look of that one sometimes sees in a very bright moonlight night—deeply intensely blue, with white clouds driven vigorously along by a strong breeze—now veiling, and now exposing the dazzling luminary around which they sail. A beautiful sky! and, in spite of its coldness, a beautiful world! The effect of this backward spring has been to arrest the early flowers, to which heat is the great enemy; whilst the leaves and the later flowers have, nevertheless, ventured to peep out slowly and cautiously in sunny places — exhibiting in the copses and hedge-rows a pleasant mixture of March and May. And we, poor chilly mortals, must follow, as nearly as we can, the wise example of the May blossoms, by avoiding bleak paths and open commons, and creeping up the sheltered road to the vicarage—the pleasant sheltered road, where the western sun steals in between two rows of bright green elms, and the east wind is fenced off by the range of woody hills which rise abruptly before us, forming so striking a boundary to the picture.

How pretty this lane is, with its tall elms, just dressed in their young leaves, bordering the sunny path, or sweeping in a semicircle behind the clear pools and the white cottages that are scattered along the way! You shall seldom see a cottage hereabout without an accompanying pond, all alive with geese and ducks, at the end of the little garden. Ah! here is Dame Simmons making a most original use of her piece of water, standing on the bank that divides it from her garden, and most ingeniously watering her onion-bed with a new mop—now a dip, and now a twirl! Really, I give her credit for the invention. It is as good an imitation of a shower as one should wish to see on a summer-day. A squirt is nothing to it!

And here is another break to the tall line of elms— the gate that leads into Farmer Thorpe's great enclosures. Eight, ten, fourteen people in this large field, wheat-hoeing. The couple nearest the gate, who keep aloof from all the rest, and are hoeing this furrow so completely in concert, step by step, and stroke for stroke, are Jem Tanner and Mabel Green. There is not a handsomer pair in the field or in the village. Jem, with his bright complexion, his curling hair, his clear blue eye, and his trim figure—set off to great advantage by his short jacket and trousers and new straw hat; Mabel, with her little stuff gown, and her white handkerchief and apron—defining so exactly her light and flexible shape—and her black eyes flashing from under a deep bonnet lined with pink, whose reflection gives to her bright dark countenance and dimpled cheeks a glow innocently artificial, which was the only charm that they wanted.

Jem and Mabel are, beyond all doubt, the handsomest couple in the field, and I am much mistaken if each have not a vivid sense of the charms of the other. Their mutual admiration was clear enough in their work; but it speaks still more plainly in their idleness. Not a stroke have they done for these five minutes; Jem, propped on his hoe, and leaning across the furrow, whispering soft nonsense; Mabel, blushing and smiling—now making believe to turn away—now listening, and looking up with a sweeter smile

than ever, and a blush that makes her bonnet-lining pale.
Ah, Mabel ! Mabel ! Now they are going to work again—
no !—after three or four strokes the hoes have somehow
become entangled, and without either advancing a step
nearer the other, they are playing with these rustic implements as pretty a game at romps—showing off as nice
a piece of rural flirtation—as ever was exhibited since
wheat was hoed.

Ah, Mabel ! Mabel ! beware of Farmer Thorpe ! He'll
see at a glance that little will his corn profit by such
labours. Beware, too, Jem Tanner !—for Mabel is, in
some sort, an heiress ; being the real niece and adopted
daughter our little lame clerk, who, although he looks
such a tattered ragamuffin that the very grave-diggers
are ashamed of him, is well to pass in the world—keeps a
scrub pony—indeed he can hardly walk up the aisle—
hath a share in the County fire-office—and money in the
funds. Mabel will be an heiress, despite the tatter-
demalion costume of her honoured uncle, which I think
he wears out of coquetry, that the remarks which might
otherwise fall on his miserable person—full as misshapen
as that of any Hunchback recorded in the Arabian Tales—
may find a less offensive vent on his raiment. Certain
such a figure hath seldom been beheld out of church or
in. Yet will Mabel, nevertheless, be a fortune ; and,
therefore, she must inter-marry with another fortune,
according to the rule made and provided in such cases ;
and the little clerk hath already looked her out a spouse,
about his own standing—a widower in the next parish,
with four children and a squint. Poor Jem Tanner !
Nothing will that smart person or that pleasant speech
avail with the little clerk—never will he officiate at your
marriage to his niece—" Amen " would " stick in his
throat." Poor things ! in what a happy oblivion of the
world and its cares, Farmer Thorpe and the wheat-hoeing,
the squinting shopkeeper and the little clerk, are they,

laughing and talking at this moment! Poor things!
poor things!

Well, I must pursue my walk. How beautiful a mixture
of flowers and leaves is in the high bank under this north
hedge—quite an illustration of the blended seasons of
which I spoke. An old irregular hedge-row is always
beautiful, especially in the spring-time, when the grass,
and mosses, and flowering weeds mingle best with the
bushes and creeping plants that overhung them. But this
bank is, most especially, various and lovely. Shall we
try to analyse it? First, the clinging white-veined ivy,
which crawls up the slope in every direction, the master-
piece of that rich mosaic; then the brown leaves and the
lilac blossoms of its fragrant namesake, the ground ivy,
which grows here so profusely; then the late-lingering
primrose; then the delicate wood-sorrel; then the regular
pink stars of the cranesbill, with its beautiful leaves;
then the golden oxslip and the cowslip, "cinque-spotted";
then the blue pansy, and the enamelled wild hyacinth;
then the bright foliage of the brier-rose, which comes
trailing its green wreaths amongst the flowers; then the
bramble and the woodbine, creeping round the foot
of a pollard oak, with its brown folded leaves; then a
verdant mass—the blackthorn, with its lingering blossoms
—the hawthorn, with its swellings buds—the bushy maple
—the long stems of the hazel—and between them, hanging
like a golden plume over the bank, a splendid tuft of the
blossomed broom; then, towering high above all, the
tall and leavy elms. And this is but a faint picture of this
hedge, on the meadowy side of which sheep are bleating,
and where every here and there a young lamb is thrusting
its pretty head between the trees.

Who is this approaching? Farmer Thorpe? Yes, of
a certainty, it is that substantial yeoman, sallying forth
from his substantial farm-house, which peeps out from
between two huge walnut-trees on the other side of the

road, with intent to survey his labourers in the wheat-field.   Farmer Thorpe is a stout, square, sturdy personage of fifty, or thereabouts, with a hard weather-beaten countenance, of that peculiar vermilion, all over alike, into which the action of the sun and wind sometimes tans a fair complexion ; sharp, shrewd features, and a keen grey eye.   He looks completely like a man who will neither cheat nor be cheated : and such is his character—an upright, downright English Yeoman— just always, and kind in a rough way—but given to fits of anger, and filled with an abhorrence of pilfering, and idleness, and trickery of all sorts, that makes him strict as a master, and somewhat stern at work-house and vestry.   I doubt if he will greatly relish the mode in which Jem and Mabel are administering the hoe in his wheat-drills.   He will not reach the gate yet ; for his usual steady, active pace is turned, by a recent accident, into an unequal, impatient halt—as if he were alike angry with his lameness and the cause.   I must speak to him as he passes—not merely as a due courtesy to a good neighbour, but to give the delinquents in the field notice to resume their hoeing ; but not a word of the limp—that is a sore subject.

" A fine day, Mr. Thorpe ! "

" We want rain, ma'am ! "

And on, with great civility, but without pausing a moment, he is gone.   He'll certainly catch Mabel and her lover philandering over his wheat-furrows.   Well, that may take its chance !—they have his lameness in their favour—only that the cause of that lameness has made the worthy farmer unusually cross.   I think I must confide the story to my readers.

Gipsies and beggars do not in general much inhabit our neighbourhood ; but about half-a-mile off there is a den so convenient for strollers and vagabonds, that it sometimes tempts the rogues to a few days' sojourn.

It is, in truth, nothing more than a deserted brick-kiln, by the side of a lonely lane. But there is something so snug and comfortable in the old building (always keeping in view gipsy notions of comfort) ; the blackened walls are so backed by the steep hill on whose side they are built—so fenced from the bleak north-east, and letting in so gaily the pleasant western sun ; and the wide, rugged, impassable lane (used only as a road to the kiln, and with that abandoned) is at once so solitary and deserted, so close to the inhabited and populous world, that it seems made for a tribe whose prime requisites in a habitation are shelter, privacy, and a vicinity to farm-yards.

Accordingly, about a month ago, a pretty strong encampment, evidently gipsies, took up their abode in the kiln. The party consisted of two or three tall, lean, sinister-looking men, who went about the country mending pots and kettles, and driving a small trade in old iron ; one or two children, unnaturally quiet, the spies of the crew ; an old woman, who sold matches and told fortunes ; a young woman with an infant strapped to her back, who begged ; several hungry-looking dogs, and three ragged donkeys. The arrival of the vagabonds spread a general consternation through the village. Game-keepers and housewives were in equal dismay. Snares were found in the preserves—poultry vanished from the farm-yards— a lamb was lost from the lea—and a damask table-cloth, belonging to the worshipful the Mayor of W——, was abstracted from the drying-ground of Rachel Strong, the most celebrated laundress in these parts, to whom it had been sent for the benefit of country washing. No end to the pilfering, and stories of pilfering ! The inhabitants of the kiln were not only thieves in themselves, but the cause of thievery in others. "The gipsies !" was the answer general to every inquiry for things missing.

Farmer Thorpe—whose dwelling, with its variety of out-

buildings—barns, ricks, and stables—is only separated by
a meadow and a small coppice from the lane that leads to
the gipsy retreat—was particularly annoyed by this visita-
tion.   Two couple of full-grown ducks, and a whole brood
of early chickens, disappeared in one night ; and Mrs.
Thorpe fretted over the loss, and the farmer was indignant
at the roguery.   He set traps, let loose mastiffs, and put
in action all the resources of village police—but in vain.
Every night property went ; and the culprits, however
strongly suspected, still continued unamenable to the law.

At last, one morning, the great Chanticleer of the
farm-yard—a cock of a million, with an unrivalled crow,
a matchless strut, and plumage all gold and green, and
orange and purple—gorgeous as a peacock, and fierce as
a he-turkey—Chanticleer, the pride and glory of the
yard, was missing ! and Mrs. Thorpe's lamentations and
her husband's anger redoubled.   Vowing vengeance
against the gipsies, he went to the door to survey a
young blood mare of his own breeding ; and as he stood
at the gate—now bemoaning Chanticleer—now cursing
the gipsies—now admiring the bay filly—his neighbour,
Dame Simmons—the identical lady of the mop, who
occasionally chared at the house—came to give him the
comfortable information that she had certainly heard
Chanticleer—she was quite ready to swear to Chanticleer's
voice—crowing in the brick-kiln.   No time, she added,
should be lost, if Farmer Thorpe wished to rescue that
illustrious cock, and to punish the culprits—since the
gipsies, when she passed the place, were preparing to
decamp.

No time *was* lost.   In one moment Farmer Thorpe was
on the bay filly's unsaddled back, with the halter for a
bridle ; and, in the next, they were on full gallop towards
the kiln.   But, alas ! alas ! " the more haste the worst
speed," says the wisdom of nations.   Just as they arrived
at the spot from which the procession—gipsies, dogs,

and donkeys—and Chanticleer in a sack, shrieking most vigorously—were proceeding on their travels, the young blood mare—whether startled at the unusual *cortège*, or the rough ways, or the hideous noise of her old friend, the cock—suddenly reared and threw her master, who lay in all the agony of a sprained ankle, unable to rise from the ground; whilst the whole tribe, with poor Chanticleer a prisoner, marched triumphantly past him, utterly regardless of his threats and imprecations. In this plight was the unlucky farmer discovered, about half-an-hour afterwards, by his wife, the constable, and a party of his own labourers, who came to give him assistance in securing the culprits; of whom, notwithstanding an instant and active search through the neighbourhood, nothing has yet transpired. We shall hardly see them again in these parts, and have almost done talking of them. The village is returned to its old state of order and honesty; the Mayor of W—— has replaced his table-cloth, and Mrs. Thorpe her cock; and the poor farmer's lame ankle is all that remains to give token of the gipsies.

Here we are at the turning, which, edging round by the coppice, branches off to their sometime den: the other bend to the right leads up a gentle ascent to the vicarage, and that is our way. How fine a view of the little parsonage we have from hence, between those arching elms, which enclose it like a picture in a frame! and how pretty a picture it forms, with its three pointed roofs, its snug porch, and its casement windows glittering from amid the china-roses! What a nest of peace and comfort! Farther on, almost at the summit of the hill, stands the old church with its massy tower—a row of superb lime-trees running along one side of the churchyard, and a cluster of dark yews shading the other. Few country churches have so much to boast in architectural beauty or in grandeur of situation.

We lose sight of it as we mount the hill, the lane narrowing and winding between deep banks, surmounted by high hedges, excluding all prospects till we reach the front of the vicarage, and catch across the gate of the opposite field a burst of country the most extensive and the most beautiful—field and village, mansion and cot, town and river, all smiling under the sparkling sun of May, and united and harmonised by the profusion of hedge-row timber in its freshest verdure, giving a rich woodland character to the scene, till it is terminated in the distance by the blue line of the Hampshire hills almost melting into the horizon. Such is the view from the vicarage. But it is too sunny and too windy to stand about out of doors, and time to finish our ramble. Down the hill, and round the corner, and past Farmer Thorpe's house, and one glance at the wheat-hoers, and then we will go home.

Ah! it is just as I feared. Jem and Mabel have been parted: they are now at opposite sides of the field—he looking very angry, working rapidly and violently, and doing more harm than good—she looking tolerably sulky, and just moving her hoe, but evidently doing nothing at all. Farmer Thorpe, on his part, is standing in the middle of the field, observing, but pretending not to observe, the little humours of the separated lovers. There is a lurking smile about the corners of his mouth that bespeaks him more amused than angry. He is a kind person after all, and will certainly make no mischief. I should not even wonder if he espoused Jem Tanner's cause; and, for certain, if any one can prevail on the little clerk to give up his squinting favourite in favour of true love, Farmer Thorpe is the man.

WHITSUN-EVE

The pride of my heart and the delight of my eyes is my garden. Our house, which is in dimensions very much like a bird-cage, and might, with almost equal convenience, be laid on a shelf or hung up in a tree, would be utterly unbearable in wet weather were it not that we have a retreat out of doors, and a very pleasant retreat it is. To make my readers comprehend it I must describe our whole territories.

Fancy a small plot of ground with a pretty, low, irregular cottage at one end; a large granary, divided from the dwelling by a little court running along one side; and a long thatched shed, open towards the garden, and supported by wooden pillars, on the other. The bottom is bounded half by an old wall and half by an old paling, over which we see a pretty distance of woody hills. The house, granary, wall, and paling, are covered with vines, cherry-trees, roses, honeysuckles, and jessamines, with great clusters of tall hollyhocks running up between them; a large elder overhanging the little gate, and a magnificent bay-tree, such a tree as shall scarcely be matched in these parts, breaking with its beautiful conical form the horizontal lines of the buildings. This is my garden; and the long pillared shed, the sort of rustic arcade, which runs along one side, parted from the flower-beds by a row of geraniums, is our out-of-door drawing-room.

I know nothing so pleasant as to sit there on a summer afternoon, with the western sun flickering through the great elder-tree, and lighting up our gay parterres, where flowers and flowering shrubs are set as thick as grass in a field, a wilderness of blossom, interwoven, intertwined, wreathy, garlandy, profuse beyond all profusion, where we may guess that there is such a thing as mould, but never see it. I know nothing so pleasant as to sit in the shade of that dark bower, with the eye resting on that bright piece of colour lighted so gloriously by the evening sun, now catching a glimpse of the little birds as they fly rapidly in and out of their nests—for there are always two or three birds'-nests in the thick tapestry of cherry-trees, honeysuckles, and china-roses, which covers our walls—now tracing the gay gambols of the common butterflies as they sport around the dahlias; now watching that rarer moth, which the country people, fertile in pretty names, call the bee-bird; * that bird-like insect, which flutters in the hottest days over the sweetest flowers, inserting its long proboscis into the small tube of the jessamine, and hovering over the scarlet blossom of the geranium, whose bright colour seems reflected on its own feathery breast : that insect which seems so thoroughly a creature of the air, never at rest; always, even when feeding, self-poised and self-supported, and whose wings, in their ceaseless motion, have a sound, so deep, so full, so lulling, so musical. Nothing so pleasant as to sit amid that mixture of rich flowers and leaves, watching the bee-bird ! Nothing so pretty to look at as my garden ! It is quite a picture ; only unluckily it resembles a picture in more qualities than one—it is fit for nothing but to look at. One might as well think of walking in a bit of framed canvas. There are walks, to be sure—tiny paths of smooth gravel, by courtesy called such—but they are so overhung by roses and lilies, and such gay encroachers— so overrun by convolvulus and heart's-ease, and mignon-ette, and other sweet stragglers, that, except to edge through them occasionally for the purpose of planting, or weeding, or watering, there might as well be no paths

* Sphinx ligustri, privet hawk-moth.

at all. Nobody thinks of walking in my garden. Even
May glides along with a delicate and trackless step, like
a swan through the water; and we, its two-footed denizens,
are fain to treat it as if it were really a saloon, and go
out for a walk towards sunset, just as if we had not been
sitting in the open air all day.

What a contrast from the quiet garden to the lively
street! Saturday night is always a time of stir and
bustle in our village, and this is Whitsun-Eve, the
pleasantest Saturday of all the year, when London
journeymen and servant lads and lasses snatch a short
holiday to visit their families. A short and precious
holiday, the happiest and liveliest of any; for even the
gambols and merry-makings of Christmas offer but a
poor enjoyment compared with the rural diversions, the
Mayings, revels, and cricket-matches of Whitsuntide.

We ourselves are to have a cricket-match on Monday,
not played by the men, who, since a certain misadventure
with the Beech-hillers, are, I am sorry to say, rather chop-
fallen, but by the boys, who, zealous for the honour of
their parish, and headed by their bold leader Ben Kirby,
marched in a body to our antagonists' ground the Sunday
after our melancholy defeat, challenged the boys of that
proud hamlet, and beat them out and out on the spot.
Never was a more signal victory. Our boys enjoyed
this triumph with so little moderation that it had like
to have produced a very tragical catastrophe. The
captain of the Beech-hill youngsters, a capital bowler, by
name Amos Stone, enraged past all bearing by the crowing
of his adversaries, flung the ball at Ben Kirby with so
true an aim that if that sagacious leader had not warily
ducked his head when he saw it coming, there would
probably have been a coroner's inquest on the case, and
Amos Stone would have been tried for manslaughter.
He let fly with such vengeance, that the cricket-ball
was found embedded in a bank of clay five hundred yards

off, as if it had been a cannon shot. Tom Coper and Farmer Thackum, the umpires, both say they never saw so tremendous a ball. If Amos Stone live to be a man (I mean to say if he be not hanged first) he'll be a pretty player. He is coming here on Monday with his party to play the return match, the umpires having respectively engaged Farmer Thackum that Amos shall keep the peace, Tom Coper that Ben shall give no unnecessary or wanton provocation—a nicely worded and lawyer-like clause, and one that proves that Tom Coper hath his doubts of the young gentleman's discretion ; and, of a truth, so have I. I would not be Ben Kirby's surety, cautiously as the security is worded—no ! not for a white double dahlia, the present object of my ambition.

This village of ours is swarming to-night like a hive of bees, and all the church bells round are pouring out their merriest peals, as if to call them together. I must try to give some notion of the various figures.

First, there is a group suited to Teniers, a cluster of out-of-door customers of the Rose, old benchers of the inn, who sit round a table smoking and drinking in high solemnity to the sound of Timothy's fiddle. Next, a mass of eager boys, the combatants of Monday, who are surrounding the shoemaker's shop, where an invisible hole in their ball is mending by Master Keep himself, under the joint superintendence of Ben Kirby and Tom Coper. Ben showing much verbal respect and outward deference for his umpire's judgment and experience, but managing to get the ball done his own way after all ; whilst outside the shop, the rest of the eleven, the less trusted commons, are shouting and bawling round Joel Brent, who is twisting the waxed twine round the handles of the bats—the poor bats, which please nobody, which the taller youths are despising as too little and too light, and the smaller are abusing as too heavy and too large. Happy critics ! winning their match can hardly be a

greater delight—even if to win it they be doomed !
Farther down the street is the pretty black-eyed girl,
Sally Wheeler, come home for a day's holiday from B.,
escorted by a tall footman in a dashing livery, whom she
is trying to curtsy off before her deaf grandmother sees
him. I wonder whether she will succeed !

Ascending the hill are two couples of a different description. Daniel Tubb and his fair Valentine, walking boldly
along like licensed lovers ; they have been asked twice
in church, and are to be married on Tuesday ; and closely
following that happy pair, near each other but not together,
come Jem Tanner and Mabel Green, the poor culprits
of the wheat-hoeing. Ah ! the little clerk hath not
relented ! The course of true love doth not yet run smooth
in that quarter. Jem dodges along, whistling " Cherry-
ripe," pretending to walk by himself, and to be thinking
of nobody ; but every now and then he pauses in his
negligent saunter, and turns round outright to steal a
glance at Mabel, who, on her part, is making believe
to walk with poor Olive Hathaway, the lame mantua-
maker, and even affecting to talk and to listen to that
gentle, humble creature, as she points to the wild flowers
on the common, and the lambs and children disporting
amongst the gorse, but whose thoughts and eyes are evidently fixed on Jem Tanner, as she meets his backward
glance with a blushing smile, and half springs forward to
meet him : whilst Olive has broken off the conversation
as soon as she perceived the pre-occupation of her companion, and begun humming, perhaps unconsciously,
two or three lines of Burns, whose " Whistle and I'll
come to ye, my lad," and " Gi'e me a glance of thy bonny
black e'e," were never better exemplified than in the couple
before her. Really, it is curious to watch them, and to
see how gradually the attraction of this tantalising vicinity
becomes irresistible, and the rustic lover rushes to his
pretty mistress like the needle to the magnet. On they

go, trusting to the deepening twilight, to the little clerk's absence, to the good-humour of the happy lads and lasses who are passing and repassing on all sides—or rather, perhaps, in a happy oblivion of the cross uncle, the kind villagers, the squinting lover, and the whole world. On they trip, arm in arm, he trying to catch a glimpse of her glowing face under her bonnet, and she hanging down her head, and avoiding his gaze with a mixture of modesty and coquetry, which well becomes the rural beauty. On they go, with a reality and intensity of affection which must overcome all obstacles ; and poor Olive follows her with an evident sympathy in their happiness which makes her almost as enviable as they ; and we pursue our walk amidst the moonshine and the nightingales, with Jacob Frost's cart looming in the distance, and the merry sounds of Whitsuntide, the shout, the laugh, and the song, echoing all around us like " noises of the air."

OUR MAYING

As party produces party and festival brings forth festival in higher life, so one scene of rural festivity is pretty sure to be followed by another. The boys' cricket-match at Whitsuntide, which was won most triumphantly by our parish, and luckily passed off without giving cause for a coroner's inquest, or indeed without injury of any sort, except the demolition of Amos Stone's new straw hat, the crown of which (Amos's head being fortunately at a distance) was fairly struck out by the cricket-ball; this match produced one between our eleven and the players of the neighbouring hamlet of Whitley; and being patronised by the young lord of the manor and several of the gentry round, and followed by jumping in sacks, riding donkey-races, grinning through horse-collars, and other diversions more renowned for their antiquity than their elegance, gave such general satisfaction, that it was resolved to hold a Maying in full form in Whitley-wood.

Now this wood of ours happens to be a common of twenty acres, with three trees on it, and the Maying was fixed to be held between hay-time and harvest; but "what's in a name?" Whitley-wood is a beautiful piece of greensward, surrounded on three sides by fields, and farm-houses, and cottages, and woody uplands, and on the other by a fine park; and the May-house was erected and the May-games held in the beginning of July, the very season of leaves and roses, when the days are at the longest, and the weather at the finest, and the whole world is longing to get out of doors. Moreover, the whole

festival was aided, not impeded, by the gentlemen amateurs,
headed by that very genial person, our young lord of the
manor ; whilst the business part of the affair was con-
fided to the well-known diligence, zeal, activity, and
intelligence of that most popular of village landlords,
mine host of the Rose. How could a Maying fail under
such auspices ? Everybody expected more sunshine and
more fun, more flowers and more laughing, than ever
was known at a rustic merrymaking—and really, considering the manner in which expectation had been raised,
the quantity of disappointment has been astonishingly
small.

Landlord Sims, the master of the revels, and our very
good neighbour, is a portly, bustling man of five-and-forty,
or thereabout, with a hale, jovial visage, a merry eye,
a pleasant smile, and a general air of good-fellowship.
This last qualification, whilst it serves greatly to recommend his ale, is apt to mislead superficial observers, who
generally account him a sort of a slenderer Boniface,
and imagine that, like the renowned hero of the spigot,
Master Sims eats, drinks, and sleeps on his own anno
domini. They were never more mistaken in their lives ;
no soberer man than Master Sims within twenty miles !
Except for the good of the house, he no more thinks of
drinking beer than a grocer of eating figs. To be sure
when the jug lags he will take a hearty pull, just by way
of example, and to set the good ale agoing. But, in general,
he trusts to subtler and more delicate modes of quickening
its circulation. A good song, a good story, a merry jest,
a hearty laugh, and a most winning habit of assentation ;
these are his implements. There is not a better companion, or a more judicious listener, in the county. His
pliability is astonishing. He shall say yes to twenty
different opinions on the same subject within the hour ;
and so honest and cordial does his agreement seem, that
no one of his customers, whether drunk or sober, ever

dreams of doubting his sincerity. The hottest conflict of politics never puzzles him : Whig or Tory, he is both or either—" the happy Mercutio, that curses both houses." Add to this gift of conformity, a cheerful, easy temper, an alacrity of attention, a zealous desire to please, which gives to his duties, as a landlord, all the grace of hospitality, and a perpetual civility and kindness, even when he has nothing to gain by them ; and no one can wonder at Master Sims's popularity.

After his good wife's death this popularity began to extend itself in a remarkable manner amongst the females of the neighbourhood : smitten with his portly person, his smooth, oily manner, and a certain soft, earnest, whispering voice, which he generally assumes when addressing one of the fairer sex, and which seems to make his very "How d'ye do " confidential and complimentary. Moreover, it was thought that the good landlord was well to do in the world, and though Betsy and Letty were good little girls, quick, civil, and active, yet, poor things, what could such young girls know of a house like the Rose ? All would go to rack and ruin without the eye of a mistress ! Master Sims must look out for a wife. So thought the whole female world, and, apparently, Master Sims began to think so himself.

The first fair one to whom his attention was directed was a rosy, pretty widow, a pastry-cook of the next town, who arrived in our village on a visit to her cousin, the baker, for the purpose of giving confectionery lessons to his wife. Nothing was ever so hot as that courtship. During the week that the lady of pie-crust stayed, her lover almost lived in the oven. One would have thought that he was learning to make the cream tarts without pepper, by which Bedreddin Hassan regained his state and his princess. It would be a most suitable match, as all the parish agreed ; the widow, for as pretty as she was (and one sha'n't often see a pleasanter open coun-

tenance, or a sweeter smile), being within ten years as
old as her suitor, and having had two husbands already.
A most proper and suitable match, said everybody;
and when our landlord carried her back to B. in his new-
painted green cart, all the village agreed that they were
gone to be married, and the ringers were just setting up a
peal, when Master Sims returned alone, single, crestfallen,
dejected; the bells stopped of themselves, and we heard
no more of the pretty pastry-cook.   For three months after
that rebuff, mine host, albeit not addicted to aversions,
testified an equal dislike to women and tartlets, widows
and plum-cake.   Even poor Alice Taylor, whose travel-
ling basket of lollypops and ginger-bread he had whilom
patronised, was forbidden the house; and not a bun or
a biscuit could be had at the Rose for love or money.

The fit, however, wore off in time; and he began again
to follow the advice of his neighbours, and to look out
for a wife, up street and down; whilst at each extremity
a fair object presented herself, from neither of whom
had he the slightest reason to dread a repetition of the
repulse which he had experienced from the blooming
widow.   The down-street lady was a widow also, the
portly, comely relict of our drunken village blacksmith,
who, in spite of her joy at her first husband's death, and
an old spite at mine host of the Rose, to whose good
ale and good company she was wont to ascribe most of
the aberrations of the deceased, began to find her shop,
her journeymen, and her eight children (six unruly,
obstreperous Pickles of boys, and two tom-boys of girls)
rather more than a lone woman could manage, and to
sigh for a helpmate to ease her of her cares, collect the
boys at night, see the girls to school of a morning, break
the larger imps off running away to revels and fairs, and
the smaller fry off birds'-nesting and orchard-robbing,
and bear a part in the lectures and chastisements which
she deemed necessary to preserve the young rebels from

the bad end which she predicted to them twenty times a-day. Master Sims was the coadjutor on whom she had inwardly pitched; and, accordingly, she threw out broad hints to that effect every time she encountered him, which, in the course of her search for boys and girls who were sure to be missing at school-time and bed-time, happened pretty often; and Mr. Sims was far too gallant and too much in the habit of assenting to listen unmoved; for really the widow was a fine, tall, comely woman; and the whispers, and smiles, and hand-pressings when they happened to meet were becoming very tender; and his admonitions and head-shakings addressed to the young crew (who, nevertheless, all liked him) quite fatherly. This was his down-street flame.

The rival lady was Miss Lydia Day, the carpenter's sister; a slim upright maiden, not remarkable for beauty, and not so young as she had been, who, on inheriting a small annuity from the mistress with whom she had spent the best of her days, retired to her native village to live on her means. A genteel, demure, quiet personage was Miss Lydia Day; much addicted to snuff and green tea, and not averse from a little gentle scandal—for the rest, a good sort of woman, and *un très-bon parti* for Master Sims, who seemed to consider it a profitable speculation, and made love to her whenever she happened to come into his head, which, it must be confessed, was hardly so often as her merits and her annuity deserved. Remiss as he was, he had no lack of encouragement to complain of—for she " to hear would seriously incline," and put on her best silk, and her best simper, and lighted up her faded complexion into something approaching to a blush whenever he came to visit her. And this was Master Sims's up-street love.

So stood affairs at the Rose when the day of the Maying arrived; and the double flirtation, which, however dexterously managed, must have been sometimes, one would think, rather inconvenient to the inamorato, proved on this occasion extremely useful. Each of the fair ladies contributed her aid to the festival ; Miss Lydia by tying up sentimental garlands for the May-house, and scolding the carpenters into diligence in the erection of the booths ; the widow by giving her whole bevy of boys and girls a holiday, and turning them loose on the neighbourhood to collect flowers as they could. Very useful auxiliaries were these light foragers ; they scoured the country far and near—irresistible mendicants ! pardonable thieves ! coming to no harm, poor children, except that little George got a black eye in tumbling from the top of an acacia tree at the Park, and that Sam (he's a sad Pickle is Sam !) narrowly escaped a horse-whipping from the head gardener at the Hall, who detected a bunch of his new rhododendron, the only plant in the county, forming the very crown and centre of the Maypole. Little harm did they do, poor children, with all their pilfery ; and when they returned, covered with their flowery loads, like the May-day figure called "Jack of the Green," they worked at the garlands and the May-houses as none but children ever do work, putting all their young life and their untiring spirit of noise and motion into their pleasant labour. Oh, the din of that building ! Talk of the Tower of Babel ! that was a quiet piece of masonry compared to the May-house of Whitley-wood, with its walls of leaves and flowers—and its canvas booths at either end for refreshments and musicians. Never was known more joyous note of preparation.

The morning rose more quietly—I had almost said more dully—and promised ill for the *fête*. The sky was gloomy, the wind cold, and the green filled as slowly as a balloon seems to do when one is watching it. The entertainments of the day were to begin with a cricket-match (two elevens to be chosen on the ground), and the wickets pitched at twelve o'clock precisely. Twelve o'clock came—but no cricketers—except, indeed, some two or three punctual and impatient gentlemen : one o'clock came and brought no other reinforcement than two or three more of our young Etonians and Wykhamites—less punctual than their precursors, but not a whit less impatient. Very provoking, certainly—but not very uncommon. Your country cricketer, the peasant, the mere rustic, does love, on these occasions, to keep his betters waiting, if only to display his power ; and when we consider that it is the one solitary opportunity in which importance can be felt and vanity gratified, we must acknowledge it to be perfectly in human nature that a few airs should be shown. Accordingly, our best players held aloof. Tom Coper would not come to the ground ; Joel Brent came indeed, but would not play ; Samuel Long coquetted—he would and he would not. Very provoking, certainly! Then two young farmers, a tall brother and a short, Hampshire men, cricketers born, whose good-humour and love of the game rendered them sure cards, had been compelled to go on business—the one ten miles south—the other, fifteen north—that very morning. No playing without the Goddards ! No sign of either of them on the B—— road or the F——. Most intolerably provoking, beyond a doubt. Master Sims tried his best coaxing and his best double X on the recusant players ; but all in vain. In short, there was great danger of the match going off altogether ; when, about two o'clock, Amos Stone, who was there with the crown of his straw hat sewed in wrong side outwards—new thatched, as it were—and who had been set to watch the B—— highway, gave notice that something was coming as tall as a Maypole—which something turning out to be the long Goddard, and his brother approaching at the same moment in the opposite direction, hope, gaiety, and good-humour revived again ; and two elevens, including Amos and another urchin of his calibre, were formed on the spot.

I never saw a prettier match. The gentlemen, the Goddards, and the boys being equally divided, the strength and luck of the parties were so well balanced that it produced quite a neck-and-neck race, won only by two notches. Amos was completely the hero of the day, standing out half of his side, and getting five notches at one hit. His side lost—but so many of his opponents give him their ribands (have not I said that Master Sims bestowed a set of ribands ?) that the straw hat was quite covered with purple trophies ; and Amos, stalking about the ground with a shy and awkward vanity, looked with his decorations like the sole conqueror—the Alexander or Napoleon of the day. The boy did not speak a word ; but every now and then he displayed a set of huge white teeth in a grin of inexpressible delight. By far the happiest and proudest personage of that Maying was Amos Stone.

By the time the cricket-match was over the world began to be gay at Whitley-wood. Carts and gigs, and horses and carriages, and people of all sorts arrived from all quarters ; and, lastly, " the blessed sun himself " made his appearance, adding a triple lustre to the scene. Fiddlers, ballad-singers, cake baskets—Punch—Master Frost, crying cherries—a Frenchman with dancing dogs —a Bavarian woman selling brooms—half-a-dozen stalls with fruit and frippery—and twenty noisy games of quoits, and bowls, and ninepins—boys throwing at boxes—girls playing at ball—gave to the assemblage the bustle, clatter, and gaiety of a Dutch fair, as one sees it in Teniers' pictures. Plenty of drinking and smoking on the green—plenty of eating in the booths : the gentlemen cricketers, at one end, dining off a round of beef which made the table totter—the players, at the other, supping off a gammon of bacon—Amos Stone crammed at both— and Landlord Sims bustling everywhere with an activity that seemed to confer upon him the gift of ubiquity,

assisted by the little light-footed maidens, his daughters,
all smiles and curtsies, and by a pretty black-eyed young
woman—name unknown—with whom, even in the midst
of his hurry, he found time, as it seemed to me, for a little
philandering. What would the widow and Miss Lydia
have said ? But they remained in happy ignorance—the
one drinking tea in most decorous primness in a distant
marquee, disliking to mingle with so mixed an assembly
—the other in full chase after the most unlucky of all
her urchins, the boy called Sam, who had gotten into
a *démêlé* with a showman, in consequence of mimicking
the wooden gentleman Punch and his wife Judy—thus,
as the showman observed, bringing his exhibition into
disrepute.

Meanwhile, the band struck up in the May-house, and
the dance, after a little demur, was fairly set afloat—
an honest English country-dance—(there had been some
danger of waltzing and quadrilling) — with ladies and
gentlemen at the top, and country lads and lasses at
the bottom ; a happy mixture of cordial kindness on the
one hand, and pleased respect on the other. It was droll,
though, to see the beplumed and beflowered French hats,
the silks and the fur-belows, sailing and rustling amidst the
straw bonnets and cotton gowns of the humbler dancers ;
and not less so to catch a glimpse of the little lame clerk,
shabbier than ever, peeping through the canvas opening
of the booth, with a grin of ineffable delight, over the
shoulders of our vicar's pretty wife. Really, considering
that Mabel Green and Jem Tanner were standing together
at that moment at the top of the set, so deeply engaged
in making love that they forgot when they ought to
begin, and that the little clerk must have seen them, I
cannot help taking his grin as a favourable omen to those
faithful lovers.

Well, the dance finished, the sun went down, and we
departed. The Maying is over, the booths carried away,

and the May-house demolished. Everything has fallen
into its old position except the love affairs of Landlord
Sims. The pretty lass, with the black eyes, who first
made her appearance at Whitley-wood, is actually staying
at the Rose Inn, on a visit to his daughters ; and the village
talk goes that she is to be the mistress of that thriving
hostelry, and the wife of its master ; and both her rivals
are jealous after their several fashions—the widow in
her tantrums, the maiden in the dumps. Nobody knows
exactly who the black-eyed damsel may be—but she's
young, and pretty, and civil, and modest ; and without
intending to depreciate the merits of either of her com-
petitors, I cannot help thinking that our neighbour has
shown his good taste.

A CASTLE IN THE AIR

" CAN any one tell me of a house to be let hereabouts ? "
asked I, this afternoon, coming into the room, with an
open letter in my hand, and an unusual animation of
feeling and of manner. " Our friends, the Camdens,
want to live amongst us again, and have commissioned
me to make inquiries for a residence."

This announcement, as I expected, gave general delight ;
for Mr. Camden is the most excellent and most agreeable
person under the sun, except his wife, who is even more
amiable than her amiable husband : to regain such
neighbours was felt to be an universal benefit, more
especially to us who were so happy as to call them friends.
My own interest in the house question was participated
by all around me, and the usual enumeration of vacant
mansions, and the several objections to each (for where
ever was a vacant mansion without its objection !) began
with zeal and rapidity.

" Cranley Hall," said one.

" Too large."

" Hinton Park ? "

" Too much land."

" The White House at Hannonby—the Belvidere, as
the late people called it ? "

" What ! Is that flourishing establishment done up ?
But Hannonby is too far off—ten miles at least."

" Queen's-bridge Cottage ? "

" Ay, that sweet place would have suited exactly, but
it's let. The Browns took it only yesterday."

" Sydenham Court ? "

" That might have done too, but it is not in the market. The Smiths intend to stay."

" Lanton Abbey ? "

" Too low ; grievously damp."

By this time, however, we had arrived at the end of our list ; nobody could remember another place to be let, or likely to be let, and confessing ourselves too fastidious, we went again over our catalogue *raisonné* with expectations much sobered, and objections much modified, and were beginning to find out that Cranley Hall was not so very large, nor Lanton Abbey so exceedingly damp, when one of our party exclaimed suddenly, " We never thought of Hatherden Hill ! surely that is small enough and dry enough ! " and it being immediately recollected that Hatherden was only a mile off, we lost sight of all faults in this great recommendation, and wrote immediately to the lawyer who had the charge of letting the place, whilst I myself and my most efficient assistant sallied forth to survey it on the instant.

It was a bright cool afternoon about the middle of August, and we proceeded in high spirits towards our destination, talking, as we went, of the excellence and agreeableness of our delightful friends, and anticipating the high intellectual pleasure, the gratification to the taste and the affections which our renewed intercourse with persons so accomplished and so amiable could not fail to afford ; both agreeing that Hatherden was the very place we wanted, the very situation, the very distance, the very size. In agreeing with me, however, my companion could not help reminding me rather maliciously how very much, in our late worthy neighbours', the Norrises, time, I had been used to hate and shun this paragon of places ; how frequently I had declared Hatherden too distant for a walk, and too near for a drive ; how constantly I had complained of fatigue in mounting the hill, and of cold in crossing the common ; and how, finally, my half-yearly visits of civility had dwindled first into annual, then into biennial calls, and would doubtless have extended themselves into triennial marks of remembrance, if our neighbours had but remained long enough. "To be sure," added he, recollecting, probably, how he, with his stricter sense of politeness, used to stave off a call for a month together, taking shame to himself every evening for his neglect, retaining "at once the conscience and the sin!" "To be sure, Norris was a sad bore! We shall find the hill easier to climb when the Camdens live on the top of it." An observation to which I assented most heartily.

On we went gaily; just pausing to admire Master Keep, the shoemaker's farming, who, having a bit of garden-ground to spare, sowed it with wheat instead of planting it with potatoes, and is now, aided by his lame apprentice, very literally carrying his crop. I fancy they mean to thresh their corn in the woodhouse, at least there they are depositing the sheaves. The produce may amount to four bushels. My companion, a better judge, says to three; and it has cost the new farmer two superb scarecrows, and gunpowder enough for a review, to keep off the sparrows. Well, it has been amusement and variety, however! and gives him an interest in the agricultural corner of the county newspaper. Master Keep is well-to-do in the world, and can afford himself such a diversion. For my part, I like these little experiments, even if they be not over gainful. They show enterprise; a shoemaker of less genius would never have got beyond a crop of turnips.

On we went—down the lane, over the bridge, up the hill—for there really is a hill, and one of some steepness for Berkshire, and across the common, once so dreary, but now bright and glittering under the double influence of an August sun and our own good spirits, until we were stopped by the gate of the lawn, which was of course locked, and obliged to wait until a boy should summon the old woman who had charge of the house, and who was now at work in a neighbouring harvest-field, to give us entrance.

Boys in plenty were there. The fine black-headed lad George Ropley, who, with his olive complexion, his bright dark eyes, and his keen intelligent features, looks so Italian, but who is yet in all his ways so thoroughly and genially English—had been gathering in his father's crop of apples, and was amusing himself with tossing some twenty amongst as many urchins of either sex who had collected round him to partake of the fruit and the sport. There he stood tossing the ripe ruddy apples ; some high in the air for a catch, some low amongst the bushes for a hunt ; some one way, some another, puzzling and perplexing the rogues, by taking care that none should go appleless in the midst of his fun. And what fun it was to them all, thrower and catchers ! What infinite delight ! How they laughed and shouted, and tumbled and ran ! How they watched every motion of George Ropley's hand ; the boys and the girls, and the " toddling wee things," of whom one could not distinctly make out whether they were the one or the other ! And how often was that hand tossed up empty, flinging nothing, in order to cheat the wary watchers ! Now he threw an apple into the midst of the group, and what a scramble ! Then at a distance, and what a race ! The five nearest started ; one, a great boy, stumbled over a mole-hill and was flung out ; two of the little ones were distanced ; and it was a neck and neck heat between a girl in a pink frock (my acquaintance, Liddy Wheeler) and a boy in a tattered jacket, name unknown. With fair play Liddy would have beaten, but he of the ragged jacket pulled her back by her new pink frock, rushed forward, and conquered— George gallantly flinging his last apple into her lap to console her for her defeat.

By this time the aged portress (Dame Wheeler, Liddy's

grandmother) had given us admittance, and we stood on the steps in front of the house, in calm survey of the scene before us. Hatherden was just the place to like or not to like, according to the feeling of the hour; a respectable, comfortable country house, with a lawn before, a paddock on one side, a shrubbery on the other; offices and a kitchen garden behind, and the usual ornaments of villas and advertisements, a green-house and a veranda. Now, my thoughts were *couleur de rose*, and Hatherden was charming. Even the beds intended for flowers on the lawn, but which, under a summer's neglect, were now dismal receptacles of seeds and weeds, did not shock my gardening eye so much as my companion evidently expected. "We must get my factotum, Clarke, here to-morrow," so ran my thoughts, "to clear away that rubbish, and try a little bold transplanting: late holly-hocks, late dahlias, a few pots of lobelias and chrysanthemums, a few patches of coreopsis and china-asters, and plenty of scarlet geraniums, will soon make this desolation flourishing. A good gardener can move anything now-a-days, whether in bloom or not," thought I, with much complacency; "and Clarke's a man to transplant Windsor forest without withering a leaf. We'll have him to-morrow."

The same happy disposition continued after I entered the house. And when left alone in the echoing empty breakfast-room, with only one shutter opened, while Dame Wheeler was guiding the companion of my survey to the stable-yard, I amused myself with making, in my own mind, comparisons between what had been, and what would be. There she used to sit, poor Mrs. Norris, in this large airy room, in the midst of its solid handsome furniture, in a great chair at a great table, busily at work for one of her seven small children; the table piled with frocks, trousers, petticoats, shirts, pinafores, hats, bonnets, all sorts of children's gear, masculine and feminine, together with spelling-books, copy-books, ivory alphabets, dissected maps, dolls, toys, and ginger-bread for the same small people. There she sat, a careful mother, fretting over their naughtiness and their ailments ; always in fear of the sun, or the wind, or the rain, of their running to heat themselves, or their standing still to catch cold : not a book in the house fit for a person turned of eight years old ! not a grown-up idea ! not a thought beyond the nursery ! One wondered what she could have talked of before she had children. Good Mrs. Norris, such was she. Good Mr. Norris was, for all purposes of neighbourhood, worse still. He was gapy and fidgety, and prosy and dozy, kept a tool-chest and a medicine-chest, weighed out manna and magnesia, constructed fishing-flies and nets for fruit trees, turned nutmeg-graters, lined his wife's work-box, and dressed his little daughter's doll ; and had a tone of conversation perfectly in keeping with his tastes and pursuits, abundantly tedious, thin, and small. One talked down to him, worthy gentleman, as one would to his son Willy. These were the neighbours that had been. What wonder that the hill was steep, and the way long, and the common dreary ! Then came pleasant thoughts of the neighbours that were to be. The lovely and accomplished wife, so sweet and womanly ; the elegant and highly-informed husband, so spirited and manly ! Art and literature, and wisdom and wit adorning with a wreathy and garlandy splendour all that is noblest in mind and purest in heart ! What wonder that Hatherden became more and more interesting in its anticipated charms, and that I went gaily about the place, taking note of all that could contribute to the comfort of its future inhabitants !

Home I came, a glad and busy creature, revolving in my mind the wants of the house and their speediest remedies—new paper for the drawing-room ; new wainscoting for the dining parlour ; a stove for the laundry :

a lock for the wine cellar ; baizing the door of the library, and new painting the hall ; to say nothing of the grand design of Clarke and the flower-beds.

So full was I of busy thoughts, and so desirous to put my plans in train without the loss of a moment, that although the tossing of apples had now resolved itself into a most irregular game of cricket, George Ropley being batting at one wicket, with little Sam Coper for his mate at the other ; Sam, an urchin of seven years old, but the son of an old player, full of cricket blood, born, as it were, with the bat in his hand, getting double the notches of his tall partner—an indignity which that well-natured stripling bore with surprising good-humour ; and although the opposite side consisted of Liddy Wheeler bowling at one end, her old competitor of the ragged jacket at the other, and one urchin in trousers, and one in petti-coats, standing out ; in spite of the temptation of watch-ing this comical parody on that manly exercise, rendered doubly amusing by the scientific manner in which little Sam stood at his wicket, the perfect gravity of the fields-man in petticoats, and the serious air with which these two worthies called Liddy to order whenever she trans-gressed any rule of the game—Sam will certainly be a great player some day or other, and so (if he be not a girl, for really there's no telling) will the young gentleman standing out—in spite, however, of the great temptation of overlooking a favourite divertisement, with variations so truly original, home we went, hardly pausing to observe the housing of Mr. Keep's wheat harvest. Home we went, adding at every step a fresh storey to our Castle in the Air, anticipating happy mornings and joyous evenings at dear Hatherden ; in love with the place and all about it, and quite convinced that the hill was nothing, the distance nothing, and the walk by far the prettiest in this neighbourhood.

Home we came, and there we found two letters, one from

Mr. Camden, sent per coach, to say he found that they must go abroad immediately, and that they, therefore, could not think of coming into Berkshire for a year or more; one from the lawyer left in charge of Hatherden, to say that we could not have the place, as the Norrisses were returning to their old house forthwith. And my castle is knocked down — blown up — which is the right word for the demolishing of such airy edifices? And Hatherden is as far off, and the hill as steep, and the common as dreary as ever.

A VISIT TO RICHMOND

THE macadamised roads, and the light open carriages lately introduced, have so abridged, I had well nigh said annihilated distance in this fair island, that what used to be judged a journey is now a drive ; our neighbourhood has become, from a reverse reason to theirs, as extensive as that of the good people in the back settlements of America ; we think nothing of thirty miles for a morning call, or forty for a dinner-party ; Richmond is quite within visiting distance, and London will shortly be our market-town.

This pleasant change was never so strongly impressed on my mind as by a hasty and most agreeable jaunt which I made to the former of these places during one of the few fine days last summer. The invitation, written one day, arrived in the course of post by breakfast-time the next, and without any uncomfortable hurry in packing or setting off, we were quietly dining with our kind inviters, rather before than after our usual hour, and might have returned very conveniently the same evening, had we been so minded.

There was some temptation to this exploit besides the very great one of whisking to and fro like a jack o' lantern, and making all the village stare at our rapidity. Our road lay through the Forest, and we might have passed again by moonlight the old romantic royal town of Windsor, with its stately palace and its Shakespearian associations—I never catch a glimpse of those antique buildings but those " Merry Wives " and all their company start up before my eyes ; might have heard the

night-wind rustle amongst the venerable oaks and beeches
of its beautiful park ; might have seen the deer crouching
in the fern, and the hare scudding across the glades ; and
as we paused to contemplate the magical effects of light
and shadow which forest scenery displays at such an hour,
might have seen the Castle in the distance, throwing its
dark masses against the sky, and looking like some
stupendous work of nature, or some grand dream of
Gothic architecture, rather than an actual erection of
man.   Everybody that has seen Windsor by moonlight
will understand how much one wishes to see that most
striking sight again ; but our friends were not people to
run away from, besides, I wanted to get better acquainted
with the celebrated spot where they resided — so we
stayed.

"God made the Country and man made the Town!"
I wonder in which of the two divisions Cowper would
have placed Richmond.   Every Londoner would laugh
at the rustic who should call it town, and with foreigners
it passes pretty generally for a sample (the only one they
see) of the rural villages of England ; and yet it is no
more like the country—the real, untrimmed, genuine
country—as we see it hereabouts, for instance, than a
garden is like a field.   I do not say this is disparagement.
Richmond is nature in a court-dress, but still nature
—ay, and very lovely nature too, gay and happy and
elegant as one of Charles the Second's beauties, and with
as little to remind one of the original penalty of labour,
or poverty, or grief, or crime.   I suppose that since no
place on the globe is wholly exempt from their influence,
care and vice may exist even there.   They are, however,
well hidden.   The inhabitants may find them, or they may
find the inhabitants, but to the casual visitor Richmond
appears as a sort of fairy-land, a piece of the old Arcadia,
a holiday spot for ladies and gentlemen, where they lead
a happy out-of-door life, like the gay folks in Watteau's

pictures, and have nothing to do with the work-a-day world.

The principal charm of this smiling landscape is the river, the beautiful river; for the hill seems to me over-rated. That celebrated prospect is, to my eye, too woody, too leafy, too green. There is a monotony of vegetation, a heaviness. The view was finer as I first saw it in February, when the bare branches admitted frequent glimpses of houses and villages, and the colouring was left to the fancy, than when arrayed in the pomp and garniture of " the leafy month of June." Canova said it only wanted crags. I rather incline to the old American criticism, and think that it wants clearing.

But the river! the beautiful river! there is no over-rating that. Brimming to its very banks of meadow or of garden; clear, pure, and calm as the bright summer sky, which is reflected in clearer brightness from its bosom; no praise can be too enthusiastic for that glorious stream. How gracefully it glides through the graceful bridge! And how the boats become it! And how pretty those boats are, from the small skiff of the market-woman laden with fruit and flowers, or the light-green pleasure vessel with its white awning and its gay freight of beaux and belles, to the heavy steamboat which comes walloping along with a regular mechanical combination of noise and motion, rumpling the quiet waters, and leaving a track of waves which vary most agreeably the level lake-like surface of the tranquil river. Certainly the Thames is the pleasantest highway in his Majesty's dominions.

Some of the happiest hours I ever passed in my life were spent on its bosom in one of those sweet and shady June mornings, when the light clouds seemed, as it were, following the sun, and enfolding him in a thousand veils of whiter alabaster, and the soft air came loaded with fragrance from gardens which were one flush of roses and

honeysuckles. I shall not easily forget that morning.
Gliding along through those beautiful scenes with companions worthy of their beauty ; sunk in that silence of
deep enjoyment, that delicious dreaminess which looks
so like thought, although in reality a much wiser and
happier thing ; listening half unconsciously to Emily
I,'s sweet Venetian ballads, the singer and her song so
united to the scene and the hour ; repeating almost as
unconsciously as we met the Queen-birds,

> " The swans on fair St. Mary's lake
> Float double, swan and shadow ; "

just roused as we passed Pope's grotto, or the arch over
Strawberry Hill ; and then landing at Hampton Court,
the palace of the Cartoons, and of the Rape of the Lock,
and coming home with my mind full of the divine Raphael,
and of that glorious portrait of Titian by himself, which,
next to the Cartoons, forms the chief ornament of that
regal mansion ; strangely chequered and intersected as
those strange things, fancy and memory, are apt to be,
by vivid images of the fair Belinda, and of that inimitable
game at Ombre which will live longer than any painting,
and can only die with the language. There is no forgetting
that morning.

Another almost as pleasant was passed in going down
the river towards Kew, amongst all sorts of royal recollections, from the remains of the house of Anne of Cleves, to
the lime trees, fragrant with blossom and musical with
bees, under which the late king and queen used to sit
of a summer evening, whilst their children were playing
round them on the grass. Kew Palace is in fine harmony
with this pretty family scene. One likes to think of
royalty so comfortable, and homely, and unconstrained,
as it must have been in that small, ugly, old-fashioned
house. Princes are the born thralls of splendour, and
to see them eased of their cumbrous magnificence pro-

duces much such a sensation of pleasure as that which
one feels in reading the fine passage of *Ivanhoe*, where
the collar is taken from the neck of Gurth, and he leaps
up a free man. At Kew, too, in those confined and ill-
furnished rooms, the royal inhabitants were not without
better luxuries; books accessible and readable, and
looking as if they had been read, and a fine collection
of cabinet pictures: superb Canalettis; the famous
Dropsical Woman, on which the queen is said, during her
last illness, to have fixed her eyes so frequently, and with
such an intense expression of self-pity; and a portrait of
Vandyke, which rivals the Titian, the elegant Vandyke
with his head over the shoulder, which has been so often
engraved. What a noble race of men those great painters
were! There is nothing in all their works grander or
fuller of intellectual beauty than some of their own heads,
as we find them recorded in their portraits of themselves,
or in the interesting collection of Vasari.

This remark will hardly apply to one great painter,
whose residence forms one of the many delightful associations of Richmond. Sir Joshua, who flattered all other
persons, did himself so little justice, that in his own
portraits he might pass for a dancing-master. His villa
is here; rich in remembrances of Johnson and Boswell,
and Goldsmith and Burke; here the spot where the poet
Thomson used to write; here the elegant house of Owen
Cambridge; close by, the celebrated villa of Pope, where
one seems to see again Swift and Gay, St. John and
Arbuthnot; a stone's throw off, the still more celebrated
Gothic toy-shop, Strawberry Hill, which we all know so
well from the minute and vivid descriptions of its master,
the most amusing of letter-writers, the most fashionable
of antiquaries, the most learned of *petit-maitres*, the
cynical, finical, delightful Horace Walpole. Here, too,
is Richmond Park, where Jeanie Deans and the Duke of
Argyle met Queen Caroline: it has been improved, un-

luckily, and the walk where the interview took place no longer exists. To make some amends, however — for everything belonging to those delicious books assumes the form of historical interest, becomes an actual reality —to compensate for this disappointment, in removing some furniture from an old house in the town, three portraits were discovered in the wainscot, George the Second, a staring likeness, between Lady Suffolk and Queen Caroline. The paintings were the worst of that bad era, but the position of the three and the recollection of Jeanie Deans was irresistible; those pictures ought never to be separated.

But of all the celebrated villas round Richmond, none pleased me better than one which seemed so unsuited to that gay scene, that one cannot look at it without wondering how it came there. I speak of Ham House, a stately old place, retired from the river, which is concealed and divided from it by rows of huge trees.

Ham House is a perfect model of the mansion of the last century, with its dark shadowy front, its steps and terraces, its marble basins, and its deep silent court, whose iron gate, as Horace Walpole used to complain, was never opened. Everything about it belongs to the time of hoops and periwigs. Harlow Place must have been just such an abode of stateliness and seclusion. Those iron gates seem to have been erected for no other purpose than to divide Lovelace from Clarissa; they look so stern and so unrelenting. We almost expect to see her through them, sweeping slowly along the terrace-walk in the pure dignity of her swan-like beauty, with her jealous sister watching her from a window; and we look for him, too, at the corner of the wall, waiting to deposit a letter, and listening with a speaking eagerness to the rustle of her silk gown. If there were any Clarissas now-a-days they would certainly be found at Ham House. And the keeping is so perfect. The very flowers are

old-fashioned. No American borders, no kalmias or
azaleas or magnolias, or such heathen shrubs! No
flimsy China roses! Nothing new-fangled! None but
flowers of the olden time, arranged in gay formal knots,
staid, and prim, and regular, and without a leaf awry.
Add but round Dutch honeysuckles, and I daresay that
Fletcher's beautiful song, which I shall borrow to conclude
my description, might comprise the whole catalogue.

> " Roses, their sharp spines being gone,
>   Not royal in their smell alone,
>   But in their hue ;
> Virgin pinks of odours faint,
> Daisies smell less but most quaint,
>   And sweet thyme true.
>
> Primrose, first-born child of Ver,
> Merry spring-time's harbinger,
>   With her bells dim,
> Oxlips in their cradles growing,
> Marigolds on death beds blowing,
>   * Lark-heels trim."

* Of course the flower that we now call larkspur. I have attri-
buted this charming song (the bridal song from the Two Noble
Kinsmen) to Fletcher—but it may belong to a still greater poet, for
certainly Shakespeare was art and part in that beautiful tragedy.

THE HAYMAKERS

AMONGST the country employments of England none
is so delightful to see or to think of as haymaking. It
comes in the pleasantest season, amidst a green, and
flowery, and sunshiny world ; it has for scene the prettiest
places—park, or lawn, or meadow, or upland pasture ;
and withal it has more of innocent merriment, more of
the festivity of an out-of-door sport, and less of the
drudgery and weariness of actual labour, than any other
of the occupations of husbandry. One looks on it, pretty
picture as it is, without the almost saddening sympathy
produced by the slow and painful toil of the harvest-field,
and, moreover, one looks on it much oftener. A very
little interval of dressed garden shall divide a great
country mansion from the demesne, where hay-cocks
repose under noble groups of oaks and elms, or mingle
their fragrance with the snowy wreaths of the acacia,
or the honeyed tassels of the lime ; and the fair and
delicate lady who cannot tell wheat from barley, and
the mincing fine gentleman who " affects an *ignorance*
if he have it not," shall yet condescend not merely to
know hay when they see it, but even to take some interest
in the process of getting it up. In short, at the most
aristocratic country tables, from the high-sheriff of the
county to the lord-lieutenant, hay is a permitted subject ;
and the state of the clouds, or of the weather-glass, shall
be inquired into as diligently, and be listened to with as
much attention, as speculations on the St. Leger or the
Derby, discussions on the breed of pheasants, or calcula-
tions on a contested election. Hay is very naturally

felt to be a gentlemanly topic, since from the richest to the poorest every country gentleman is a hay-owner.

I have been used all my life to take a lively interest, and even so much participation as may belong to a mere spectator, in this pleasant labour ; for I cannot say that I ever actually handled the fork or the rake. In former times our operations were on a grand scale, since the lawn before and around our old house, and the park-like paddock behind, were of such an extent as to make the getting in of the crop an affair of considerable moment in a pecuniary point of view. Now we have in our own hands only two small fields, the one a meadow of some three acres, about a mile off, the other a bit of upland pasture not much bigger, and rather nearer. The consequence of which diminution of property is, that I am ten times more interested in our small possession than ever I was in our large demesne, and that the produce of these two little bits of land—the minikin rick, not much better than a hay-cock itself, all of which is to be consumed by that special friend of mine, our pretty, frisky cream-coloured horse,* of whom it is every day predicted that he will break our necks—appears much more important in my eyes than the mountains of dried grass, which, after feeding some dozen horses, and half-a-dozen cows, were sold out amongst the inn-keepers, coach proprietors, cattle-dealers, and hay-buyers of all sorts, and sometimes, in a plentiful year, had even the honour to be advertised in a country newspaper, put up to public sale, puffed by the auctioneer, abused by the bidders, talked about, and lied about, and finally knocked down by the hammer— as great a piece of promotion as a hay-rick can well come to.

This trick of estimating one's possessions in an inverse

---

* Now, alas ! no more ! Would that the beauty were alive again, even if he did put our lives in jeopardy ! I shall never entertain so strong a personal friendship for any steed.

ratio to their real value is, I believe, strange as the assertion may seem, no uncommon freak of that whimsical, but good-for-*something* piece of perversity called human nature. In my own case I can, besides, claim in mitigation for the mistake (if mistake it be to take an interest in anything innocent !) the extreme beauty of the two patches of ground on which grows the hay in question.

One of these grassplots is a breezy, airy, upland field, abutting on the southernmost nook of an open common, forming, so to say, one side of a sunny bay, half filled with a large clear pond of bright water, water always bright ; the first swallows of the year are regularly seen there ; a great farm-house with its bustling establishment directly opposite ; a winding road leading across the green ; and trees, cottages, children, horses, cows, sheep, and geese, scattered around in the gayest profusion—a living and moving picture. The most populous street of a populous city gives a less vivid idea of habitation than the view from the gate, or from the high bank, feathered with broom and hazel—for the fence consists rather of a ditch than of a hedge, the field being, as it were, moated—of that lightsome and cheerful bit of pasture land.

The more distant meadow is prettier still ; it has no regular approach, and is reached only through a chain of fields belonging to different neighbours, whose gates, close locked upon all other occasions, open only to admit the ponderous hay waggon, creaking under its burthen, and the noisy procession of pitchers and rakers by which it is accompanied. Surrounded by close and high hedges, richly studded by hedge-row timber, no spot can be more completely shut out from the world than this small meadow. A stream of considerable variety and beauty winds along one end, fringed on each margin by little thickets of copse wood, hawthorn, and hazel, mixed with trees of a larger growth, and clothed, intertwisted, matted, by garlands of wild rose and wild

honeysuckle; whilst here and there a narrow strip of
turf intervenes between these natural shrubberies and
the sparkling, glittering, babbling stream, which runs so
clearly over its narrow bed that every shoal of minnows
is visible as they pass. Every vagary that a nameless
brooklet well can play does this brook show off in its
short course across the end of our meadow; now driven
rapidly through a narrow channel by the curvature
of the banks, fretting, and fuming, and chafing over
the transparent pebbles; now creeping gently between
clusters of the rich willow herb and golden flag; now
sleeping quietly in a wider and deeper pool, where the
white waterlily has found room for its dark leaves and its
snowy flowers, and where those quiet but treacherous
waters seem about to undermine the grassy margent
which already overhangs them, and to lay bare the roots
of the old willows. On the banks of that tricksy stream
lies the scene of our little story.

Last summer was, as most of my readers probably
remember, one of no small trial to haymakers in general,
the weather being what is gently and politely termed
"unsettled," which in this pretty climate of ours, during
" the leafy month of June," may commonly be construed
into cloudy, stormy, drizzly, cold. In this instance the
silky, courtly, flattering epithet, being translated, could
hardly mean other than wet—fixed, determined, settled
rain. From morning to night the clouds were dropping;
roses stood tottering on their stalks; strawberries lay
sopping in their beds; cherries and currants hung all
forlorn on their boughs, with the red juice washed out
of them; gravel roads turned into sand; pools into ponds;
ditches into rivulets; rivers overflowed their channels;
and that great evil—a summer flood—appeared in-
evitable. "The rain it raineth every day" was the
motto for the month. Sheridan's wicked interpolation in
Mr. Coleridge's tragedy, " drip, drip, drip, there's nothing

here but dripping," seemed made expressly for the season. Cut or uncut, the grass was spoiling ; the more the hay was made the clearer it appeared that it would never make to any purpose ; the poor cattle shook their ears as if aware of an impending scarcity ; salt, the grand remedy for sopped hay, rose in the market ; farmers fretted, and gentlemen fumed.*

So passed the "merry month of June." Towards the beginning of July, however, matters mended. A new moon made her appearance in the world, and that great stranger, the sun, as if out of compliment to his fair, cold sister, ventured out of the clouds to salute her across the sky, one evening just before his usual time of setting, and even continued the civility by leaving behind him such a glow of purple rosiness, and such a line of golden light, as illumined the whole horizon, and gave the most gracious promise for the ensuing day—a promise unusually well kept for so great a personage—that is to say, not quite forgotten. The weather, to be sure, was not quite perfect—when was the weather ever known to be so ?— it was, on the contrary, of that description which is termed " catching " ; but still there were intervals of brightness ; the rain was less heavy ; the sun did shine sometimes ; and even when he refused to show that resplendent face of his, a light stirring breeze answered all haymaking purposes almost as well. In short, between wind and sunshine, we managed to get in our upland crop with little danger and less damage, and encouraged by that success, and by the slow, gentle rising of the weather-glass, which the knowing in such matters affirm to be much more reliable than a sudden and violent jump

* It is well if they did no worse. A fair young friend of mine, whose father, one of the most accomplished persons that I have ever known, and by no means addicted to the use of naughty words on common occasions, rented about thirty acres of water-meadow, known by the name of " the moors," used always to call the hay-making time his " swearing month." He was wont to laugh at the expression—but I never heard him deny that it was true.

of the quicksilver, we gave orders to cut the little mead
without delay, and prepared for a day's haymaking in that
favourite spot.

We were not without other encouragements with
respect to the weather. The sun himself had had the
goodness to make " a golden set " and a rosy dawning,
and those vegetable barometers, the scarlet pimpernel
in the hedge-rows, and the purple Venus's looking-glass
in the garden, threw open their rich cups to receive his
earliest beams, with a fulness of expansion seldom shown
by those, I had almost said, sentient flowers, when there
is the slightest appearance of rain. Our good neighbour
the shoemaker, too, an in-door oracle, whose speculations
on the atmosphere are not very remarkable for their
correctness, prognosticated wet ; whilst our other good
neighbour, Farmer Bridgwater, an out-of-door, practical
personage, whose predictions—and it is saying much for
them—are almost as sure to come true as the worthy
cordwainer's to prove false, boldly asseverated that the day
would prove fine, and made his preparations and mus-
tered his troops (for Farmer Bridgwater is generalissimo
in our hay-field) with a vigour and energy that would
have become a higher occasion. He set six men on to
mowing by a little after sunrise, and collected fourteen
efficient haymakers by breakfast-time. Fourteen active
haymakers for our poor three acres ! not to count the
idle assistants ; we ourselves, with three dogs and two
boys to mind them, advisers who came to find fault and
look on, babies who came to be nursed, children who
came to rock the babies, and other children who came
to keep the rockers company and play with the dogs ;
to say nothing of this small rabble, we had fourteen able-
bodied men and women in one hay-field, besides the six
mowers who had got the grass down by noon, and finding the strong beer good and plentiful, magnanimously
volunteered to stay and help to get in the crop. N.B.—

This abundance of aid is by no means so extravagant as it seems, especially in catching weather. Beer, particularly in country affairs, will go twice as far as money, and, if discreetly administered (for we must not make even haymakers quite tipsy), really goes as near to supply the place of the sun as anything well can do. In our case the good double X was seconded by this bright luminary, and our operations prospered accordingly.

Besides being a numerous, ours was a merry group, very merry and very noisy ; for amongst the country people, as amongst children, those two words may almost be reckoned synonymous. There was singing that might pass for screaming ; laughter that burst forth in peals and in shouts ; and talking in every variety of key, from the rough, bluff, commanding halloo of Farmer Bridgwater, issuing his orders from one end of the field to another, to the shrill cry of Dame Wilson's baby, which seemed to pierce upwards, and cleave the very sky. A mingled buzz of talking was, however, the predominant sound, talking of which little could be collected except a general expression of happiness, Dame Wilson's roaring infant being, with one exception, the only dissatisfied person in the field.

Nobody could imagine the joyous din of that little place. A "jovial crew" they were, though by no means "merry beggars" ; for our haymakers were for that profession persons of respectability, rather, indeed, amateurs than professors—saving, perhaps, Dame Wilson and her set of boys and girls, who might be accounted poor, and a certain ragged Irishman called Jerry, who comes over every year harvesting, and is a general favourite with high and low ; with these small drawbacks (N.B.—Dame Wilson is a mountain of a woman, at least five feet in the girth, and Jerry a maypole of a man, who stands six feet three without his shoes), with these trifling exceptions, our troop of haymakers might really pass for people of substance.

First came the commander-in-chief, Farmer Bridgwater, a hearty sturdy old bachelor, rough and bluff, and merry, and kind, a great although a general admirer of our pretty lasses, to whom his blunt compliments and rustic raillery, of which the point lay rather in a knowing wink, a sly turn of the head, and a peculiar dryness of manner, than in the words, added to his unfailing good nature, rendered him always welcome.

Next in the list figures our respectable neighbour, Aaron Keep, the shoemaker, who came to help us and to watch the weather. He is an excellent person is Aaron Keep, and he came, as he said, to help us; and I dare say he would have been very sorry if the hay had been quite spoiled; nevertheless, having predicted that it would rain, I cannot help thinking he considered it a little hard that no rain came. The least little shower, just to confirm his prognostics, would have made him happy, and he kept watching the clouds, and hoping and foretelling a thunderstorm; but the clouds were obstinate, and the more he predicted that a storm would come, the more it stayed away.

Then arrived Master Wheatley, our worthy neighbour, the wheelwright, who, being also parish constable, might have abated the noise if he himself had not been the noisiest. I think he came to please his daughter Mary, a smiling airy damsel of thirteen, who never made hay before in her life. How enraptured the little girl was with the holiday! My dog Dash was the only creature in the field gay enough to keep pace with her frolics. They were playmates during the whole day.

Mine host of the Rose was also present, that model of all village landlords, mine host in his red waistcoat; and he also brought with him his pretty daughters, lasses of eighteen and twenty, who care no more for poor Dash than I do for a wax doll; I dare say they don't even know that he's a spaniel. Lucy had been to London this spring, and brought home a beau, whom she had picked up there, as a visitor to her papa, and, our hay-field being a good place for love-making, there too was he, displaying in handling a prong all the awkwardness that might be expected from a Cheapside haberdasher accustomed to the yard. He laughed at himself, however, with a very good grace, and seemed a well-conditioned and well-behaved person, his misfortune of cockneyism notwithstanding. They said that Miss Lucy would soon leave the Rose and take to measuring ribands herself. Patty, too, the round-faced, rosy-cheeked, fair-haired, younger sister, my favourite (but that is a secret, for both are equally civil, and, as far as I know, equally good; I would not make any difference in the world, only—Patty is my favourite); Patty, said the world—the village world—was also not unlikely to leave the Rose, though for an abode only two doors removed from it; Mr. George Waring, our smart young saddler, having, they affirmed, won her heart; but upon looking out for Patty and George, thinking to find them engaged as the other couple were, what was my astonishment to see the poor little lass, her smiles gone and her roses faded, moping under the hedge alone, rather making believe to rake than actually raking; whilst Mr. George Waring was tossing about the hay in company with the handsome brunette Sally Wheeler, who was just (as I remembered to have heard) come home from service to be married, and looked prodigiously as if the young saddler was her intended spouse. Nothing was ever more suspicious. He looked brighter and gayer than ever, and so did Sally, and for certain they were talking of something interesting, something at which the gentleman smiled and the lady blushed, talking so earnestly that they even forgot to toss the hay about, and that Farmer Bridgwater's loudest reprimand, although it startled every one else in the field, was apparently unheard by either of them.

" Alas ! I fear Mr. George Waring will play poor Patty false," was my involuntary thought, as I glided amongst the thickets by the side of the stream, and established myself in a verdant nook quite out of sight of the gay scene I had quitted, from which I was parted by a natural shrubbery of honeysuckle and wild roses, covered with blossoms and over-canopied by the spreading branches of a large oak. A pleasant seat was that green bank, with the clear water flowing at my feet, gay with the yellow flag, the white lily, and the blue forget-me-not, and fragrant with the rich tufts of the elegant meadow-sweet, mingling its delicious odour with that of the wild rose, the honeysuckle, and the new-mown hay. A pleasant seat was that turfy bank, and, as the haymakers adjourned to the farther end of the field to dinner, a quiet one ; until suddenly I heard first a deep sigh, and then two voices, from the other side of the oak tree. I listened with somewhat of curiosity, but more of interest, to the following dialogue :—

" Why, my queen," said the bluff, good-humoured voice of Farmer Bridgwater, " what are you moping here for ? And what have you done with your rosy cheeks ? A'nt you well ? "

" Yes," answered the sighing Patty.

" Go to dinner, then," responded the generalissimo of the hay-field.

" No," sighed the damsel ; " I'd rather stay here."

" Shall Lucy bring you something to eat ? " pursued the good farmer.

" No."

" Or your father ? "

" No."

" Or Aaron Keep ? I see he has done."

" No."

" Or little Mary Wheatley ? she'll be here like a bird."

"No, I don't want any dinner, thank you;" and then came a deep sigh—such a sigh!

"Or I myself?" continued the honest farmer, not at all diverted from his purpose.

"No. It's very good of you," said Patty, half crying, "and I am very much obliged—but——"

"Perhaps you'd rather George Waring should bring it?" pursued the pertinacious inquirer, with a slight change of voice. "I'll go and send him directly."

"Don't think of such a thing," interrupted Patty, breathlessly; "he's engaged."

"No," chuckled the farmer; "that business is over; Sally and he have settled the wedding-day, and I have recommended you for bridesmaid."

"Me!"

"Ay, you! One wedding leads to another. Wednesday week is to be the day; and after George Waring has given Sally to his brother Tom, he'll have an excellent opportunity for courting you."

"Tom! Tom Waring! Of whom are you speaking?"

"Of George's brother, to be sure, and Sally's beau. There he is, just come into the field. Did you never hear of Tom Waring? He only arrived from Andover last night, where Sally and he have been living next door to each other; and now they are going to marry and settle, as true lovers should. Why, what's the girl crying for?" exclaimed the good farmer, "crying and smiling, and blushing, and looking so happy! Did you think George was making love to her in his own proper person, you goosecap? Will you come to dinner now, you simpleton? you'd better, or I'll tell."

"Oh, Farmer Bridgwater!"

"Wipe your eyes and come to dinner, or I'll send George Waring to fetch you; come along, I say."

" Oh, Farmer Bridgwater ! " and off they marched ; and the next I saw of the haymakers, George and Patty were at work together, and so were Tom and Sally, looking as happy all the four as ever people could do in this world.

LOST AND FOUND

ANYBODY may be lost in a wood. It is well for me to have so good an excuse for my wanderings! for I am rather famous for such misadventures, and have sometimes been accused by my kindest friends of committing intentional blunders, and going astray out of *malice prepense*. To be sure, when in two successive rambles I contrived to get mazed on Burghfield Common, and bewildered in Kibe's Lane, those exploits did seem to overpass the common limits of stupidity. But in a wood, and a strange wood, a new place, a fresh country, untrodden ground beneath the feet, unknown land-marks before the eyes, wiser folks than I might require the silken clue of Rosamond, or the bag of ashes given to Finette Cendron (*Anglicè*, Cinderella) by the good fairy her godmother, to help them home again. Now, my luck exceeded even hers of the Glass Slipper, for I found something not unlike the good fairy herself, in the pleasant earthly guise of an old friend. But I may as well begin my story.

About two years ago we had the misfortune to lose one of the most useful and popular inhabitants of our village, Mrs. Bond, the butterwoman. She—for although there was a very honest and hard-working Farmer Bond, who had the honour to be Mrs. Bond's husband, she was so completely the personage of the family that nobody ever thought of him—she lived on a small dairy-farm at the other side of the parish, where she had reared ten children in comfort and respectability, contriving in all years and in all seasons to look and to be flourishing,

happy, and contented, and to drive her tilted cart twice
a-week into B., laden with the richest butter, the freshest
eggs, and the finest poultry of the county. Never was
market-woman so reliable as Mrs. Bond, so safe to deal
with, or so pleasant to look at. She was a neat, comely
woman of five-and-forty, or thereabout, with dark hair,
laughing eyes, a bright smile, and a brighter complexion—
red and white like a daisy. People used to say how pretty
she must have been; but I think she was then in the
prime of her good looks; just as a full-blown damask
rose is more beautiful than the same flower in the bud.

Very pleasant she was to look at, and still pleasanter
to talk to; she was so gentle, so cheerful, so respectful,
and so kind. Everybody in the village loved Mrs. Bond.
Even Lizzy and May, the two most aristocratical of its
inhabitants, and the most tenacious of the distinctions
of rank, would run to meet the butter cart as if it were a
carriage and four; a mark of preference which the good-
humoured dairywoman did not fail to acknowledge and
confirm by gifts suited to their respective tastes—an
occasional pitcher of butter-milk to May, and a stick
with cherries tied round it to poor Lizzy.

Nor was Mrs. Bond's bounty confined to largesses of
so suspicious a nature as presents to the pets of a good
customer. I have never known any human being more
thoroughly and universally generous, more delicate in her
little gifts, or with so entire an absence of design or artifice
in her attentions. It was a prodigality of kindness that
seemed never weary of well-doing. What posies of pinks
and sweet-williams, backed by marjoram and rosemary,
she used to carry to the two poor old ladies who lodged
at the pastry-cook's at B.! What faggots of lilac and
laburnum she would bring to deck the poor widow
Hay's open hearth! What baskets of water-cresses, the
brownest, the bitterest, and the crispest of the year,
for our fair neighbour, the nymph of the shoe-shop, a

delicate girl, who could only be tempted into her break-fast by that pleasant herb! What pots of honey for John Brown's cough! What gooseberries and currants for the baker's little children! And as soon as her great vine ripened, what grapes for everybody! No wonder that when Mrs. Bond left the parish to occupy a larger farm in a distant county, her absence was felt as a misfortune by the whole village; that poor Lizzy inquired after her every day for a week; and that May watched for the tilted cart every Wednesday and Friday for a month or more.

I myself joined very heartily in the general lamentation. But time and habit reconcile us to most privations, and I must confess that, much as I liked her, I had nearly forgotten our good butterwoman, until an adventure which befell me last week placed me once more in the way of her ready kindness.

I was on a visit at a considerable distance from home, in one of the most retired parts of Oxfordshire. Nothing could be more beautiful than the situation, or less accessible; shut in amongst woody hills, remote from great towns, with deep chalky roads, almost impassable, and a broad bridgeless river, coming, as if to intercept your steps, whenever you did seem to have fallen into a beaten track. It was exactly the country and the season in which to wander about all day long.

One fair morning I set out on my accustomed ramble. The sun was intensely hot; the sky almost cloudless; I had climbed a long abrupt ascent, to enjoy the sight of the magnificent river, winding like a snake amidst the richly-clothed hills; the pretty village, with its tapering spire; and the universal freshness and brilliancy of the gay and smiling prospect—too gay, perhaps! I gazed till I became dazzled with the glare of the sunshine, oppressed by the very brightness, and turned into a beech wood by the side of the road, to seek relief from the

overpowering radiance. These beech woods should rather
be called coppices. They are cut down occasionally,
and consist of long flexible stems, growing out of the old
roots. But they are like no other coppices, or rather
none other can be compared with them. The young
beechen stems, perfectly free from underwood, go arching
and intertwining overhead, forming a thousand mazy
paths, covered by a natural trellis ; the shining green
leaves, just bursting from their golden sheaths, contrasting
with the smooth silvery bark, shedding a cool green light
around, and casting a thousand dancing shadows on the
mossy flowery path, pleasant to the eye and to the tread,
a fit haunt for wood-nymph or fairy. There is always
much of interest in the mystery of a wood ; the un-
certainty produced by the confined boundary ; the
objects which crowd together, and prevent the eye from
penetrating to any distance ; the strange flickering
mixture of shadow and sunshine, the sudden flight of
birds—oh, it was enchanting ! I wandered on, quite
regardless of time or distance, now admiring the beautiful
wood-sorrel which sprang up amongst the old roots—
now plucking the fragrant wood-roof—now trying to
count the countless varieties of woodland-moss, till, at
length, roused by my foot's catching in a rich trail of the
white-veined ivy, which crept, wreathing and interlaced,
over the ground, I became aware that I was completely
lost, had entirely forsaken all track, and out-travelled
all landmarks. The wood was, I knew, extensive, and
the ground so tumbled about, that every hundred yards
presented some flowery slope or broken dell, which added
greatly to the picturesqueness of the scenery, but much
diminished my chance of discovery or extrication.

In this emergency I determined to proceed straight
onward, trusting in this way to reach at last one side
of the wood, although I could not at all guess which ;
and I was greatly solaced, after having walked about a

quarter of a mile, to find myself crossed by a rude cart track ; and still more delighted, on proceeding a short distance farther, to hear sounds of merriment and business ; none of the softest, certainly, but which gave token of rustic habitation ; and to emerge suddenly from the close wood, amongst an open grove of huge old trees, oaks with their brown-plaited leaves, cherries covered with snowy garlands, and beeches almost as gigantic as those of Windsor Park, contrasting, with their enormous trunks and majestic spread of bough, the light and flexible stems of the coppice I had left.

I had come out at one of the highest points of the wood, and now stood on a platform overlooking a scene of extraordinary beauty. A little to the right, in a very narrow valley, stood an old farm-house, with pointed roofs and porch and pinnacles, backed by a splendid orchard, which lay bathed in the sunshine, exhaling its fresh aromatic fragrance, all one flower ; just under me was a strip of rich meadow land, through which a stream ran sparkling, and directly opposite a ridge of hanging coppices, surrounding and crowning, as it were, an immense old chalk-pit, which, overhung by bramble, ivy, and a hundred pendent weeds, irregular and weather stained, had an air as venerable and romantic as some grey ruin. Seen in the gloom and stillness of evening, or by the pale glimpses of the moon, it would have required but little aid from the fancy to picture out the broken shafts and mouldering arches of some antique abbey. But, besides that daylight is the sworn enemy of such illusions, my attention was imperiously claimed by a reality of a very different kind. One of the gayest and noisiest operations of rural life—sheep-washing—was going on in the valley below—

> " the turmoil that unites
> Clamour of boys with innocent despites
> Of barking dogs, and bleatings from strange fear."
>   —WORDSWORTH.

All the inhabitants of the farm seemed assembled in the meadow. I counted a dozen, at least, of men and boys of all ages, from the stout, sunburnt, vigorous farmer of fifty, who presided over the operation, down to the eight-year old urchin, who, screaming, running, and shaking his ineffectual stick after an eloped sheep, served as a sort of aide-de-camp to the sheep-dog. What a glorious scene of confusion it was! what shouting! what scuffling! what glee! Four or five young men, and one amazon of a barefooted girl, with her petticoats tucked up to her knees, stood in the water where it was pent between two hurdles, ducking, sousing, and holding down by main force, the poor, frightened, struggling sheep, who kicked, and plunged, and bleated, and butted, and, in spite of their imputed innocence, would certainly, in the ardour of self-defence, have committed half-a-dozen homicides, if their power had equalled their inclination. The rest of the party were fully occupied ; some in conducting the purified sheep, who showed a strong disposition to go the wrong way, back to their quarters ; others in leading the uncleansed part of the flock to their destined ablution, from which they also testified a very ardent and active desire to escape. Dogs, men, boys, and girls, were engaged in marshalling these double processions, the order of which was constantly interrupted by the outbreaking of some runaway sheep, who turned the march into a pursuit, to the momentary increase of the din which seemed already to have reached the highest possible pitch.

The only quiet persons in the field were a delicate child of nine years old and a blooming woman of forty-five— a comely, blooming woman, with dark hair, bright eyes, and a complexion like a daisy, who stood watching the sheep-washers with the happiest smiles, and was evidently the mother of half the lads and lasses in the *melée*. It would be, and it was, no other than my friend Mrs. Bond, and resolving to make myself and my difficulties known to her, I scrambled down no very smooth or convenient path and keeping a gate between me and the scene of action, contrived, after sundry efforts, to attract her attention.

Here, of course, my difficulties ceased. But if I were to tell how glad she was to see her old neighbour, how full of kind questions and of hospitable cares—how she would cut the great cake intended for the next day's sheep-shearing, would tap her two-year-old currant wine, would gather a whole bush of early honeysuckles, and finally would see me home herself, I being, as she observed, rather given to losing my way—if I were to tell all these things, when should I have done ? I will rather conclude in the words of an old French fairy tale :—" *Je crains déjà d'avoir abusé de la patience du lecteur. Je finis avant qu'il me dise de finir.*"

THE OLD GIPSY

We have few gipsies in our neighbourhood. In spite
of our tempting green lanes, our woody dells and healthy
commons, the rogues don't take to us. I am afraid that
we are too civilised, too cautious ; that our sheep-folds
are too closely watched ; our barn-yards too well guarded ;
our geese and ducks too fastly penned ; our chickens
too securely locked up ; our little pigs too safe in their
sty ; our game too scarce ; our laundresses too careful.
In short, we are too little primitive ; we have a snug
brood of vagabonds and poachers of our own, to say
nothing of their regular followers, constables and justices
of the peace :—we have stocks in the village, and a tread-
mill in the next town ; and therefore we go gipsyless—
a misfortune of which every landscape painter, and every
lover of that living landscape, the country, can appreciate
the extent. There is nothing under the sun that har-
monises so well with nature, especially in her woodland
recesses, as that picturesque people, who are, so to say,
the wild genus—the pheasants and roebucks of the human
race.

Sometimes, indeed, we used to see a gipsy procession
passing along the common, like an eastern caravan, men,
women, and children, donkeys and dogs ; and sometimes a patch of bare earth, strewed with ashes and
surrounded with scathed turf, on the broad green margin
of some cross road, would give token of a gipsy halt ; but
a regular gipsy encampment has always been so rare an
event, that I was equally surprised and delighted to
meet with one in the course of my walks last autumn,

particularly as the party was of the most innocent description, quite free from those tall, dark, lean, Spanish-looking men, who it must be confessed, with all my predilection for the caste, are rather startling to meet when alone in an unfrequented path : and a path more solitary than that into which the beauty of a bright October morning had tempted me could not well be imagined.

Branching off from the high road, a little below our village, runs a wide green lane, bordered on either side by a row of young oaks and beeches just within the hedge, forming an avenue, in which, on a summer afternoon, you may see the squirrels disporting from tree to tree, whilst the rooks, their fellow denizens, are wheeling in noisy circles over their heads. The fields sink gently down on each side, so that, being the bottom of a natural winding valley, and crossed by many little hills and rivulets, the turf exhibits even in the dryest summers an emerald verdure. Scarcely any one passes the end of that lane without wishing to turn into it ; but the way is in some sort dangerous and difficult for foot passengers, because the brooklets which intersect it are in many instances bridgeless, and in others bestridden by planks so decayed that it were rashness to pass them ; and the nature of the ground treacherous and boggy, and in many places as unstable as water, renders it for carriages wholly impracticable.

I however, who do not dislike a little difficulty where there is no absolute danger, and who am moreover almost as familiar with the one only safe track as the heifers who graze there, sometimes venture along this seldom-trodden path, which terminates, at the end of a mile and a half, in a spot of singular beauty. The hills become abrupt and woody, the cultivated enclosures cease, and the long narrow valley ends in a little green, bordered on one side by a fine old park, whose mossy paling, overhung with thorns and hollies, comes sweeping round it, to meet

the rich coppices which clothe the opposite acclivity.
Just under the high and irregular paling, shaded by the
birches and sycamores of the park, and by the venerable
oaks which are scattered irregularly on the green, is a
dark deep pool, whose broken banks, crowned with fern
and wreathed with brier and bramble, have an air of
wildness and grandeur that might have suited the pencil
of Salvator Rosa.

In this lonely place (for the mansion to which the park
belongs has long been uninhabited) I first saw our gipsies.
They had pitched their tent under one of the oak trees,
perhaps from a certain dim sense of natural beauty,
which those who live with nature in the fields are seldom
totally without; perhaps because the neighbourhood of
the coppices, and of the deserted hall, was favourable to
the acquisition of game, and of the little fuel which their
hardy habits required.   The party consisted only of four—
an old crone, in a tattered red cloak and black bonnet,
who was stooping over a kettle, of which the contents
were probably as savoury as that of Meg Merrilees, renowned in story ; a pretty black-eyed girl, at work under
the trees ; a sun-burnt urchin of eight or nine, collecting
sticks and dead leaves to feed their out-of door fire, and
a slender lad two or three years older, who lay basking
in the sun, with a couple of shabby dogs, of the sort called
mongrel, in all the joy of idleness, whilst a grave, patient
donkey stood grazing hard-by.   It was a pretty picture,
with its soft autumnal sky, its rich woodiness, its sunshine,
its verdure, the light smoke curling from the fire, and the
group disposed around it so harmless, poor outcasts !
and so happy—a beautiful picture ! I stood gazing on
it till I was half ashamed to look longer, and came
away half afraid that they should depart before I could
see them again.

This fear I soon found to be groundless. The old
gipsy was a celebrated fortune-teller, and the post having

been so long vacant, she could not have brought her talents to a better market. The whole village rang with the predictions of this modern Cassandra—unlike her Trojan predecessor, inasmuch as her prophecies were never of evil. I myself could not help admiring the real cleverness, the genuine gipsy tact with which she adapted her fore-tellings to the age, the habits, and the known desires and circumstances of her clients.

To our little pet, Lizzy, for instance, a damsel of seven, she predicted a fairing; to Ben Kirby, a youth of thirteen, head batter of the boys, a new cricket-ball; to Ben's sister Lucy, a girl some three years his senior, and just pro-moted to that ensign of womanhood a cap, she promised a pink top-knot; whilst for Miss Sophia Matthews, our old-maidish schoolmistress, who would be heartily glad to be a girl again, she foresaw one handsome husband, and for the smart widow Simmons, two. These were the least of her triumphs. George Davis, the dashing young farmer of the hill-house, a gay sportsman, who scoffed at fortune-tellers and matrimony, consulted her as to whose greyhound would win the courser's cup at the beacon meeting: to which she replied, that she did not know to whom the dog would belong, but that the winner of the cup would be a white greyhound, with one blue ear, and a spot on its side, being an exact description of Mr. George Davis's favourite Helen, who followed her master's steps like his shadow, and was standing behind him at this very instant. This prediction gained our gipsy half-a-crown. And Master Welles—the thriving, thrifty yeoman of the Lea—she managed to win sixpence from his hard, honest, frugal hand, by a prophecy that his old brood mare, called Blackfoot, should bring forth twins. And Ned the blacksmith, who was known to court the tall nursemaid at the mill—she got a shilling from Ned, simply by assuring him that his wife should have the longest coffin that ever was made in our wheelwright's shop. A most tempting prediction! ingeniously combining the prospect of winning and of surviving the lady of his heart—a promise equally adapted to the hot and cold fits of that ague called love; lightening the fetters of wedlock; uniting in a breath the bridegroom and the widower. Ned was the best pleased of all her customers, and enforced his suit with such vigour, that he and the fair giantess were asked in church the next Sunday, and married at the fortnight's end.

No wonder that all the world—that is to say, all our world—were crazy to have their fortunes told—to enjoy the pleasure of hearing from such undoubted authority that what they wished to be should be. Amongst the most eager to take a peep into futurity was our pretty maid Harriet, although her desire took the not unusual form of disclamation—"Nothing should induce her to have her fortune told, nothing upon earth! She never thought of the gipsy, not she!" and, to prove the fact, she said so at least twenty times a day. Now Harriet's fortune seemed told already; her destiny was fixed. She, the belle of the village, was engaged, as everybody knows, to our village beau, Joel Brent; they were only waiting for a little more money to marry; and as Joel was already head carter to our head farmer, and had some prospect of a bailiff's place, their union did not appear very distant. But Harriet, besides being a beauty, was a coquette, and her affection for her betrothed did not interfere with certain flirtations which came in like Isabella, "by-the-bye," and occasionally cast a shadow of coolness between the lovers, which, however, Joel's cleverness and good-humour generally contrived to chase away. There had probably been a little fracas in the present instance, for at the end of one of her daily professions of unfaith in gipsies and their predictions, she added, "that none but fools did believe them; that Joel had had his fortune told, and wanted to treat her to a prophecy—but she was not such a simpleton."

About an hour after the delivery of this speech, I happened, in tying up a chrysanthemum, to go to our wood-yard for a stick of proper dimensions, and there, enclosed between the faggot-pile and the coal-shed, stood the gipsy, in the very act of palmistry, conning the lines of fate in Harriet's hand. Never was a stronger contrast than that between the old withered sibyl, dark as an Egyptian, with bright laughing eyes, and an expression of keen humour under all her affected solemnity, and our village beauty, tall and plump and fair, blooming as a rose, and simple as a dove. She was listening too intently to see me, but the fortune-teller did, and stopped so suddenly that her attention was awakened, and the intruder discovered.

Harriet at first meditated a denial. She called up a pretty innocent unconcerned look ; answered my silence (for I never spoke a word) by muttering something about "coals for the parlour"; and catching up my new-painted green watering-pot, instead of the coal-scuttle, began filling it with all her might, to the unspeakable discomfiture of that useful utensil, on which the dingy dust stuck like birdlime—and of her own clean apron, which exhibited a curious interchange of black and green on a white ground. During the process of filling the watering-pot, Harriet made divers signs to the gipsy to decamp. The old sibyl, however, budged not a foot, influenced probably by two reasons—one, the hope of securing a customer in the new-comer, whose appearance is generally, I am afraid, the very reverse of dignified, rather merry than wise ; the other, a genuine fear of passing through the yard-gate, on the outside of which a much more imposing person, my greyhound May-flower, who has a sort of beadle instinct anent drunkards and pilferers, and disorderly persons of all sorts, stood barking most furiously.

This instinct is one of May's remarkable qualities.

Dogs are all, more or less, physiognomists, and commonly pretty determined aristocrats, fond of the fine and averse to the shabby, distinguishing, with a nice accuracy, the master castes from the pariahs of the world. But May's power of perception is another matter, more, as it were, moral. She has no objection to honest rags ; can away with dirt, or age, or ugliness, or any such accident, and, except just at home, makes no distinction between kitchen and parlour. Her intuition points entirely to the race of people commonly called suspicious, on whom she pounces at a glance. What a constable she would have made ! What a jewel of a thief-taker ! Pity that those four feet should stand in the way of her preferment ! she might have risen to be a Bow Street officer. As it is we make the gift useful in a small way. In the matter of hiring and marketing the whole village likes to consult May. Many a chap has stared when she has been whistled up to give her opinion as to his honesty ; and many a pig bargain has gone off on her veto. Our neighbour, mine host of the Rose, used constantly to follow her judgment in the selection of his lodgers. His house was never so orderly as when under her government. At last he found out that she abhorred tipplers as well as thieves—indeed, she actually barked away three of his best customers : and he left off appealing to her sagacity, since which he has, at different times, lost three silver spoons and a leg of mutton. With every one else May is an oracle. Not only in the case of wayfarers and vagrants, but amongst our own people, her fancies are quite a touchstone. A certain hump-backed cobbler, for instance—May cannot abide him, and I don't think he has had so much as a job of heel-piecing to do since her dislike became public. She really took away his character.

Longer than I have taken to relate Mayflower's accomplishments stood we, like the folks in *The Critic*, at a dead lock ; May, who probably regarded the gipsy as a sort of rival, an interloper on her oracular domain, barking with the voice of a lioness—the gipsy trying to persuade me into having my fortune told—and I endeavouring to prevail on May to let the gipsy pass. Both attempts were unsuccessful : and the fair consulter of destiny, who had by this time recovered from the shame of her detection, extricated us from our dilemma by smuggling the old woman away through the house.

Of course Harriet was exposed to some raillery, and a good deal of questioning about her future fate, as to which she preserved an obstinate but evidently satisfied silence. At the end of three days, however—my readers are, I hope, learned enough in gipsy lore to know, that unless kept secret for three entire days, no prediction can come true—at the end of three days, when all the family except herself had forgotten the story, our pretty soubrette, half bursting with the long retention, took the opportunity of lacing on my new half-boots to reveal the prophecy. " She was to see within the week, and this was Saturday, the young man, the real young man, whom she was to marry."—" Why, Harriet, you know poor Joel."—" Joel, indeed ! the gipsy said that the young man, the real young man, was to ride up to the house dressed in a dark great-coat (and Joel never wore a great-coat in his life—all the world knew that he wore smock-frocks and jackets), and mounted on a white horse—and where should Joel get a white horse ? "— " Had this real young man made his appearance yet ? " —" No ; there had not been a white horse past the place since Tuesday ; so it must certainly be to-day."

A good look-out did Harriet keep for white horses during this fateful Saturday, and plenty did she see. It was the market-day at B., and team after team came by with one, two, and three white horses ; cart after cart, and gig after gig, each with a white steed : Colonel M.'s carriage, with its prancing pair—but still no horseman. At length one appeared; but he had a great-coat whiter than the animal he rode; another, but he was old farmer Lewington, a married man; a third, but he was little Lord L., a schoolboy, on his Arabian pony. Besides, they all passed the house; and as the day wore on, Harriet began, alternately, to possess her old infidelity on the score of fortune-telling, and to let out certain apprehensions that, if the gipsy did really possess the power of foreseeing events, and no such horseman arrived, she might possibly be unlucky enough to die an old maid—a fate for which, although the proper destiny of a coquette, our village beauty seemed to entertain a very decided aversion.

At last, at dusk, just as Harriet, making believe to close our casement shutters, was taking her last peep up the road, something white appeared in the distance coming leisurely down the hill. Was it really a horse? Was it not rather Titus Strong's cow driving home to milking? A minute or two dissipated that fear; it certainly was a horse, and as certainly it had a dark rider. Very slowly he descended the hill, pausing most provokingly at the end of the village, as if about to turn up the Vicarage lane. He came on, however, and after another short stop at the Rose, rode up full to our little gate, and catching Harriet's hand as she was opening the wicket, displayed to the half-pleased, half-angry damsel, the smiling, triumphant face of her own Joel Brent, equipped in a new great-coat, and mounted on his master's newly purchased market nag. Oh, Joel! Joel! The gipsy! the gipsy!

THE YOUNG GIPSY

THE weather continuing fine and dry, I did not fail to revisit my gipsy encampment, which became more picturesque every day in the bright sun-gleams and lengthening shadows of a most brilliant autumn. A slight frost had strewed the green lane with the light yellow leaves of the elm—those leaves on whose yielding crispness it is so pleasant to tread, and which it is so much pleasanter to watch whirling along, "thin dancers upon air," in the fresh October breeze ; whilst the reddened beech, and spotted sycamore, and the rich oaks drooping with acorns, their foliage just edging into its deep orange brown, added all the magic of colour to the original beauty of the scenery. It was undoubtedly the prettiest walk in the neighbourhood, and the one which I frequented the most.

Ever since the adventure of May, the old fortune-teller and I understood each other perfectly. She knew that I was no client, no patient, no customer (which is the fittest name for a goosecap who goes to a gipsy to ask what is to befall her ?), but she also knew that I was no enemy to either her or her profession ; for, after all, if people choose to amuse themselves by being simpletons, it is no part of their neighbours' business to hinder them. I, on my side, liked the old gipsy exceedingly ; I liked both her humour and her good-humour, and had a real respect for her cleverness. We always interchanged a smile and a nod, meet where we might. May, too, had become accustomed to the whole party. The gift of a bone from the cauldron—a bare bone—your well-fed dog likes nothing so well as such a windfall, and if stolen the relish is higher—a bare bone brought about that reconciliation. I am sorry to accuse May of accepting a bribe, but such was the fact. She now looked at the fortune-teller with great complacency, would let the boys stroke her long neck, and, in her turn, would condescend to frolic with their shabby curs, who, trained to a cat-like caution and mistrust of their superiors, were as much alarmed at her advances as if a lioness had offered herself as their playfellow. There was no escaping her civility, however, so they submitted to their fate, and really seemed astonished to find themselves alive when the gambol was over. One of them, who from a tail turned over his back like a squirrel, and an amazingly snub nose, had certainly some mixture of the pug in his composition, took a great fancy to her when his fright was past; which she repaid by the sort of scornful kindness, the despotic protection, proper to her as a beauty, and a favourite, and a high-blooded greyhound—always a most proud and stately creature. The poor little mongrel used regularly to come jumping to meet her, and she as regularly turned him over and over and over, and round and round and round, like a teetotum. He liked it apparently, for he never failed to come and court the tossing whenever she went near him.

The person most interesting to me of the whole party was the young girl. She was remarkably pretty, and of the peculiar prettiness which is so frequently found amongst that singular people. Her face resembled those which Sir Joshua has often painted—rosy, round, and bright, set in such a profusion of dark curls, lighted by such eyes, and such a smile! and she smiled whenever you looked at her—she could not help it. Her figure was light and small, of low stature, and with an air of great youthfulness. In her dress she was, for a gipsy, surprisingly tidy. For the most part, that ambulatory

race have a preference for rags, as forming their most
appropriate wardrobe, being a part of their tools of
trade, their insignia of office. I do not imagine that
Harriet's friend, the fortune-teller, would have exchanged
her stained tattered cloak for the thickest and brightest
red cardinal that ever came out of a woollen-draper's
shop. And she would have been a loser if she had.
Take away that mysterious mantle, and a great part
of her reputation would go too. There is much virtue
in an old cloak. I question if the simplest of her clients,
even Harriet herself, would have consulted her in a new
one. But the young girl was tidy ; not only accurately
clean, and with clothes neatly and nicely adjusted to her
trim little form, but with the rents darned, and the holes
patched, in a way that I should be glad to see equalled
by our own villagers.

Her manners were quite as ungipsy-like as her apparel,
and so was her conversation ; for I could not help talking
to her, and was much pleased with her frankness and
innocence, and the directness and simplicity of her
answers. She was not the least shy ; on the contrary,
there was a straightforward look, a fixing of her sweet
eyes full of pleasure and reliance right upon you, which, in
the description, might seem almost too assured, but which,
in reality, no more resembled vulgar assurance than
did the kindred artlessness of Shakespeare's Miranda. It
seems strange to liken a gipsy girl to that loveliest creation
of genius ; but I never saw that innocent gaze without
being sure that just with such a look of pleased attention,
of affectionate curiosity, did the island princess listen to
Ferdinand.

All that she knew of her little story she told without
scruple, in a young liquid voice, and with a little curtesy
between every answer, that became her extremely.
" Her name," she said, " was Fanny. She had no father
or mother ; they were dead ; and she and her brothers

lived with her grandmother. They lived always out of doors, sometimes in one place—sometimes in another; but she should like always to live under that oak tree, it was so pleasant. Her grandmother was very good to them all, only rather particular. She loved her very much; and she loved Dick (her eldest brother), though he was a sad unlucky boy, to be sure. She was afraid he would come to some bad end."

And, indeed, Dick at that moment seemed in imminent danger of verifying his sister's prediction. He had been trying for a gleaning of nuts amongst the tall hazels on the top of a bank, which, flanked by a deep ditch, separated the coppice from the green. We had heard him for the last five minutes smashing and crashing away at a prodigious rate, swinging himself from stalk to stalk, and tugging and climbing like a sailor or a monkey; and now, at the very instant of Fanny's uttering this prophecy, having missed a particularly venturesome grasp, he was impelled forward by the rebound of the branches, and fell into the ditch with a tremendous report, bringing half the nuttery after him, and giving us all a notion that he had broken his neck. His time, however, was not yet come; he was on his feet again in half a minute, and in another half minute we again heard him rustling among the hazel boughs; and Fanny and I went on with our talk, which the fright and scolding, consequent on this accident, had interrupted. My readers are of course aware that when any one meets with a fall, the approved medicament of the most affectionate relatives is a good dose of scolding.

"She liked Dick," she continued, "in spite of his unluckiness—he was so quick and good-humoured; but the person she loved most was her youngest brother, Willy. Willy was the best boy in the world, he would do anything she told him" (indeed the poor child was in the very act of picking up acorns under her inspection, to sell, as I afterwards found, in the village), "and never got into mischief, or told a lie in his life ; she had had the care of him ever since he was born, and she wished she could get him a place." By this time the little boy had crept towards us, and, still collecting the acorns in his small brown hands, had turned up his keen intelligent face, and was listening with great interest to our conversation. "A place ! " said I, much surprised. "Yes," replied she firmly, "a place. 'Twould be a fine thing for my poor Willy to have a house over him in the cold winter nights." And with a grave tenderness, that might have beseemed a young mother, she stooped her head over the boy and kissed him. "But *you* sleep out of doors in the cold winter nights, Fanny ? "—"Me ! oh, I don't mind it, and sometimes we creep into a barn. But poor Willy ! If I could but get Willy a place, my lady ! "

This "my lady," the first gipsy word that Fanny had uttered, lost all that it would have had of unpleasing in the generosity and affectionateness of the motive. I could not help promising to recommend her Willy, although I could not hold out any very strong hopes of success, and we parted, Fanny following me, with thanks upon thanks, almost to the end of the lane.

Two days after I again saw my pretty gipsy ; she was standing by the side of our gate, too modest even to enter the court, waiting for my coming out to speak to me. I brought her into the hall, and was almost equally delighted to see her, and to hear her news ; for although I had most faithfully performed my promise, by mentioning Master Willy to everybody likely to want a servant of his qualifications, I had seen enough in the course of my canvass to convince me that a gipsy boy of eight years old would be a difficult *protégé* to provide for.

Fanny's errand relieved my perplexity. She came to tell me that Willy had gotten a place—"That Thomas Lamb, my lord's head gamekeeper, had hired him to tend his horse and his cow, and serve the pigs, and feed the dogs, and dig the garden, and clean the shoes and knives, and run on errands—in short, to be a man of all work. Willy was gone that very morning. He had cried to part with her, and she had almost cried herself, she should miss him so ; he was like her own child. But then it was such a great place ; and Thomas Lamb seemed such a kind master—talked of new clothing him, and meant him to wear shoes and stockings, and was very kind indeed. But poor Willy had cried sadly at leaving her,"—and the sweet matronly elder sister fairly cried too.

I comforted her all I could, first by praises of Thomas Lamb, who happened to be of my acquaintance, and was indeed the very master whom, had I had the choice, I would have selected for Willy ; and secondly, by the gift of some unconsidered trifles, which one should have been ashamed to offer to any one who had ever had a house over her head, but which the pretty gipsy girl received with transport, especially some working materials of the commonest sort. Poor Fanny had never known the luxury of a thimble before ; it was as new to her finger as shoes and stockings were likely to be to Willy's feet. She forgot her sorrows, and tripped home to her oak-tree, the happiest of the happy.

Thomas Lamb, Willy's new master, was, as I have said, of my acquaintance. He was a remarkably fine young man, and as well-mannered as those of his calling usually are. Generally speaking, there are no persons, excepting real gentlemen, so gentlemanly as gamekeepers. They keep good company. The beautiful and graceful creatures whom they at once preserve and pursue, and the equally noble and generous animals whom they train, are their principal associates ; and even by their masters they are regarded rather as companions than as servants. They attend them in their sports more as

guides and leaders than as followers, pursuing a common
recreation with equal enjoyment, and often with superior
skill.   Gamekeepers are almost always well behaved, and
Thomas Lamb was eminently so.   He had quite the
look of a man of fashion ; the person, the carriage, the
air.   His figure was tall and striking ; his features
delicately carved, with a paleness of complexion, and a
slight appearance of ill-health that added to their elegance.
In short, he was exactly what the ladies would have called
interesting in a gentleman ; and the gentleness of his
voice and manner, and the constant propriety of his
deportment, tended to confirm the impression.

Luckily for him, however, this delicacy and refinement
lay chiefly on the surface.   His constitution, habits, and
temper were much better fitted to his situation much
hardier and heartier, than they appeared to be.   He was
still a bachelor, and lived by himself in a cottage, almost
as lonely as if it had been placed in a desert island.   It
stood in the centre of his preserves, in the midst of a
wilderness of coppice and woodland, accessible only by a
narrow winding path, and at least a mile from the nearest
habitation.   When you have threaded the labyrinth,
and were fairly arrived in Thomas's dominion, it was a
pretty territory.   A low thatched cottage, very irregularly built, with a porch before the door, and a vine
half covering the casements ; a garden a good deal
neglected, (Thomas Lamb's four-footed subjects, the
hares, took care to eat up all his flowers :· hares are
animals of taste, and are particularly fond of pinks
and carnations, the rogues !) an orchard, and a meadow
completed the demesne.   There was also a commodious
dog-kennel, and a stable, of which the outside was
completely covered with the trophies of Thomas's industry—kites, jackdaws, magpies, hawks, crows, and
owls, nailed by the wings, *displayed*, as they say in
heraldry, against the wall, with polecats, weasels, stoats,

and hedgehogs figuring at their side, a perfect menagerie of dead game-killers.*

But the prettiest part of this woodland cottage was the real living game that flitted about it, as tame as barn-door fowls ; partridges flocking to be fed, as if there were not a dog, or a gun, or a man in the world ; pheasants, glorious creatures ! coming at a call ; hares almost as fearless as Cowper's, that would stand and let you look at them : would let you approach quite near, before they raised one quivering ear and darted off ; and that even then, when the instinct of timidity was aroused, would turn at a safe distance to look again.

Such was to be Willy's future habitation. The day after he entered upon his place, I had an opportunity of offering my double congratulations, to the master on his new servant, to the servant on his new master. Whilst taking my usual walk, I found Thomas Lamb, Dick, Willy, and Fanny, about half-way up the lane, engaged in the animating sport of unearthing a weasel, which one of the gipsy dogs followed into a hole by the ditch-side. The boys showed great sportsmanship on this occasion : and so did their poor curs, who, with their whole bodies inserted into the different branches of the burrow, and nothing visible but their tails (the one, the long puggish brush, of which I have already made mention, the other a terrier-like stump, that maintained an incessant wag), continued to dig and scratch, throwing out showers of earth, and whining with impatience and eagerness. Every now and then, when quite gasping and exhausted, they came out for a moment's air ; whilst the boys took their turn, poking with a long stick, or loosening the

* Foxes, the destruction of which is so great an object in a pheasant preserve, never are displayed, especially if there be a pack of hounds in the neighbourhood. That odious part of a gamekeeper's occupation is as quietly and unostentatiously performed as any operation of gunnery can be. Lords of manors will even affect to preserve foxes—Heaven forgive them ! just as an unpopular ministry is sure to talk of protecting the liberty of the subject.

ground with their hands, and Thomas stood by, superintending and encouraging both dog and boy, and occasionally cutting a root or a bramble that impeded their
progress. Fanny also entered into the pursuit with
great interest, dropping here and there a word of advice,
as nobody can help doing when they see others in perplexity.   In spite of all these aids, the mining operation
proceeded so slowly, that the experienced keeper sent off
his new attendant for a spade to dig out the vermin,
and I pursued my walk.

After this encounter, it so happened that I never went
near the gipsy tent without meeting Thomas Lamb—
sometimes on foot, sometimes on his pony ; now with a
gun, and now without ; but always loitering near the
oak-tree, and always, as it seemed, reluctant to be seen.
It was very unlike Thomas's usual manner to seem
ashamed of being caught in any place, or in any company ;
but so it was. Did he go to the ancient sibyl to get his
fortune told ? or was Fanny the attraction ? A very
short time solved the query.

One night, towards the end of the month, the keeper
presented himself at our house on justice business. He
wanted a summons for some poachers who had been
committing depredations in the preserve. Thomas was
a great favourite ; and was of course immediately admitted, his examination taken, and his request complied
with. "But how," said the magistrate, looking up
from the summons which he was signing, " how can you
expect, Thomas, to keep your pheasants, when that
gipsy boy with his finders has pitched his tent just in
the midst of your best coppices, killing more game than
half the poachers in the country ? "—" Why, as to the
gipsy, sir," replied Thomas ; " Fanny is as good a
girl——" " I was not talking of Fanny," interrupted
the man of warrants, smiling,—" as good a girl," pursued
Thomas—" A very pretty girl ! " ejaculated his worship,

—" as good a girl," resumed Thomas, " as ever trod the earth ! "—" A sweet, pretty creature, certainly," was again the provoking reply. " Ah, sir, if you could but hear how her little brother talks of her ! "—" Why, Thomas, this gipsy has made an impression."—" Ah, sir ! she is such a good girl ! "—and the next day they were married.

It was a measure to set every tongue in the village a-wagging ; for Thomas, besides his personal good gifts, was well-to-do in the world—my lord's head keeper, and prime favourite. He might have pretended to any farmer's daughter in the parish : everybody cried out against the match. It was rather a bold measure, certainly ; but I think it will end well. They are, beyond a doubt, the handsomest couple in these parts ; and as the fortune-teller and her eldest grandson have had the good sense to decamp, and Fanny, besides being the most grateful and affectionate creature on earth, turns out clever and docile, and comports herself just as if she had lived in a house all her days, there are some hopes that in process of time her sin of gipsyism may be forgiven, and Mrs. Lamb be considered as visitable, at least by her next neighbours, the wives of the shoemaker and the parish clerk. At present, I am sorry to say that those worthy persons have sent both Thomas and her to Coventry—a misfortune which they endure with singular resignation.

OLD MASTER GREEN

A VILLAGE SKETCH

A PARTICULAR sort of mould, which in this county is scarcely to be found except in the tract of land called Chittling Moor, being wanted to form a compost for that very dear part of my small possessions, my beautiful geraniums, we determined to accompany, or rather to follow, in our pretty pony phaeton, the less aristocratic *cortège*, consisting of two boys with wheelbarrows, and old Master Green with a donkey-cart, who had been despatched to collect it some two hours before.

The day was one of the latest in August, and the weather splendidly beautiful, clear, bright, breezy, sunny. It would have been called too warm by one half of the world, and by the other too cold, which I take to be as near an approach to perfection as our climate, or any climate, can well compass. We had been sitting in our large parlour-like greenhouse; a superb fuchsia, bending with the weight of its own blossoms, reaching almost to the top of the house, on one side of the door, and a splendid campanula, with five distinct stems, covered with large yet delicate lilac bells, on the other; the rich balmy scent of the campanula blending with the exquisite odours of tuberoses, jessamine, mignonette, full-blown myrtles, and the honey-sweet clematis, and looking out on gay beds of the latest flowers, China-asters, dahlias, hydrangeas blue and pink, phlox white and purple, the scarlet lobelia, and the scarlet geranium. In short, all within my little garden was autumn, beautiful autumn.

On the other side of our cottage the season seemed to have changed. The China roses and honeysuckles, with which it is nearly covered, were in the profuse bloom of early June, and the old monthly rose by the door-way, (the sweetest of roses !) together with a cluster of sweet-peas that grew among its branches, were literally smelling of summer. The quantity of rain that had fallen had preserved the trees in their most vivid freshness, and the herbage by the roadside and the shorter turf on the common had all the tender verdure of spring.

As we advanced, however, through the narrow lanes, autumn and harvest reasserted their rights. Every here and there, at the corners where branches jutted out, and in the straits where the hedges closed in together, loose straws of oats and barley, torn from their different waggons, hung dangling from the boughs, mixed with straggling locks of hay, the relics of the after-crop. We ourselves were fain to drive into a ditch, to take shelter from a dingy procession of bean-carriers. My companion, provoked at the ditchy indignity, which his horse relished no better than himself, asserted that the beans could not be fit to carry ; but, to judge from the rattling and crackling which the huge black sheaves made in their transit, especially when the loaded wain was jerked a little on one side, to avoid entirely driving over our light and grace-ful open carriage, which it overtopped, and threatened to crush, as the giant in the fairy tale threatens Tom Thumb—to judge by that noisy indication of ripeness, ripe they were. The hedge-rows too gave abundant proofs in their own vegetation of the advancing season. The fragrant hazel-nuts were hardening in their shells, and tempting the school-boy's hand by their swelling clusters ; the dewberries were colouring ; the yellow St. John's wort, and the tall mealy-leaved mullein, had succeeded the blush-ing bells of the foxglove, which, despoiled of its crimson beauty, now brandished its long spikes of seed-vessels upon the bank, above which the mountain-ash waved its scarlet berries in all the glory of autumn; whilst, as we emerged from the close narrow lanes into the open tract of Hartley Common, patches of purple heath just bursting into flower, and the gorse and broom pushing forth fresh blossom under the influence of the late rainy weather, waved over the light harebell, the fragrant thyme, and the springing fungi of the season. In short, the whole of our Berkshire world, as well as that very dear and very tiny bit of it called my garden, spoke of autumn, beautiful autumn, the best if not the only time for a visit to the Chittling Moor.

These Moors were pretty much what the word commonly indicates, a long level tract of somewhat swampy pasture land, extending along the margin of the Kennet, which, in other parts so beautiful, rolled heavily and lazily through its abundant, but somewhat coarse, herbage; a dreary and desolate place when compared with the general scenery of our richly-wooded and thickly-peopled country, and one where the eye, wandering over the dull expanse, unbroken by hill, or hedge, or timber tree, conveyed, as is often the case in flat, barren, and desolate scenes, an idea of space more than commensurate with the actual extent.

The divisions of this large piece of ground are formed of wide ditches, which at once serve to drain and to irrigate these marshy moors, so frequently over-flowed by the river in spring and winter, and sometimes even in summer; it being no unusual catastrophe for the coarse and heavy crops to be carried away by a sudden flood, disappointing the hopes of the farmer, and baffling the efforts of the haymaker. A weary thing was a wet summer in the Chittling Moor, with the hay-field one day a swamp and the next a lake; and the hay, or rather the poor drowned grass, that should have been hay, choking the ditches, or sailing down the stream! The best that could befall it was to be carried off in waggons in its grassy shape, and made comfortably and snugly on dry ground, in some upland meadow; but people cannot always find room for the outer integuments of three hundred acres of grass land, and, besides that difficulty, the intersecting ditches, with their clattering, hollow-sounding wooden bridges, presented no ordinary peril to the heavy wains, so that the landlord was fain to put up with little rent, and the farmer with small profit—too happy if the subsequent grazing paid the charge or the loss of the prolonged and often fruitless hay-harvest.

A dreary scene was the Chittling Moor; a few old willow pollards, the most melancholy of trees, formed the sole break to its dull uniformity, and one small dwelling, whose curling smoke rose in the distance above a clustering orchard, was the only sign of human habitation. This small cottage had been built chiefly to suit the circumstances of the Moor, which rendered a public-house necessary during the long hay-making; and it was kept by a widow, who contrived to make the profits of that watery but drouthy season pay for the want of custom during the rest of the year. Not that the Widow Knight was absolutely without customers at any period; the excellence and celebrity of her home-brewed having insured to her a certain number of customers, who, especially on Sundays, used to walk down to the Chittling Gate (so was her domicile entitled) to partake of the luxuries of a pipe and a pot of ale, scream to the deaf widow, gossip with her comely daughter, or flirt with her pretty grandchild (for the whole establishment was female), as their several ages or dispositions might prompt.

Of this number none was more constant than our present attendant, old Master Green, and it is by no means certain whether his familiarity with the banks and pollards which afforded the true geranium mould may not have been acquired by his hebdomadal visits to the Widow Knight's snug and solitary ale-house.

Old George Green was indeed a veteran of the tap-room, one to whom strong beer had been for nearly seventy years the best friend and the worst enemy, making him happy and keeping him poor. He called himself eighty-five; and I presume, from the report of other people, as well as his own (for when approaching that age, vanity generally takes the turn of making itself older), that he might really be past fourscore. A wonderful man he was of his years, both in appearance and constitution. Hard work had counteracted the ill effects of hard drinking, as an equal quantity of labour, under the form of hard riding, sometimes used to do by a jovial fox-hunting squire of former times, and had kept him light, vigorous, and active, as little bent or stiffened by age as the two boys who were delving out the earth under his direction. The only visible mark which age had set upon him—mark, did I say? a brand, a fire-brand—was in his nose, which was of the true Bardolphian size and colour, and a certain roll of the eye, which might perhaps, under any circum stances, have belonged to the man and his humour, but which much resembled that of a toper, when half-tipsy, and fancying himself particularly wise.

The very Nestor of village topers was Master Green, hearty, good-humoured, merry, and jolly, very civil, and a little sly. He was quite patriarchal in the number of his descendants, having had the Mahommedan allow-ance of four wives, although, after the Christian fashion, successively, and more children and grandchildren than he could conveniently count. Indeed, his computation varied a little, according as he happened to be drunk or sober; for he was proud of his long train of descendants, just as his betters may be proud of a long line of ancestry; and, being no disciple of the Malthusian doctrine, thought he " had done the state " (that is, the parish) " some service," in rearing up a goodly tribe of sons and daughters, many of them in their turn grandfathers and grandmothers, and most of whom had conducted themselves passably in the world, as times go—thanks probably to a circumstance which he sometimes lamented, their being, men and women, but puny tipplers compared with their jolly progenitor. Even his favourite grandson and namesake, only son and heir of the most prosperous of his innumerous family, Master Green, the thriving carpenter of East Hartley, who, like a dutiful lad, came every Sunday afternoon to the Chittling Gate to meet his grandfather, abandoning for that purpose the cricket-ground at Hartley, where he, a singularly fine young man, had long been accounted the best player—even this favourite grandson was, he declared, little better than a milk-sop, a swallower of tea and soda-water. "I verily believe," said Master Green, "that a pot of double X would upset him!"

A friend and a promoter of matrimony in all its shapes, especially in a guise of a love-match, was our worthy great-grandfather, whether in his own person, or in the person of his descendants. Four wives had he had of happy memory, and he spoke of them all with mingled affection and philosophy, as good sort of women in the main, though the first was somewhat of a slut, the second ugly, the third silly, and the last a scold, which, as he observed, "might be one reason that he missed her so much, poor woman! the house seemed so quiet and *unked*; "—whereupon he sighed, and then, with a roll of his eye and a knowing twist of his Bardolphian nose, began to talk of the necessity of his looking out for a fifth helpmate.

By this time the operation of collecting the geranium mould was in full activity; and the conversation of the old man and the two lively boys, to which we were authorised listeners, and in which my companion soon became an interlocutor, gave us to understand that they

were in possession of some further information respecting
Master Green's matrimonial intentions.

"We all know why he goes to the Chittling Gate every
Sunday," said Ben, an arch saucy lad, of whom we have
before heard in this volume.

"Any child may know that," responded Master Green,
trying to look demure and innocent, like a young lady
when rallied on her admirers; "any child can tell that.
The Widow Knight brews the best ale in the parish."

"Ay, but that's not the only reason," said John, a
modest youth of sixteen; "is it, Ben?"

"It's reason enough," rejoined Master Green.

"But not *the* reason," retorted Ben.

"What! the widow herself?" quoth my companion.

"Lord, no, sir," interrupted Ben.

"'Twould be a very suitable match, and a snug resting-
place, only I'm afraid he would drink up all the ale in
the cellar," pursued the interrogator.

"Lord, no, sir!" again exclaimed Ben. "Master
Green thinks the widow too old."

"Too old! Why she's a score of years younger than
himself, but I suppose he prefers the daughter?"

"No, no, sir," rejoined Ben; "she's too old, too. The
grand-daughter, the grand-daughter! That's the match
for Master Green."

"What! the young pretty girl, Susan Parker, a girl
of eighteen, marry a man of eighty! nonsense, Ben."

"They've been asked in church, sir," said John,
quietly; "I heard it myself."

"Asked in church! But I thought the young carpenter was after Susan? Asked in church! Master
Green, are you rivalling your own grandson?"

"His father, the sick carpenter, would not hear of
that match," cried Ben, "because Susan had no money."

"And what does he say to this match, Ben?"

"Sir, he says that he likes it worse than t'other, but

that he can't help this ; that his father is an old fool, and must answer for his own folly."

" Well, but Susan ! she never can be such a goose. It must be a mistake. Have you really been asked in church, Master Green ? Have the banns actually been published ? "

" Twice, sir, in full form," answered the old man gravely. " I wonder your honour did not hear them."

" And is the match really to take place ? "

" Next Monday, your honour, God willing."

" Pshaw ! nonsense ! the thing's impossible ! you are all joking."

" Time will prove, sir," rejoined Master Green, still more gravely ; and, the geranium mould being now fairly collected, we parted.

And on the next Monday the marriage did take place sure enough, though not exactly in the way anticipated, George Green the younger proving to be the bridegroom, to the surprise of bridemaid, parson, and clerk : whilst the rich carpenter, unable to resist the double pleadings of his father and his son, and somewhat pleased to be spared the scandal of so youthful a step-mother, forgave the trick and the stolen match ; and old George Green, in the fulness of his delight, got tipsier than ever, in honour of his success, and toasted the Widow Knight so often and so heartily in her own home-brewed, that it's odds but he becomes the landlord of that snug ale-house, the Chittling Gate, after all.

JACK HATCH

I PIQUE myself on knowing by sight, and by name, almost every man and boy in our parish, from eight years old to eighty—I cannot say quite so much for the women. They—the elder of them at least—are more within doors, more hidden. One does not meet them in the fields and highways; their duties are close housekeepers, and live under cover. The girls, to be sure, are often enough in sight, " true creatures of the element," basking in the sun, racing in the wind, rolling in the dust, dabbling in the water,—hardier, dirtier, noisier, more sturdy defiers of heat, and cold, and wet, than boys themselves. One sees them quite often enough to know them; but then the little elves alter so much at every step of their approach to womanhood, that recognition becomes difficult, if not impossible. It is not merely growing,—boys grow;—it is positive, perplexing, and perpetual change: a butter-fly hath not undergone more transmogrifications in its progress through this life, than a village belle in her arrival at the age of seventeen.

The first appearance of the little lass is something after the manner of a caterpillar, crawling and creeping upon the grass, set down to roll by some tired little nurse of an elder sister, or mother with her hands full. There it lies—a fat, boneless, rosy piece of health, aspiring to the accomplishments of walking and talking; stretch-ing its chubby limbs; scrambling and sprawling; laugh-ing and roaring; there it sits, in all the dignity of the baby, adorned in a pink-checked frock, a blue-spotted pinafore, and a little white cap, tolerably clean, and quite whole. One is forced to ask if it be boy or girl ; for these hardy country rogues are all alike, open-eyed, and weather-stained, and nothing fearing. There is no more mark of sex in the countenance than in the dress.

In the next stage, dirt-encrusted enough to pass for the chrysalis, if it were not so very unquiet, the gender remains equally uncertain. It is a fine, stout, curly-pated creature of three or four, playing and rolling about, amongst grass or mud, all day long ; shouting, jumping, screeching— the happiest compound of noise and idleness, rags and rebellion, that ever trod the earth.

Then comes a sunburnt gipsy of six, beginning to grow tall and thin, and to find the cares of the world gathering about her ; with a pitcher in one hand, a mop in the other, an old straw bonnet of ambiguous shape, half hiding her tangled hair ; a tattered stuff petticoat, once green, hanging below an equally tattered cotton frock, once purple ; her longing eyes fixed on a game of baseball at the corner of the green, till she reaches the cottage door, flings down the mop and pitcher, and darts off to her companions, quite regardless of the storm of scolding with which the mother follows her runaway steps.

So the world wags till ten ; then the little damsel gets admission to the charity school, and trips mincingly thither every morning, dressed in the old-fashioned blue gown, and white cap and tippet, and bib and apron of that primitive institution, looking as demure as a Nun, and as tidy ; her thoughts fixed on button-holes and spell-ing-books—those ensigns of promotion ; despising dirt and baseballs, and all their joys.

Then at twelve the little lass comes home again, un-capped, untippeted, unschooled ; brown as a berry, wild as a colt, busy as a bee—working in the fields, digging in the garden, frying rashers, boiling potatoes, shelling beans, darning stockings, nursing children, feeding pigs ; —all these employments varied by occasional fits of romping and flirting, and idle play, according as the nascent coquetry or the lurking love of sport happens to preponderate; merry, and pretty, and good with all her little faults. It would be well if a country girl could stand at thirteen. Then she is charming. But the clock will move forward, and at fourteen she gets a service in a neighbouring town; and her next appearance is in the perfection of the butterfly state, fluttering, glittering, inconstant, vain,—the gayest and gaudiest insect that ever skimmed over a village green. And this is the true progress of a rustic beauty, the average lot of our country girls; so they spring up, flourish, change, and disappear. Some indeed marry and fix amongst us, and then ensues another set of changes, rather more gradual perhaps, but quite as sure, till grey hairs, wrinkles, and linsey-woolsey wind up the picture.

All this is beside the purpose. If woman be a mutable creature, man is not. The wearers of smock frocks, in spite of the sameness of the uniform, are almost as easily distinguished by an interested eye as a flock of sheep by the shepherd, or a pack of hounds by the huntsman; or, to come to less affronting similes, the members of the House of Commons by the Speaker, or the gentlemen of the bar by the Lord Chief Justice. There is very little change in them from early boyhood. "The child is father to the man" in more senses than one. There is a constancy about them; they keep the same faces, however ugly; the same habits, however strange; the same fashions, however unfashionable; they are in nothing new-fangled. Tom Coper, for instance, man and boy, is and has been addicted to posies,—from the first polyanthus to the last China rose, he has always a nosegay in his button-hole; George Simmons may be known a mile off, by an eternal red waistcoat; Jem Tanner, summer and winter, by the smartest of all smart straw hats; and Joel Brent, from the day that he left off petticoats, has always, in every dress and every situation, looked like a study for a painter—no mistaking him. Yes! I know every man and boy of note in the parish, with one exception—one most singular exception, which " haunts, and startles, and waylays " me at every turn. I do not know, and I begin to fear that I never shall know, Jack Hatch.

The first time I had occasion to hear of this worthy was on a most melancholy occurrence. We had lost— I do not like to talk about it, but I cannot tell my story without—we had lost a cricket match, been beaten, and soundly too, by the men of Beech-hill, a neighbouring parish. How this accident happened, I cannot very well tell; the melancholy fact is sufficient. The men of Beech-hill, famous players, in whose families cricket is an hereditary accomplishment, challenged and beat us. After our defeat, we began to comfort ourselves by endeavouring to discover how this misfortune could possibly have befallen. Every one that has ever had a cold must have experienced the great consolation that is derived from puzzling out the particular art of imprudence from which it sprang; and we, on the same principle, found our affliction somewhat mitigated by the endeavour to trace it to its source. One laid the catastrophe to the wind—a very common scapegoat in the catarrhal calamity—which had, as it were, played us booty, carrying our adversaries' balls right and ours wrong; another laid it to a certain catch missed by Tom Willis, by which means Farmer Thackum, the pride and glory of the Beech-hillers, had two innings; a third to the aforesaid Thackum's remarkable manner of bowling, which is circular, so to say —that is, after taking aim, he makes a sort of chassée on one side, before he delivers his ball, which pantomimic motion had a great effect on the nerves of our eleven, unused to such quadrilling; a fourth imputed our defeat to the over-civility of our umpire, George Gosseltine, a sleek, smooth, silky, soft-spoken person, who stood with

his little wand under his arm, smiling through all our
disasters—the very image of peace and good-humour ;
whilst their umpire, Bob Coxe, a roystering, roaring,
bullying blade, bounced, and hectored, and blustered
from his wicket, with the voice of a twelve-pounder ;
the fifth assented to this opinion, with some extension,
asserting that the universal impudence of their side took
advantage of the meekness and modesty of ours,—(N.B.—
It never occurred to our modesty that they might be the
best players),—which flattering persuasion appeared likely
to prevail, in fault of a better, when all on a sudden the
true reason of our defeat seemed to burst at once from
half-a-dozen voices, re-echoed like a chorus by all the
others—" It was entirely owing to the want of Jack
Hatch ! How could we think of playing without Jack
Hatch ! "

This was the first I heard of him. My inquiries as
to this great player were received with utter astonishment.
" Who is Jack ? "   " Not know Jack Hatch ! "   There
was no end of the wonder—" not to know him, argued
myself unknown."   " Jack Hatch—the best cricketer
in the parish, in the county, in the country ! Jack
Hatch, who had got seven notches at one hit ! Jack
Hatch, who had trolled and caught out a whole eleven !
Jack Hatch, who, besides these marvellous gifts in cricket,
was the best bowler and the best musician in the hundred,
—could dance a hornpipe and a minuet, sing a whole
song-book, bark like a dog, mew like a cat, crow like a
cock, and go through Punch from beginning to end !
Not know Jack Hatch ! "

Half ashamed of my non-acquaintance with this
Admirable Crichton of rural accomplishments, I determined to find him out as soon as possible, and I have
been looking for him more or less ever since.

The cricket-ground and the bowling-green were of
course the first places of search ; but he was always

just gone, or not come, or he was there yesterday, or
he is expected to-morrow—a to-morrow which, as
far as I am concerned, never arrives ;—the stars
were against me. Then I directed my attention to
his other acquirements ; and once followed a ballad-
singer half a mile, who turned out to be a strapping
woman in a man's great-coat ; and another time pierced
a whole mob of urchins to get at a capital Punch—when
behold it was the genuine man of puppets, the true
squeakery, the " real Simon Pure," and Jack was as much
to seek as ever.

At last I thought that I had actually caught him, and
on his own peculiar field, the cricket-ground. We abound
in rustic fun, and good-humour, and of course in nick-
names. A certain senior of fifty, or thereabout, for
instance, of very juvenile habits and inclinations, who
plays at ball, and marbles, and cricket with all the boys
in the parish, and joins a kind merry buoyant heart to
an aspect somewhat rough and careworn, has no other
appellation that ever I heard but " Uncle " ; I don't
think, if by any strange chance he were called by it, that
he would know his own name. On the other hand, a
little stunted pragmatical urchin, son and heir of Dick
Jones, an absolute old man cut shorter, so slow, and stiff,
and sturdy, and wordy, passes universally by the title of
" Grandfather "—I have not the least notion that he
would answer to Dick. Also a slim, grim-looking, white-
headed lad, whose hair is bleached, and his skin browned
by the sun, till he is as hideous as an Indian idol, goes, good
lack ! by the pastoral misnomer of the " Gentle Shepherd."
Oh, manes of Allan Ramsay ! the Gentle Shepherd !

Another youth, regular at cricket, but never seen
except then, of unknown parish and parentage, and
singular uncouthness of person, dress, and demeanour,
rough as a badger, ragged as a colt, and sour as verjuice,
was known, far more appropriately, by the cognomen of

"Oddity" Him, in my secret soul, I pitched on for
Jack Hatch. In the first place, as I had in the one case
a man without a name, and in the other a name without
a man, to have found these component parts of individu-
ality meet in the same person, to have made the man
to fit the name, and the name fit the man, would have been
as pretty a way of solving two enigmas at once as hath been
heard of since Œdipus his day. But besides the obvious
convenience and suitability of this belief, I had divers
other corroborating reasons. Oddity was young, so was
Jack ;—Oddity came up the hill from leaward, so must
Jack ;—Oddity was a capital cricketer, so was Jack ;—
Oddity did not play in our unlucky Beech-hill match,
neither did Jack ;—and last of all, Oddity's name was
Jack, a fact I was fortunate enough to ascertain from
a pretty damsel who walked up with him to the ground
one evening, and who, on seeing him bowl out Tom Coper,
could not help exclaiming in soliloquy, as she stood a few
yards behind us, looking on with all her heart, "Well
done, Jack!" That moment built up all my hopes ;
the next knocked them down. I thought I had clutched
him, but willing to make assurance doubly sure, I turned
to my pretty neighbour (Jack Hatch too had a sweetheart),
and said in a tone half affirmative, half interrogatory,
"That young man who plays so well is Jack Hatch ?"—
"No, ma'am, Jack Bolton!" and Jack Hatch remained
still a sound, a name, a mockery.

Well! at last I ceased to look for him, and might
possibly have forgotten my curiosity, had not every week
produced some circumstance to relumine that active
female passion.

I seemed beset by his name, and his presence, invisibly
as it were. Will-o'-the-wisp is nothing to him ; Puck,
in that famous Midsummer Dream, was a quiet goblin
compared to Jack Hatch. He haunts one in dark places.
The fiddler, whose merry tones come ringing across the

orchard on a winter's night from Farmer White's barn, setting the whole village a-dancing, is Jack Hatch. The whistler, who trudges homeward at dusk up Kibe's lanes, out-piping the nightingale, in her own month of May, is Jack Hatch. And the indefatigable learner of the bassoon, whose drone, all last harvest, might be heard in the twilight, issuing from the sexton's dwelling on the Little Lea, " making night hideous," that iniquitous practiser is Jack Hatch.

The name meets me in all manner of ways. I have seen it in the newspaper for a prize of pinks ; and on the back of a warrant on the charge of poaching ;— N.B. the constable had my luck, and could not find the culprit, otherwise I might have had some chance of seeing him on that occasion. Things the most remote and discrepant issue in Jack Hatch. He caught Dame Wheeler's squirrel ; the Magpie at the Rose owes to him the half-dozen phrases with which he astounds and delights the passers-by ; the very dog Tero,—an animal of singular habits, who sojourns occasionally at half the houses in the village, making each his home till he is affronted—Tero himself, best and ugliest of finders—a mongrel compounded of terrier, cur, and spaniel—Tero, most remarkable of ugly dogs, inasmuch as he constantly squints, and commonly goes on three legs, holding up first one, and then the other, out of a sort of quadrupedal economy to ease those useful members—Tero himself is said to belong of right and origin to Jack Hatch.

Everywhere that name meets me. 'Twas but a few weeks ago that I heard him asked in church, and a day or two afterwards I saw the tail of the wedding procession, the little lame clerk handing the bridemaid, and a girl from the Rose running after them with pipes, passing by our house. Nay, this very morning, some one was speaking—Dead ! what dead ? Jack Hatch dead ?—a name, a shadow, a Jack-o'-lantern ! Can Jack Hatch die ? Hath he the property of mortality ? Can the bell toll for him ? Yes ! there is the coffin and the pall— all that I shall ever see of him is there !—There are his comrades following in decent sorrow—and the poor pretty bride, leaning on the little clerk.—My search is over— Jack Hatch is dead !

THE MOLE-CATCHER

THERE are no more delightful or unfailing associations
than those afforded by the various operations of the
husbandman, and the changes on the fair face of nature.
We all know that busy troops of reapers come with the
yellow corn; whilst the yellow leaf brings a no less busy
train of ploughman and seedsmen preparing the ground
for fresh harvests; that woodbines and wild roses,
flaunting in the blossomy hedge-rows, give token of the
gay bands of haymakers which enliven the meadows;
and that the primroses, which begin to unfold their pale
stars by the side of the green lanes, bear marks of the
slow and weary female processions, the gangs of tired
yet talkative bean-setters, who defile twice a day through
the intricate mazes of our cross-country roads. These
are general associations, as well known and as universally
recognised as the union of mince-pies and Christmas.
I have one, more private and peculiar, one, perhaps,
the more strongly impressed on my mind, because the
impression may be almost confined to myself. The full
flush of violets, which, about the middle of March, seldom
fails to perfume the whole earth, always brings to my
recollection one solitary and silent coadjutor of the
husbandman's labours, as unlike a violet as possible—
Isaac Bint, the mole-catcher.

I used to meet him every spring, when we lived at
our old house, whose park-like paddock, with its finely-
clumped oaks and elms, and its richly-timbered hedge-
rows, edging into wild, rude, and solemn fir plantations,
dark, and rough, and hoary, formed for so many years

my constant and favourite walk. Here, especially under the great horse-chestnut, and where the bank rose high and naked above the lane, crowned only with a tuft of golden broom; here the sweetest and prettiest of wild flowers, whose very name hath a charm, grew like a carpet under one's feet, enamelling the young green grass with their white and purple blossoms, and loading the air with their delicious fragrance; here I used to come almost every morning, during the violet-tide; and here, almost every morning, I was sure to meet Isaac Bint.

I think that he fixed himself the more firmly in my memory by his singular discrepancy with the beauty and cheerfulness of the scenery and the season. Isaac is a tall, lean, gloomy personage, with whom the clock of life seems to stand still. He has looked sixty-five for these last twenty years, although his dark hair and beard, and firm manly stride, almost contradict the evidence of his sunken cheeks and deeply-lined forehead. The stride is awful: he hath the stalk of a ghost. His whole air and demeanour savour of one that comes from underground. His appearance is "of the earth, earthy." His clothes, hands, and face are of the colour of the mould in which he delves. The little round traps which hang behind him over one shoulder, as well as the strings of dead moles which embellish the other, are encrusted with dirt like a tombstone; and the staff which he plunges into the little hillocks, by which he traces the course of his small quarry, returns a hollow sound, as if tapping on the lid of a coffin. Images of the church-yard come, one does not know how, with his presence. Indeed he does officiate as assistant to the sexton in his capacity of grave-digger, chosen, as it should seem, from a natural fitness; a fine sense of congruity in good Joseph Reed, the functionary in question, who felt, without knowing why, that, of all men in the parish, Isaac Bint was best fitted to that solemn office.

His remarkable gift of silence adds much to the impression produced by his remarkable figure. I don't think that I ever heard him speak three words in my life. An approach of that bony hand to that earthy leather cap was the greatest effort of courtesy that my daily salutations could extort from him. For this silence, Isaac has reasons good. He hath a reputation to support. His words are too precious to be wasted. Our mole-catcher, ragged as he looks, is the wise man of the village, the oracle of the village inn, foresees the weather, charms away agues, tell fortunes by the stars, and writes notes upon the almanack—turning and twisting about the predictions after a fashion so ingenious, that it's a moot point which is oftenest wrong—Isaac Bint, or Francis Moore. In one eminent instance, our friend was, however, eminently right. He had the good luck to prophesy, before sundry witnesses—some of them sober—in the tap-room of the Bell—he then sitting, pipe in mouth, on the settle at the right-hand side of the fire, whilst Jacob Frost occupied the left—he had the good fortune to foretell, on New Year's Day, 1812, the downfall of Napoleon Bonaparte—a piece of soothsayership which has established his reputation, and dumbfounded all doubters and cavillers ever since; but which would certainly have been more striking if he had not annually uttered the same prediction, from the same place, from the time that the aforesaid Napoleon became First Consul. But this small circumstance is entirely overlooked by Isaac and his admirers, and they believe in him, and he believes in the stars, more firmly than ever.

Our mole-catcher is, as might be conjectured, an old bachelor. Your married man hath more of this world about him—is less, so to say, planet-struck. A thorough old bachelor is Isaac, a contemner and maligner of the sex, a complete and decided woman-hater. Female frailty is the only subject on which he hath ever been known to dilate; he will not even charm away their agues, or tell their fortunes, and, indeed, holds them to be unworthy the notice of the stars.

No woman contaminates his household. He lives on the edge of a pretty bit of woodland scenery, called the Pinge, in a snug cottage of two rooms, of his own building, surrounded by a garden cribbed from the waste, well fenced with quick-set, and well stocked with fruit trees, herbs, and flowers. One large apple tree extends over the roof—a pretty bit of colour when in blossom, contrasted with the thatch of the little dwelling, and relieved by the dark wood behind. Although the owner be solitary, his demesne is sufficiently populous. A long row of bee-hives extends along the warmest side of the garden— for Isaac's honey is celebrated far and near; a pig occupies a commodious stye at one corner; and large flocks of ducks and geese (for which the Pinge, whose glades are intersected by water, is famous) are generally waiting round a back gate leading to a spacious shed, far larger than Isaac's own cottage, which serves for their feeding and roosting-place. The great tameness of all these creatures—for the ducks and geese flutter round him the moment he approaches, and the very pig follows him like a dog—gives no equivocal testimony of the kindness of our mole-catcher's nature. A circumstance of recent occurrence puts his humanity beyond doubt.

Amongst the probable causes of Isaac's dislike to women may be reckoned the fact of his living in a female neighbourhood (for the Pinge is almost peopled with duck-rearers and goose-crammers of the duck and goose gender) and being himself exceedingly unpopular amongst the fair poultry-feeders of that watery vicinity. He beat them at their own weapons; produced at Midsummer geese fit for Michaelmas; and raised ducks so precocious, that the gardeners complained of them as fore-running their vegetable accompaniments; and

" panting *peas* toiled after them in vain." In short, the Naiads of the Pinge had the mortification to find themselves driven out of B—— market by an interloper, and that interloper a man, who had no manner of right to possess any skill in an accomplishment so exclusively feminine as duck-rearing; and being no ways inferior in another female accomplishment, called scolding, to their sister-nymphs of Billingsgate, they set up a clamour and a cackle which might rival the din of their own gooseries at feeding-time, and would inevitably have frightened from the field any competitor less impenetrable than our hero. But Isaac is not a man to shrink from so small an evil as female objurgation. He stalked through it all in mute disdain—looking now at his mole-traps, and now at the stars—pretending not to hear, and very probably not hearing. At first this scorn, more provoking than any retort, only excited his enemies to fresh attacks; but one cannot be always answering another person's silence. The flame which had blazed so fiercely at last burnt itself out, and peace reigned once more in the green alleys of Pinge-wood.

One, however, of his adversaries—his nearest neighbour —still remained unsilenced.

Margery Grover was a very old and poor woman, whom age and disease had bent almost to the earth; shaken by palsy, pinched by penury, and soured by misfortune—a moving bundle of misery and rags. Two centuries ago she would have been burnt for a witch; now she starved and grumbled on the parish allowance; trying to eke out a scanty subsistence by the dubious profits gained from the produce of two geese and a lame gander, once the unmolested tenants of a greenish pool, situate right between her dwelling and Isaac's, but whose watery dominion had been invaded by his flourishing colony.

This was the cause of feud; and although Isaac would

willingly, from a mingled sense of justice and of pity, have yielded the point to the poor old creature, especially as ponds are there almost as plentiful as blackberries, yet it was not so easy to control the habits and inclinations of their feathered subjects, who all perversely fancied that particular pool ; and various accidents and skirmishes occurred, in which the ill-fed and weak birds of Margery had generally the worst of the fray. One of her early goslings was drowned—an accident which may happen even to water-fowl ; and her lame gander, a sort of pet with the poor old woman, injured in his well leg ; and Margery vented curses as bitter as those of Sycorax ; and Isaac, certainly the most superstitious personage in the parish—the most thorough believer in his own gifts and predictions—was fain to nail a horse-shoe on his door for the defence of his property, and to wear one of his own ague charms about his neck for his personal protection.

Poor old Margery ! A hard winter came ; and the feeble, tottering creature shook in the frosty air like an aspen-leaf ; and the hovel in which she dwelt—for nothing could prevail on her to try the shelter of the workhouse —shook, like herself, at every blast. She was not quite alone either in the world or in her poor hut : husband, children, and grandchildren had passed away ; but one young and innocent being, a great-grandson, the last of her descendants, remained, a helpless dependant on one almost as helpless as himself.

Little Harry Grover was a shrunken, stunted boy, of five years old ; tattered and squalid, like his grandame, and, at first sight, presented almost as miserable a specimen of childhood as Margery herself did of age. There was even a likeness between them ; although the fierce blue eye of Margery had, in the boy, a mild, appealing look, which entirely changed the whole expression of the countenance. A gentle and a peaceful boy was

Harry, and, above all, a useful. It was wonderful how many ears of corn in the autumn, and sticks in the winter, his little hands could pick up! how well he could make a fire, and boil the kettle, and sweep the hearth, and cram the goslings! Never was a handier boy or a trustier; and when the united effects of cold, and age, and rheumatism, confined poor Margery to her poor bed, the child continued to perform his accustomed offices; fetching the money from the vestry, buying the loaf at the baker's, keeping house, and nursing the sick woman, with a kindness and thoughtfulness, which none but those who know the careful ways to which necessity trains cottage children, would deem credible; and Margery, a woman of strong passions, strong prejudices, and strong affections, who had lived in and for the desolate boy, felt the approach of death embittered by the certainty that the workhouse, always the scene of her dread and loathing, would be the only refuge for the poor orphan.

Death, however, came on visibly and rapidly; and she sent for the overseer to beseech him to put Harry to board in some decent cottage; she could not die in peace until he had promised; the fear of the innocent child's being contaminated by wicked boys and godless women preyed upon her soul; she implored, she conjured. The overseer, a kind but timid man, hesitated, and was beginning a puzzled speech about the bench and the vestry, when another voice was heard from the door of the cottage.

"Margery," said our friend Isaac, "will you trust Harry to me? I am a poor man, to be sure; but, between earning and saving, there'll be enough for me and little Harry. 'Tis as good a boy as ever lived, and I'll try to keep him so. Trust him to me, and I'll be a father to him. I can't say more."

"God bless thee, Isaac Bint! God bless thee!" was all poor Margery could reply.

They were the last words she ever spoke. And little Harry is living with our good mole-catcher, and is growing plump and rosy; and Margery's other pet, the lame gander, lives and thrives with them too.

THE VILLAGE SCHOOLMISTRESS

WOMEN, fortunately perhaps for their happiness and their virtue, have, as compared with men, so few opportunities of acquiring permanent distinction, that it is rare to find a female unconnected with literature, or with history, whose name is remembered after her monument is defaced, and the brass on her coffin-lid corroded. Such, however, was the case with Dame Eleanor, the widow of Sir Richard Lacy, whose name, at the end of three centuries, continued to be as freshly and as frequently spoken, as " familiar " a " household word " in the little village of Aberleigh, as if she had flourished there yesterday. Her memory was embalmed by a deed of charity and of goodness. She had founded and endowed a girls' school for " the instruction " (to use the words of the deed) " of twenty poor children, and the maintenance of one discreet and godly matron " ; and the school still continued to be called after its foundress, and the very spot on which the schoolhouse stood, to be known by the name of Lady Lacy's Green.

It was a spot worthy of its destination, a spot of remarkable cheerfulness and beauty. The Green was small, of irregular shape, and situated at a confluence of shady lanes. Half the roads and paths of the parish meet there, probably for the convenience of crossing, in that place by a stone bridge of one arch covered with ivy, the winding rivulet which intersected the whole village, and which, sweeping in a narrow channel round the school garden, widened into a stream of some consequence, in the richly wooded meadows beyond. The banks of the brook, as it wound its glittering course over the green, were set, here and there, with clumps of forest trees, chiefly bright green elms, and aspens with their quivering leaves and their pale shining bark ; whilst a magnificent beech stood alone near the gate leading to the school, partly overshadowing the little court in which the house was placed. The building itself was a beautiful small structure, in the ornamented style of Elizabeth's day, with pointed roofs and pinnacles, and clustered chimneys, and casement windows ; the whole house enwreathed and garlanded by a most luxuriant vine. The date of the erection, 1563, was cut in a stone inserted in the brick-work above the porch ; but the foundress had, with an unostentatious modesty, withheld her name, leaving it, as she safely might, to the grateful recollection of the successive generations who profited by her benevolence. Altogether it was a most gratifying scene to the eye and to the heart. No one ever saw Lady Lacy's schoolhouse without admiration, especially in the play hour at noon, when the children, freed from " restraint that sweetens liberty," were clustered under the old beech tree, revelling in their innocent freedom, running, jumping, shouting, and laughing with all their might, the only sort of riot which it is pleasant to witness. The painter and the philanthropist might contemplate that scene with equal delight.

The right of appointing both the mistress and the scholars had been originally vested in the Lacy family, to whom nearly the whole of the parish had at one time belonged. But the estates, the manor, the hall-house had long passed into other hands and other names, and this privilege of charity was now the only possession which the heirs of Lady Lacy retained in Aberleigh. Reserving to themselves the right of nominating the matron, her descendants had therefore delegated to the vicar and the parish officers the selection of the children, and the general regulation of the school—a sort of council of regency, which, for as simple and as peaceful as the government seems, a disputatious churchwarden or a sturdy overseer would sometimes contrive to render sufficiently stormy.   I have known as much canvassing and almost as much ill-will in a contested election for one of Lady Lacy's scholarships, as for a scholarship in grander places, or even for an M.P.-ship in the next borough ; and the great schism between the late Farmer Brookes and all his coadjutors, as to whether the original uniform of little green stuff gowns, with white bibs and aprons, tippets and mob, should be commuted for modern cotton frocks and cottage bonnets, fairly set the parish by the ears.   Owing to the good farmer's glorious obstinacy (which I suppose he called firmness), the green gownians lost the day.   I believe that, as a matter of calculation, the man might be right, and that his costume was cheaper and more convenient ; but I am sure that I should have been against him, right or wrong ; the other dress was so pretty, so primitive, so neat, so becoming ; the little lasses looked like rose-buds in the midst of their leaves : besides, it was the old traditionary dress—the dress contrived and approved by Lady Lacy.   Oh ! it should never have been changed, never !

Since there was so much contention in the election of pupils, it was perhaps lucky for the vestry that the exercise of the more splendid piece of patronage, the appointment of a mistress, did not enter into its duties.   Mr. Lacy, a representative of the foundress, a man of fortune in a distant county, generally bestowed the situation on some old dependant of his family.   During the churchwarden-ship of Farmer Brookes, no less than three village gouvernantes arrived at Aberleigh—a quick succession !   It made more than half the business of our zealous and bustling man of office, an amateur in such matters, to instruct and overlook them.   The first importation was

Dame Whitaker, a person of no small importance, who
had presided as head nurse over two generations of the
Lacys, and was now, on the dispersion of the last set
of her nurslings to their different schools, and an unlucky
quarrel with a favourite lady's-maid, promoted and
banished to this distant government. Nobody could
well be more unfit for her new station, or better suited
to her old. She was a nurse from top to toe. Round,
portly, smiling, with a coaxing voice and an indolent
manner ; much addicted to snuff and green tea, to sitting
still, to telling long stories, and to humouring children.
She spoiled every brat she came near, just as she had been
used to spoil the little Master Edwards and Miss Julias
of her ancient dominions. She could not have scolded if
she would—the gift was not in her. Under her misrule
the school grew into sad disorder ; the girls not only
learnt nothing, but unlearnt what they knew before ;
work was lost—even the new shifts of the Vicar's lady ;
books were torn ; and, for the climax of evil, no sampler
was prepared to carry round at Christmas, from house
to house—the first time such an omission had occurred
within the memory of man. Farmer Brookes was at his
wits' end. He visited the school six days in the week, to
admonish and reprove; he even went nigh to threaten
that he would work a sampler himself ; and finally
bestowed on the unfortunate ex-nurse the nickname of
Queen Log, a piece of disrespect, which, together with
other grievances, proved so annoying to poor Dame
Whitaker, that she found the air of Aberleigh disagree
with her, patched up a peace with her old enemy, the
lady's-maid, abdicated that unruly and rebellious prin-
cipality, the school, and retired with great delight to her
quiet home in the deserted nursery, where, as far as I
know, she still remains.

The grief of the children on losing this most indulgent
non-instructress was not mitigated by the appearance or

demeanour of her successor, who at first seemed a preceptress after Farmer Brookes's own heart, a perfect Queen Stork. Dame Banks was the widow of Mr. Lacy's gamekeeper, a little thin woman, with a hooked nose, a sharp voice, and a prodigious activity of tongue. She scolded all day long, and, for the first week, passed for a great teacher. After that time it began to be discovered, that, in spite of her lessons, the children did not learn ; notwithstanding her rating they did not mind, and in the midst of a continual bustle nothing was ever done. Dame Banks was in fact a well-intentioned, worthy woman, with a restless irritable temper, a strong desire to do her duty, and a woeful ignorance how to set about it. She was rather too old to be taught either ; at least she required a gentler instructor than the good churchwarden ; and so much ill-will was springing up between them, that he had even been heard to regret the loss of Dame Whitaker's quietness, when very suddenly poor Dame Banks fell ill and died. The sword had worn the scabbard ; but she was better than she seemed ; a thoroughly well-meaning woman—grateful, pious, and charitable ; even our man of office admitted this.

The next in succession was one with whom my trifling pen, dearly as that light and fluttering instrument loves to dally and disport over the surfaces of things, must take no saucy freedom ; one of whom we all felt it impossible to speak or think without respect ; one who made Farmer Brookes's office of adviser a sinecure, by putting the whole school, himself included, into its proper place, setting everybody in order, and keeping them so. I don't know how she managed, unless by good sense and good-humour, and that happy art of government, which seems no art at all, because it is so perfect ; but the children were busy and happy, the vestry pleased, and the churchwarden contented. All went well under Mrs. Allen.

She was an elderly woman, nearer perhaps to seventy than to sixty, and of an exceedingly venerable and prepossessing appearance. Delicacy was her chief characteristic, a delicacy so complete that it pervaded her whole person, from her tall, slender figure, her fair, faded complexion, and her silver hair, to the exquisite nicety of dress by which, at all hours and seasons, from Sunday morning to Saturday night, she was invariably distinguished. The soil of the day was never seen on her apparel ; dust would not cling to her snowy caps and handkerchiefs : such was the art magic of her neatness. Her very pins did their office in a different manner from those belonging to other people. Her manner was gentle, cheerful, and courteous, with a simplicity and propriety of expression that perplexed all listeners ; it seemed so exactly what belongs to the highest birth and the highest breeding. She was humble, very humble ; but her humility was evidently the result of a truly Christian spirit, and would equally have distinguished her in any station. The poor people, always nice judges of behaviour, felt, they did not know why, that she was their superior ; the gentry of the neighbourhood suspected her to be their equal—some clergyman's or officer's widow, reduced in circumstances, and would have treated her as such, had she not, on discovering their mistake, eagerly undeceived them. She had been, she said, all her life a servant, the personal attendant of one dear mistress, on whose decease she had been recommended to Mr. Lacy, and to his kindness, under Providence, was indebted for a home and a provision for her helpless age, and the still more helpless youth of a poor orphan, far dearer to her than herself. This avowal, although it changed the character of the respect paid to Mrs. Allen, was certainly not calculated to diminish its amount ; and the new mistress of Lady Lacy's school, and the beautiful order of her house and garden,

continued to be the pride and admiration of
Aberleigh.

The orphan of whom she spoke was a little girl about
eleven years old, who lived with her, and whose black
frock bespoke the recent death of some relative. She
had lately, Mrs. Allen said, lost her grandmother, her
only remaining parent, and had now no friend but herself
on earth; but there was one above who was a Father to
the fatherless, and He would protect poor Jane! And as
she said this, there was a touch of emotion, a break of the
voice, a tremor on the lip, very unlike the usual cheerfulness and self-command of her manner. The child was
evidently very dear to her. Jane was, indeed, a most
interesting creature : not pretty—a girl of that age seldom
is ; the beauty of childhood is outgrown, that of youth
not come ; and Jane could scarcely ever have had any
other pretensions to prettiness than the fine expression
of her dark grey eyes, and the general sweetness of her
countenance. She was pale, thin, and delicate ; serious
and thoughtful far beyond her years ; averse from play,
and shrinking from notice. Her fondness for Mrs. Allen,
and her constant and unremitting attention to her health
and comforts, were peculiarly remarkable. Every part
of their small housewifery that her height and strength
and skill would enable her to perform, she insisted on doing,
and many things far beyond her power she attempted.
Never was so industrious or so handy a little maiden.
Old Nelly Chun, the charwoman, who went once a week
to the house, to wash and bake and scour, declared that
Jane did more than herself ; and to all who knew Nelly's
opinion of her own doings, this praise appeared super-
lative.

In the schoolroom she was equally assiduous, not as a
learner, but as a teacher. None so clever as Jane in
superintending the different exercises of the needle, the
spelling-book, and the slate. From the little work-

woman's first attempt to insert thread into a pocket-hand-kerchief, that digging and ploughing of cambric, miscalled hemming, up to the nice and delicate mysteries of stitch-ing and button-holing; from the easy junction of *a b*, *ab* and *b a*, *ba*, to that tremendous sesquipedalian word *irrefragibility*, at which even I tremble as I write; from the Numeration Table to Practice, nothing came amiss to her. In figures she was particularly quick. Generally speaking, her patience with the other children, however dull or tiresome or giddy they might be, was exemplary; but a false accomptant, a stupid arithmetician, would put her out of humour. The only time I ever heard her sweet, gentle voice raised a note above its natural key, was in reprimanding Susan Wheeler, a sturdy, square-made, rosy-cheeked lass, as big again as herself, the dunce and beauty of the school, who had three times cast up a sum of three figures, and three times made the total wrong. Jane ought to have admired the ingenuity evinced by such a variety of error; but she did not; it fairly put her in a passion. She herself was not only clever in figures, but fond of them to an extraordinary degree— luxuriated in Long Division, and revelled in the Rule-of-Three. Had she been a boy, she would probably have been a great mathematician, and have won that fickle, fleeting, shadowy wreath, that crown made of the rainbow, that vainest of all earthly pleasures, but which yet *is* a pleasure—Fame.

Happier, far happier was the good, the lowly, the pious child, in her humble duties! Grave and quiet as she seemed, she had many moments of intense and placid enjoyment, when the duties of the day were over, and she sat reading in the porch, by the side of Mrs. Allen, or walked with her in the meadows on a Sunday evening after church. Jane was certainly contented and happy, and yet every one that saw her thought of her with that kind of interest which is akin to pity. There was a pale,

fragile grace about her, such as we sometimes see in a
rose which has blown in the shade ; or rather, to change
the simile, the drooping and delicate look of a tender
plant removed from a hothouse to the open air. We could
not help feeling sure (notwithstanding our mistake with
regard to Mrs. Allen) that *this* was indeed a transplanted
flower, and that the village school, however excellently
her habits had become inured to her situation, was not her
proper atmosphere.

Several circumstances corroborated our suspicions.
My lively young friend Sophia Grey, standing with me
one day at the gate of the schoolhouse, where I had been
talking with Mrs. Allen, remarked to me, in French, the
sly, demure vanity with which Susan Wheeler, whose
beauty had attracted her attention, was observing and
returning her glances. The playful manner in which
Sophia described Susan's " regard furtif " made me
smile ; and looking accidentally at Jane, I saw that
she was smiling too, clearly comprehending, and enjoying
the full force of the pleasantry. She must understand
French ; and when questioned, she confessed she did, and
thankfully accepted the loan of books in that language.
Another time, being sent on a message to the vicarage,
and left for some minutes alone in the parlour, with a
piano standing open in the room, she could not resist
the temptation of touching the keys, and was discovered
playing an air of Mozart, with great taste and execution.
At this detection she blushed, as if caught in a crime, and
hurried away in tears and without her message. It was
clear that she had once learnt music. But the surest
proof that Jane's original station had been higher than
that which she now filled, was the mixture of respect and
fondness with which Mrs. Allen treated her, and the deep
regret she sometimes testified at seeing her employed
in any menial office.

At last, elicited by some warm praise of the charming

72—J

child, our good schoolmistress disclosed her story. Jane
Mowbray was the granddaughter of the lady in whose
service Mrs. Allen had passed her life. Her father had
been a man of high family and splendid fortune; had
married beneath himself, as it was called, a friendless
orphan, with no portion but beauty and virtue; and,
on her death, which followed shortly on the birth of her
daughter, had plunged into every kind of vice and extra-
vagance. What need to tell a tale of sin and suffering?
Mr. Mowbray had ruined himself, had ruined all belonging
to him, and finally had joined our armies abroad as a
volunteer, and had fallen undistinguished in his first
battle. The news of his death was fatal to his indulgent
mother; and when she too died, Mrs. Allen blessed the
Providence which, by throwing in her way a recommendation to Lady Lacy's school, had enabled her to support
the dear object of her mistress's love and prayers. "Had
Miss Mowbray no connections?" was the natural question.
"Yes; one very near—an aunt, the sister of her father,
richly married in India. But Sir William was a proud,
and a stern man, upright in his own conduct, and implac-
able to error. Lady Ely was a sweet, gentle creature, and
doubtless would be glad to extend a mother's protection
to the orphan; but Sir William—oh! he was so unrelenting! He had abjured Mr. Mowbray and all connected
with him. She had written to inform them where the
dear child was, but had no expectation of any answer from
India."

Time verified this prediction. The only tidings from
India, at all interesting to Jane Mowbray, were contained in the paragraph of a newspaper which announced
Lady Ely's death, and put an end to all hopes of protection in that quarter. Years passed on, and found
her still with Mrs. Allen at Lady Lacy's Green, more and
more beloved and respected from day to day. She had
now attained almost to womanhood. Strangers, I believe,

called her plain ; we, who knew her, thought her pretty. Her figure was tall and straight as a cypress, pliant and flexible as a willow, full of gentle grace, whether in repose or in motion. She had a profusion of light brown hair, a pale complexion, dark grey eyes, a smile of which the character was rather sweet than gay, and such a countenance! no one could look at her without wishing her well, or without being sure that she deserved all good wishes. Her manners were modest and elegant, and she had much of the self-taught knowledge which is, of all knowledge, the surest and the best, because acquired with most difficulty, and fixed in the memory by the repetition of effort. Every one had assisted her to the extent of his power, and of her willingness to accept assistance ; for both she and Mrs. Allen had a pride— call it independence—which rendered it impossible, even to the friends who were most honoured by their good opinion, to be as useful to them as they could have wished. To give Miss Mowbray time for improvement had, however, proved a powerful emollient to the pride of our dear schoolmistress ; and that time had been so well employed, that her acquirements were considerable ; whilst in mind and character she was truly admirable ; mild, grateful, and affectionate, and imbued with a deep religious feeling, which influenced every action and pervaded every thought. So gifted, she was deemed by her constant friends, the vicar and his lady, perfectly competent to the care and education of children ; it was agreed that she should enter a neighbouring family, as a successor to their then governess, early in the ensuing spring ; and she, although sad at the prospect of leaving her aged protectress, acquiesced in their decision.

One fine Sunday in the October preceding this dreaded separation, as Miss Mowbray, with Mrs. Allen leaning on her arm, was slowly following the little train of Lady Lacy's scholars from church, an elderly gentleman, sickly-looking and emaciated, accosted a pretty young woman, who was loitering with some other girls at the churchyard gate, and asked her several questions respecting the school and its mistress. Susan Wheeler (for it happened to be our old acquaintance) was delighted to be singled out by so grand a gentleman, and being a kind-hearted creature in the main, spoke of the school-house and its inhabitants exactly as they deserved. " Mrs. Allen," she said, " was the best woman in the world—the very best, except just Miss Mowbray, who was better still,—only too particular about summing, which, you know, sir," added Susan, " people can't learn if they can't. She is going to be a governess in the spring," continued the loquacious damsel, " and it's to be hoped the little ladies will take kindly to their tables, or it will be a sad grievance to Miss Jane." —" A governess ! Where can I make inquiries concerning Miss Mowbray ? "—" At the vicarage, sir," answered Susan, dropping her little courtesy, and turning away, well pleased with the gentleman's condescension, and with half-a-crown which he had given her in return for her intelligence. The stranger, meanwhile, walked straight to the vicarage, and in less than half an hour the vicar repaired with him to Lady Lacy's Green.

This stranger, so drooping, so sickly, so emaciated, was the proud Indian uncle, the stern Sir William Ely ! Sickness and death had been busy with him and with his. He had lost his health, his wife, and his children ; and, softened by affliction, was returned to England a new man, anxious to forgive and to be forgiven, and, above all, desirous to repair his neglect and injustice toward the only remaining relative of the wife whom he had so fondly loved and so tenderly lamented. In this frame of mind, such a niece as Jane Mowbray was welcomed with no common joy. His delight in her, and his gratitude toward her protectress, were unbounded. He wished them both to accompany him home, and reside with him constantly. Jane promised to do so; but Mrs. Allen, with her usual admirable feeling of propriety, clung to the spot which had been to her a "city of refuge," and refused to leave it in spite of all the entreaties of uncle and of niece. It was a happy decision for Aberleigh; for what could Aberleigh have done without its good schoolmistress?

She lives there still, its ornament and its pride; and every year Jane Mowbray comes for a long visit, and makes a holiday in the school and in the whole place. Jane Mowbray, did I say? No; not Jane Mowbray now. She has changed that dear name for the only name that could be dearer: she is married—married to the eldest son of Mr. Lacy, the lineal representative of Dame Eleanor Lacy, the honoured foundress of the school. It was in a voice, tremulous more from feeling than from age, that Mrs. Allen welcomed the young heir, when he brought his fair bride to Aberleigh; and it was with a yet stronger and deeper emotion that the bridegroom, with his own Jane in his hand, visited the asylum which she and her venerable guardian owed to the benevolence and the piety of his ancestress, whose good deeds had thus showered down blessings on her remote posterity.

THE RAT-CATCHER

A SKETCH

BEAUTIFULLY situated on a steep knoll, over-hanging
a sharp angle in the turnpike road, which leads through
our village of Aberleigh, stands a fantastic rustic building,
with a large yew tree on one side, a superb weeping ash
hanging over it on the other, a clump of elms forming
a noble back-ground behind, and all the prettiness of
porches garlanded with clematis, windows mantled with
jessamine, and chimneys wreathed with luxuriant ivy,
adding grace to the picture. To form a picture, most
assuredly, it was originally built,—a point of view, as it is
called, from Allonby Park, to which the byroad that winds
round this inland cape, or headland, directly leads; and
most probably it was also copied from some book of tasteful
designs for lodges or ornamented cottages, since not only
the building itself, but the winding path that leads up the
acclivity, and the gate which gives entrance to the little
garden, smack of the pencil and the graver.

For a picture certainly, and probably from a picture
was that cottage erected, although its ostensible purpose
was merely that of a receiving-house for letters and
parcels for the Park, to which the present inhabitant, a
jolly, bustling, managing dame, of great activity and
enterprise in her own peculiar line, has added the profitable occupation of a thriving and well-accustomed village-
shop; contaminating the picturesque, old-fashioned bay-
window of the fancy letter-house by the vulgarities of
red herrings, tobacco, onions, and salt-butter—a sight

which must have made the projector of her elegant dwelling stare again—and forcing her customers to climb up and down an ascent almost as steep as the roof of a house, whenever they wanted a pennyworth of needles, or a halfpennyworth of snuff, a toil whereat some of our poor old dames groaned aloud. Sir Henry threatened to turn her out, and her customers threatened to turn her off; but neither of these events happened. Dinah Forde appeased her landlord and managed her customers; for Dinah Forde was a notable woman; and it is really surprising what great things, in a small way, your notable woman will compass.

Besides Mrs. Dinah Forde, and her apprentice, a girl of ten years old, the letter-house had lately acquired another occupant in the shape of Dinah's tenant or lodger—I don't know which word best expresses the nature of the arrangement—my old friend Sam Page, the rat-catcher, who, together with his implements of office, two ferrets, and four mongrels, inhabited a sort of shed or outhouse at the back of the premises—serving, "especially the curs," as Mrs. Forde was wont to express herself, "as a sort of guard and protection to a lone woman's property."

Sam Page was, as I have said, an old acquaintance of ours, although neither as a resident of Aberleigh, nor in his capacity of rat-catcher, both of which were recent assumptions. It was, indeed, a novelty to see Sam Page as a resident anywhere. His abode seemed to be the highway. One should as soon have expected to find a gipsy within stone walls, as soon have looked for a hare in her last year's form, or a bird in her old nest, as for Sam Page in the same place a month together; so completely did he belong to that order which the lawyers call vagrants, and the common people designate by the significant name of trampers; and so entirely of all rovers did he seem the most roving, of all wanderers the most unsettled. The winds, the clouds, even our English weather, were but a type of his mutability.

Our acquaintance with him had commenced above twenty years ago, when, a lad of some fifteen or thereaway, he carried muffins and cakes about the country. The whole house was caught by his intelligence and animation, his light active figure, his keen grey eye, and the singular mixture of shrewdness and good-humour in his sharp but pleasant features. Nobody's muffins could go down but Sam Page's. We turned off our old stupid deaf cakeman, Simon Brown, and appointed Sam on the instant. (N.B.—This happened at the period of a general election, and Sam wore the right colour, and Simon the wrong.) Three times a week he was to call. Faithless wretch! he never called again! He took to selling election ballads, and carrying about handbills. We waited for him a fortnight, went muffinless for fourteen days, and then, our candidate being fairly elected, and blue and yellow returned to their original nonimportance, were fain to put up once more with poor old deaf Simon Brown.

Sam's next appearance was in the character of a letterboy, when he and a donkey set up a most spirited opposition to Thomas Hearne and the post-cart. Everybody was dissatisfied with Thomas Hearne, who had committed more sins than I can remember, of forgetfulness, irregularity, and all manner of postman-like faults; and Sam, when applying for employers, made a most successful canvass, and for a week performed miracles of punctuality. At the end of that time he began to commit, with far greater vigour than his predecessor, Thomas Hearne, the several sins for which that worthy had been discarded. On Tuesday he forgot to call for the bag in the evening; on Wednesday he omitted to bring it in the morning; on Thursday he never made his appearance at all; on Friday his employers gave him warning; and on Saturday they turned him off. So ended this hopeful experiment.

Still, however, he continued to travel the country in various capacities. First, he carried a tray of casts; then a basket of Staffordshire ware; then he cried cherries; then he joined a troop of ruddle-men, and came about redder than a red Indian; then he sported a barrel-organ, a piece of mechanism of no small pretensions, having two sets of puppets on the top, one of girls waltzing, the other of soldiers at drill; then he drove a knife-grinder's wheel; then he led a bear and a very accomplished monkey; then he escorted a celebrated company of dancing dogs; and then, for a considerable time, during which he took a trip to India and back, we lost sight of him.

He reappeared, however, at B. Fair, where one year he was showman to the Living Skeleton, and the next a performer in the tragedy of the Edinburgh Murders, as exhibited every half-hour at the price of a penny to each person. Sam showed so much talent for melodrama, that we fully expected to find him following his new profession, which offered all the advantage of the change of place and of character which his habits required; and on his being again, for several months, an absentee, had little doubt but he had been promoted from a booth to a barn, and even looked for his name amongst a party of five strollers, three men and two women, who issued play-bills at Aberleigh, and performed tragedy, comedy, opera, farce, and pantomime, with all the degrees and compounds thereof described by Polonius, in the great room at the Rose, divided for the occasion into a row of chairs called the Boxes, at a shilling per seat, and two of benches called the Pit, at sixpence. I even suspected that a Mr. Theodore Fitzhugh, the genius of the company, might be Sam Page fresh christened. But I was mistaken. Sam, when I saw him again, and mentioned my suspicion, pleaded guilty to a turn for the drama; he confessed that he liked acting of all things, especially tragedy, " it was such fun." But there was a small obstacle to his pursuit of the more regular branches of the histrionic art—the written drama : our poor friend could not read. To use his own words, " he was no scholar " ; and on recollecting certain small aberrations which had occurred during the three days that he carried the letter-bag, and professed to transact errands, such as the misdelivery of notes, and the non-performance of written commissions, we were fain to conclude that, instead of having, as he expressed it, " somehow or other got rid of his learning," learning was a blessing which Sam had never possessed, and that a great luminary was lost to the stage simply from the accident of not knowing his alphabet.

Instead of being, as we had imagined, ranting in " Richard " or raving in " Lear," our unlucky hero had been amusing himself by making a voyage to the West Indies and home by the way of America, having had some thoughts of honouring the New World by making it the scene of his residence, or rather of his peregrinations ; and a country where the whole population seems movable, would, probably, have suited him ; but the yellow fever seized him, and pinned him fast at the very beginning of his North American travels ; and, sick and weary, he returned to England, determined, as he said, " to take a room and live respectably."

The apartment on which he fixed was, as I have intimated, an outhouse belonging to Mrs. Dinah Forde, in which he took up his abode the beginning of last summer with his two ferrets, harmless, foreign-looking things (no native English animal has so outlandish an appearance as the ferret, with its long limber body, its short legs, red eyes, and ermine-looking fur), of whose venom, gentle as they looked, he was wont to boast amain ; four little dogs, of every variety of mongrel ugliness, whose eminence in the same quality nobody could doubt, for one had lost an eye in battle, and one an ear, the third halted in his fore-quarters, and the fourth limped behind ; and a jay of great talent and beauty, who turned his pretty head this way and that, and bent and bowed most courteously when addressed, and then responded in words equally apt and courteous to all that was said to him. Mrs. Dinah Forde fell in love with that jay at first sight ; borrowed him of his master, and hung him at one side of the door, where he soon became as famous all through the parish as the talking bird in the Arabian tales, or the parrot Vert-vert, immortalised by Gresset.

Sam's own appearance was as rat-catcher-like, I had almost said as venomous, as that of his retinue. His features sharper than ever, thin, and worn, and sallow, yet arch and good-humoured withal ; his keen eye and knowing smile, his pliant active figure, and the whole turn of his equipment, from the shabby straw hat to the equally shabby long gaiters, told his calling almost as plainly as the sharp heads of the ferrets, which were generally protruded from the pockets of his dirty jean jacket, or the bunch of dead rats with which he was wont to parade the streets of B. on a market-day. He seemed, at last, to have found his proper vocation ; and having stuck to it for four or five months, with great success and reputation, there seemed every chance of his becoming stationary at Aberleigh.

In his own profession his celebrity was, as I have said, deservedly great. The usual complaint against rat-catchers, that they take care not to ruin the stock, that they are sure to leave breeders enough, could not be applied to Sam ; who, poor fellow, never was suspected of forethought in his life ; and who, in this case, had evidently too much delight in the chase himself, to dream of checking or stopping it, whilst there was a rat left unslain. On the contrary, so strong was the feeling of

his sportsmanship, and that of his poor curs, that one of
his grand operations, on the taking in of a wheat-rick,
for instance, or the clearing out of a barn, was sure to be
attended by all the idle boys and unemployed men in the
village,—by all, in short, who, under the pretence of
helping, could make an excuse to their wives, their con-
sciences, or the parish officers. The grand battue, on
emptying Farmer Brookes's great barn, will be long remembered in Aberleigh ; there was more noise made,
and more beer drunk, than on any occasion since the
happy marriage of Miss Phœbe and the patten-maker ;
it even emulated the shouts and the tipsiness of the B.
election—and that's a bold word ! The rats killed were
in proportion to the din—and that is a bold word too ! I
am really afraid to name the number, it seemed to myself,
and would appear to my readers, so incredible. Sam and
Farmer Brookes were so proud of the achievement, that
they hung the dead game on the lower branches of the
great oak outside the gate, after the fashion practised by
mole-catchers, to the unspeakable consternation of a
cockney cousin of the good farmer's, a very fine lady,
who had never in her life before been out of the sound of
Bow-bell, and who, happening to catch sight of this
portentous crop of acorns in passing under the tree,
caused her husband, who was driving her, to turn the
gig round, and notwithstanding remonstrance and persuasion, and a most faithful promise that the boughs
should be dismantled before night, could not be induced
to set foot in a place where the trees were, to use her own
words, " so heathenish," and betook herself back to her
own domicile at Holborn Bars, in great and evident
perplexity as to the animal or vegetable quality of the
oak in question.*

* Moles are generally, and rats occasionally, strung on willows
when killed ; not much to the improvement of the beauty of the
scenery. I don't know anything that astounds a Londoner more
than the sight of a tree bearing such fruit. The plum-pudding tree,

Another cause of the large assemblage at Sam's rat-hunts was, besides the certainty of good sport, the eminent popularity of the leader of the chase. Sam was a universal favourite. He had good fellowship enough to conciliate the dissipated, and yet stopped short of the licence which would have disgusted the sober,—was pleasant-spoken, quick, lively, and intelligent,—sang a good song, told a good story, and had a kindness of temper, and a lightness of heart, which rendered him a most exhilarating and coveted companion to all in his own station. He was, moreover, a proficient in country games, and so eminent at cricket especially, that the men of Aberleigh were no sooner able, from his residence in the parish, to count him amongst their eleven, than they challenged their old rivals, the men of Hinton, and beat them forthwith.

Two nights before the return match, Sam, shabbier even than usual, and unusually out of spirits, made his appearance at the house of an old Aberleigh cricketer, still a patron and promoter of that noble game, and the following dialogue took place between them :—

"Well, Sam, we are to win this match."

"I hope so, please your honour. But I'm sorry to say I shan't be at the winning of it."

"Not here, Sam! What, after rattling the stumps about so gloriously last time, won't you stay to finish them now! Only think how those Hinton fellows will crow! You must stay over Wednesday."

"I can't, your honour. 'Tis not my fault. But here I've had a lawyer's letter on the part of Mrs. Forde, about the trifle of rent, and bill that I owe her ; and if I'm not off to-night, Heaven knows what she'll do with me ! "

"The rent—that can't be much. Let's see if we can't manage——"

whereof mention is made in the pleasant and veracious travels of the Baron Munchausen, could not appear more completely a *lusus naturæ*.

"Aye, but there's a longish bill, sir," interrupted Sam. "Consider, we are seven in family."

"Seven!" interrupted, in his turn, the other interlocutor.

"Aye, sir, counting the dogs and the ferrets, poor beasts! for I suppose she has not charged for the jay's board, though 'twas that unlucky bird made the mischief."

"The jay! What could he have to do with the matter? Dinah used to be as fond of him as if he had been her own child! and I always thought Dinah Forde a good-natured woman."

"So she is, in the main, your honour," replied Sam, twirling his hat, and looking half-shy and half-sly, at once knowing and ashamed. "So she is, in the main; but this, somehow, is a particular sort of an affair. You must know, sir," continued Sam, gathering courage as he went on, "that at first the widow and I were very good friends, and several of these articles which are charged in the bill, such as milk for the ferrets, and tea and lump-sugar, and young onions for myself, I verily thought were meant as presents; and so I do believe at the time she did mean them. But, howsoever, Jenny Dobbs, the nurserymaid at the Park (a pretty black-eyed lass—perhaps your honour may have noticed her walking with the children), she used to come out of an evening like to see us play cricket, and then she praised my bowling, and then I talked to her, and so at last we began to keep company; and the jay, owing, I suppose, to hearing me say so sometimes, began to cry out, "Pretty Jenny Dobbs!""

"Well, and this affronted the widow?"

"Past all count, your honour. You never saw a woman in such a tantrum. She declared I had taught the bird to insult her, and posted off to Lawyer Latitat. And here I have got this letter, threatening to turn me out, and put me in gaol, and what not, from the lawyer;

and Jenny, a false-hearted jade, finding how badly matters are going with me, turns round and says that she never meant to have me, and is going to marry the French Mounseer (Sir Henry's French valet), a foreigner and a papist, who may have a dozen wives before for anything, she can tell. These women are enough to drive a man out of his senses!" And poor Sam gave his hat a mighty swing, and looked likely to cry from a mixture of grief, anger, and vexation. "These women are enough to drive a man mad!" reiterated Sam, with increased energy.

"So they are, Sam," replied his host, administering a very efficient dose of consolation, in the shape of a large glass of Cognac brandy, which, in spite of its coming from his rival's country, Sam swallowed with hearty goodwill. "So they are. But Jenny's not worth fretting about : she's a poor feckless thing after all, fitter for a Frenchman than an Englishman. If I were you, I would make up to the widow : she's a person of property, and a fine comely woman into the bargain. Make up to the widow, Sam, and drink another glass of brandy to your success!"

And Sam followed both pieces of advice. He drank the brandy and he made up to the widow, the former part of the prescription probably inspiring him with courage to attempt the latter ; and the lady was propitious, and the wedding speedy : and the last that I heard of them was, the jay's publishing the banns of marriage, under a somewhat abridged form, from his cage at the door of Mrs. Dinah's shop, (a proceeding at which she seemed, outwardly, scandalised ; but over which, it may be suspected, she chuckled inwardly, or why not have taken in the cage ?) and the French valet's desertion of Jenny Dobbs, whom he, in his turn, jilted ; and the dilemma of Lawyer Latitat, who found himself obliged to send in his bill for the threatening letter to the identical gentleman to whom it was addressed. For the rest, the cricket match was won triumphantly, the wedding went off with great *éclat*, and our accomplished rat-catcher is, we trust, permanently fixed in our good village of Aberleigh.

AUNT MARTHA

ONE of the pleasantest habitations I have ever known is an old white house, built at right angles, with the pointed roofs, and clustered chimneys of Elizabeth's day, covered with roses, vines, and passion-flowers, and parted by a green sloping meadow from a straggling, picturesque village street. In this charming abode resides a more charming family : a gentleman,

> " Polite as all his life in courts had been,
>   And good as he the world had never seen ; "

two daughters full of sweetness and talent ; and Aunt Martha, the most delightful of old maids ! She has another appellation, I suppose—she must have one—but I scarcely know it : Aunt Martha is the name that belongs to her—the name of affection. Such is the universal feeling which she inspires, that all her friends, all her acquaintances, (in this case the terms are almost synonymous,) speak of her like her own family—she is everybody's Aunt Martha—and a very charming Aunt Martha she is.

First of all, she is, as all women should be if they can, remarkably handsome. She may be—it is a delicate matter to speak of a lady's age—she must be five-and-forty ; but few beauties of twenty could stand a comparison with her loveliness. It is such a fulness of bloom, so luxuriant, so satiating : just tall enough to carry off the plumpness which at forty-five is so becoming ; a brilliant complexion ; curled pouting lips ! long, clear, bright grey eyes—the colour for expression, that which unites the quickness of the black with the softness of

the blue ; a Roman regularity of feature ; and a profusion of rich brown hair. Such is Aunt Martha. Add
to this a very gentle and pleasant speech, always kind,
and generally lively ; the sweetest temper ; the easiest
manner ; a singular rectitude and singleness of mind ;
a perfect open-heartedness, and a total unconsciousness
of all these charms, and you will wonder a little that she
is Aunt Martha still. I have heard hints of an early
engagement broken by the fickleness of man ; and there
is about her an aversion to love in one particular direction
—the love matrimonial—and an overflowing of affection
in all other channels, that it seems as if the natural course
of the stream had been violently dammed up. She has
many lovers—admirers I should say—for there is amidst
her good-humoured gaiety, a coyness that forbids their
going farther ; a modesty almost amounting to shyness,
that checks even the laughing girls, who sometimes
accuse her of stealing away their beaux. I do not think
any man on earth could tempt her into wedlock : it would
be a most unpardonable monopoly if any one should ;
an intolerable engrossing of a general blessing ; a theft
from the whole community.

Her usual home is the white house covered with roses ;
and her station in the family is rather doubtful. She is
not the mistress, for her charming nieces are old enough
to take and to adorn the head of the table ; nor the
housekeeper, though, as she is the only lady of the establishment who wears pockets, those ensigns of authority, the
keys, will sometimes be found, with other strays, in that
goodly receptacle ; nor a guest—her spirit is too active
for that lazy post ; her real vocation there, and everywhere, seems to be comforting, cheering, welcoming, and
spoiling everything that comes in her way ; and, above all,
nursing and taking care. Of all kind employments, these
are her favourites. Oh, the shawlings, the cloakings,
the cloggings ! the cautions against cold, or heat, or rain,

or sun ! the remedies for diseases not arrived ! colds
uncaught ! incipient toothaches ! rheumatisms to come !
She loves nursing so well, that we used to accuse her of
inventing maladies for other people, that she might have
the pleasure of curing them ; and when they really come—
as come they will sometimes, in spite of Aunt Martha—
what a nurse she is ! It is worth while to be a little sick
to be so attended. All the cousins, and cousins' cousins
of her connection, as regularly send for her on the occasion
of a lying-in, as for the midwife. I suppose she has undergone the ceremony of dandling the baby, sitting up with
the new mamma, and dispensing the caudle, twenty times
at least. She is equally important at weddings or funerals.
Her humanity is inexhaustible. She has an intense feeling
of fellowship with her kind, and grieves or rejoices in the
sufferings or happiness of others with a reality as genuine
as it is rare.

Her accomplishments are exactly of this sympathetic
order : all calculated to administer much to the pleasure
of her companions, and nothing to her own importance or
vanity. She leaves to the sirens, her nieces, the higher
enchantments of the piano, the harp, and the guitar,
and that noblest of instruments, the human voice ;
ambitious of no other musical fame than such as belongs
to the playing of quadrilles and waltzes for their little
dances, in which she is indefatigable ; she neither carica-
tures the face of man nor of nature under pretence of
drawing figures or landscapes ; but she ornaments the
reticules, bell-ropes, ottomans, and chair-covers of all her
acquaintance, with flowers as rich and luxuriant as her
own beauty. She draws patterns for the ignorant,
and works flounces, frills, and baby-linen, for the idle ;
she reads aloud to the sick, plays at cards with the old,
and loses at chess to the unhappy. Her gift in gossiping,
too, is extraordinary ; she is a gentle newsmonger, and
turns her scandal on the sunny side. But she is an old maid

still; and certain small peculiarities hang about her.
She is a thorough hoarder; whatever fashion comes up,
she is sure to have something of the sort by her, or, at
least, something thereunto convertible. She is a little
superstitious; sees strangers in her teacup, gifts in her
finger nails, letters and winding-sheets in the candle,
and purses and coffins in the fire; would not spill the
salt " for all the worlds that one ever has to give "; and
looks with dismay on a crossed knife and fork. Moreover,
she is orderly to fidgetiness—that is her greatest calamity !
—for young ladies nowadays are not quite so tidy as they
should be, and ladies'-maids are much worse; and drawers
are tumbled, and drawing-rooms in a litter. Happy she
to whom a disarranged drawer can be a misery ! Dear
and happy Aunt Martha !

THE END

PRINTED BY THE EAST OF ENGLAND PRINTING WORKS, LONDON AND NORWICH